Flowering Plants of
Edgewood Natural Preserve

Flowering Plants of Edgewood Natural Preserve

Second Edition

Toni Corelli

Illustrated by Judy Mason & Linda Bea Miller

x

HALF MOON BAY, CALIFORNIA

Monocot Press

Published by Monocot Press
PO Box 773
Half Moon Bay, CA 94019
corelli@coastside.net

First Edition: March 2002
Second Edition: October 2004

ISBN 0-9646994-2-7

Illustrations from *Illustrated Flora of the Pacific States, Washington, Oregon and California* by LeRoy Abrams and Roxana Stinchfield Ferris (Stanford, Calif.: Stanford University Press) are copyright ©1960 Board of Trustees, Leland Stanford Junior University. Used with permission.

Manufactured in the United States of America

10 9 8 7 6 5 4 3 2 1

This book is dedicated to
Susan Sommers,
Edgewood Sage,
and to the memory of
Brenda Butner,
Preservation Advocate

Contents

Acknowledgements

I acknowledge my illustrators, Judy Mason and Linda Bea Miller, who worked endless hours on the illustrations. For sharing field notes and observations I would like to thank John Allen, Paul Heiple, Ken Himes, Susan Sommers, and the many other members of the Friends of Edgewood and the Santa Clara Valley Chapter of the California Native Plant Society. For help in the field, thanks to the San Mateo County Staff and Park Rangers. For editorial assistance, thank you Carolyn Curtis, Ann Lambrecht, Pat Lisin, and Sara Timby. Thank you to all of the Edgewood Natural Preserve Docents who bring to the public the wonders of Edgewood. For the second edition I thank Guenther Machol, Drew Shell, and Herb Fischgrund for sharing their observations and Emily Cubbon for prepress assistance. Also to my family Richard and Alexander for their unselfish help and support.

Financial assistance in the production of this book has been provided by the Santa Clara Valley Chapter of the California Native Plant Society.

– Toni Corelli

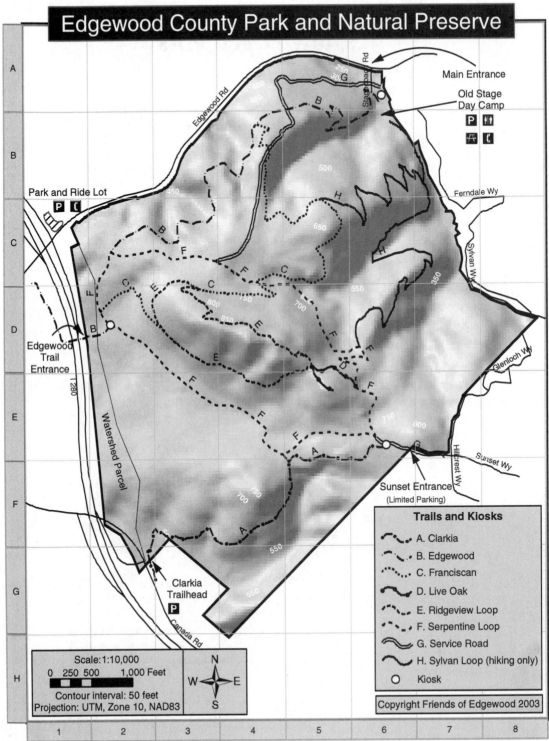

Edgewood County Park and Natural Preserve

Main Entrance

Old Stage Day Camp

Park and Ride Lot

Ferndale Wy

Edgewood Rd

Stagecoach Rd

Sylvan Wy

Edgewood Trail Entrance

Watershed Parcel

Glenloch Wy

Sunset Entrance
(Limited Parking)

Hillcrest Wy

Sunset Wy

Clarkia Trailhead

Canada Rd

Trails and Kiosks

- A. Clarkia
- B. Edgewood
- C. Franciscan
- D. Live Oak
- E. Ridgeview Loop
- F. Serpentine Loop
- G. Service Road
- H. Sylvan Loop (hiking only)
- O Kiosk

Scale: 1:10,000

0 250 500 1,000 Feet

Contour interval: 50 feet
Projection: UTM, Zone 10, NAD83

N
W E
S

Copyright Friends of Edgewood 2003

Introduction

Edgewood County Park and Natural Preserve is a public park within San Mateo County Department Parks and Recreation. The park is located east of Highway 280 and south of Edgewood Road in Redwood City, California (see the trail and location map on page XII. It is a protected wilderness area of 467 acres with an extensive trail system with 481 vascular plant species identified to date. Edgewood is famous in the San Francisco Bay Area as a place to see fields of spring wildflowers. This is mostly because of the serpentine soils that occur within the park.

Edgewood has a very active Docent Program run by The Friends of Edgewood Natural Preserve. Nature walks are given by Docents on the weekends during spring. The Friends are also involved in restoration of disturbed area within the park, eradication of invasive plants and other activities involved in the preservation of Edgewood. For more information visit their web site:

www.friendsofedgewood.org/
e-mail: info@friendsofedgewood.org
or call (866) GO-EDGEWOOD

History

Native American archeological sites occur nearby at Filoli and the Phleger property now a part of the Golden Gate National Recreation Area (GGNRA). The Ohlone-speaking people came into the San Francisco Bay area about 500 A.D. from the San Joaquin and Sacramento areas. They were probably the largest tribe in California at the time of Spanish contact. They enjoyed a diversity of climate and an abundance of foods within a few miles of the coast, baylands, freshwater streams, forests and grasslands. They lived off the land, hunting, gathering and moving short distances during the seasons to make use of the abundant foods and natural resources available.

The first Spanish-Ohlone contact probably occurred in 1769 when Captain Don Gaspar de Portola arrived and camped on the San Francisquito Creek in the baylands. This is when domestic livestock was introduced into the area. By 1776 Franciscan priests began the Mission and Presidio in San Francisco and natives began to enter the Spanish Mission system. Spanish expansion continued along the San Francisco Peninsula and more of the land was used for domestic livestock such as sheep, cattle and horses. By 1786 most of the natives had left their villages for the missions.

By 1830 the area between San Mateo and San Francisquito Creek and the area that is now San Carlos and Menlo Park was used extensively for grazing. In 1876 a small farmhouse was built on the western slope of what is now Edgewood Park. Little development occurred at Edgewood and several families owned and lived on the property for the next 90 years. The concrete bridge that is still in use upon entering the Day Camp was built in 1917. The last family who owned the Edgewood property sold it in 1967.

In 1967 the State of California bought the site for a State College campus but this project was abandoned in 1970. In 1971 the site, along with part of the southern San Francisco watershed, was proposed as a recreation complex with swimming pools, tennis courts, and an 18-hole golf course. At this time the Edgewood site was misused by off-road vehicles and motorcycles which scarred the hillsides. During this time Susan Sommers began to document the flora of Edgewood, discovering rare plant species and a diversity of wildflowers seen no where else in the San Francisco Bay Area. Using her camera to document plants and working with John Hunter Thomas she began her plant list for Edgewood which grew into more than 400 species.

In 1980 the Edgewood site was purchased using money from the U.S. Land and Water Conservation Fund, the Midpeninsula Regional Open Space District and the County Charter for Parks Fund. The plans for a golf course proceeded until 1985 when the California Native Plant Society filed a lawsuit to stop the project because of the endangered Checkerspot butterfly and San Mateo thornmint. Opposition to a golf course continued with over 40 organizations forming a coalition to preserve Edgewood. On August 27, 1993 the San Mateo County Board of Supervisors declared all of Edgewood County Park a Natural Area Preserve.

Vegetation

So far over 481 plant species within 9 plant communities have been identified at Edgewood. This includes garden plants that are not invasive and are not described within the text of the book. These mostly occur in and near the Day Camp area:

Crocosmia sp.	crocosmia
Hypericum sp.	St. John's wort
Iris foetidissima	brown stinking iris
Iris germanica	bearded iris
Kniphofia uvaria	red hot poker
Leucojum sp.	snowflake
Narcissus jonquilla	daffodil
Narcissus pseudonarcissus	daffodil
Rosa sp.	ornamental rose
Zantedeschia aethiopica	calla lily

For the purpose of this book the vegetation types used are the same as were used in the Edgewood Master Plan.

Woodland 30-70% cover. (Forest has denser cover, savanna has more open cover)
Approximately 35% area.

Oak Woodland including Foothill Woodland dominant plants:

Aesculus californica	California buckeye
Arbutus menziesii	Pacific madrone
Artemisia douglasiana	mugwort
Heteromeles arbutifolia	Christmas berry / toyon
Pedicularis densiflora	Indian warrior
Quercus agrifolia	coast live oak / encina
Quercus douglasii	blue oak
Quercus lobata	valley oak
Ribes californica	hillside gooseberry
Rosa californica	wood rose
Rubus ursinus	California blackberry
Sambucus mexicana	blue elderberry
Sanicula crassicaulis	Pacific sanicle
Symphoricarpos mollis	creeping snowberry
Toxicodendron diversilobum	western poison oak
Umbellularia californica	California bay

Mixed Evergreen Woodland including Mixed Hardwood dominant plants:

Aesculus californica	California buckeye
Arbutus menziesii	Pacific madrone
Pseudotsuga menziesii	Douglas fir
Quercus agrifolia	coast live oak / encina
Rubus ursinus	California blackberry
Symphoricarpos alba	snowberry
Toxicodendron diversilobum	western poison oak
Umbellularia californicum	California bay

Grassland
Approximately 45% area.

Serpentine Bunchgrass and Wildflower Field dominant plants:

Achillea millefolium	yarrow
Achyrachaena mollis	blow-wives
Castilleja densiflora	owl's-clover
Chlorogalum pomeridianum	amole / soap plant
Clarkia purpurea	four-spot
Delphinium variegatum	royal larkspur
Dichelostemma capitatum	blue dicks
Dodecatheon clevelandii	lowland shooting star

Elymus multisetus	big squirreltail
Hemizonia congesta	hayfield tarweed
Lasthenia californica	goldfields
Layia platyglossa	tidy-tips
Linanthus parviflorus	small-flowered linanthus
Nassella pulchra	purple needlegrass
Plantago erecta	California plantain
Triteleia laxa	Ithuriel's spear

Nonserpentine Native and Nonnative Grassland dominant plants:

Avena barbata	slender wild oat
Bromus hordeaceus	soft chess
Centaurea solstitialis	yellow star-thistle
Erodium botrys	long-beaked storksbill
Lolium multiflorum	Italian ryegrass
Nassella pulchra	purple needlegrass

Shrub (Chaparral)

Approximately 15% area.

Chamise Chaparral dominant plants:

Adenostoma fasciculatum	chamise
Ceanothus cuneatus	buck brush
Eriodictyon californicum	yerba santa
Lotus scoparius	California broom / deerweed
Prunus ilicifolia	holly-leaved cherry

Mixed Serpentine Chaparral dominant plants:

Adenostoma fasciculatum	chamise
Ceanothus cuneatus	buck brush
Eriodictyon californicum	yerba santa
Pickeringia montana	chaparral pea
Quercus durata	leather oak

Mixed Northern Coastal Scrub dominant plants:

Artemisia californica	California sagebrush
Baccharis pilularis	coyote brush
Eriophyllum confertiflorum	golden-yarrow
Lupinus albifrons	silver bush lupine
Mimulus aurantiacus	sticky monkeyflower
Rhamnus californicus	California coffeeberry
Toxicodendron diversilobum	western poison oak

Wetland

Approximately 5% area.

Riparian corridors and riparian woodland
Freshwater marsh, ponds, springs and seeps

Floristic Analysis

The vascular flora of Edgewood Natural Preserve includes 481 species within 9 plant community types.

Floristic Components

Number of Plant Families: 76

TAXONOMIC TREATMENTS	NUMBER OF SPECIES
Ferns	7
Gymnosperms	4
Dicotyledons	363
Monocotyledons	107

Relationships to the Surrounding Areas

The flora of Edgewood is represented in *The Flora of the Santa Cruz Mountains of California, A Manual of the Vascular Plants* by John Hunter Thomas. *The Flora of Santa Cruz Mountains* (SCM) lists 1,800 taxa (this includes subspecies, varieties, forms, and hybrids), occurring within 1,386 square miles. Edgewood Natural Preserve has 481 taxa, approximately 27% of the flora that is included in *The Flora of the Santa Cruz Mountains* occurring within 467 acres or .73 square miles. Edgewood Natural Preserve has 9 of the 12 represented plant communities included in *The Flora of the Santa Cruz Mountains.*

	ACRES	SQUARE MILES	TAXA	PLANT COMMUNITIES
SCM	887,000	1,386.00	1,800	12
Edgewood	467	.73	481	9

Alien Species (Nonnative)

Within Edgewood 28% of the species are aliens. In *The Flora of the Santa Cruz Mountains,* Dr. John Hunter Thomas lists 31% of the flora within the Santa Cruz Mountains as aliens. Many of these were introduced during the founding of the Spanish Missions, some accidental, some deliberate.

Rare and Endangered Plants

There are 11 plants listed in the California Native Plant Society's *Inventory of Rare and Endangered Plants of California, Sixth Edition* that occur at Edgewood. They are:

Acanthomintha duttonii	San Mateo thornmint
Allium peninsulare var. franciscanum	Franciscan onion
Arctostaphylos regismontana	Kings Mountain manzanita

Collinsia multicolor	San Francisco collinsia
Dirca occidentalis	western leatherwood
Fritillaria liliacea	fragrant fritillary
Hesperolinon congestum	dwarf flax
Lessingia hololeuca	woolly-headed lessingia
Linanthus ambiguus	serpentine linanthus
Malacothamnus arcuatus	chaparral mallow
Pentachaeta bellidiflora	white-rayed pentachaeta

Historically there was one population of *Cirsium fontinale* var. *fontinale*, fountain thistle that was documented in the 1980s but no longer occurs at Edgewood.

Geology

Edgewood is situated immediately east of the San Andreas Fault. The dominant soils in this area are derived from various types of sandstone referred to as the Franciscan Formation. At Edgewood this consists of sandstone, shale which consists of mud and silt, alluvial deposits, greenstone and serpentine. Serpentine derived soils provide unique plant communities represented by serpentine grassland and serpentine chaparral at Edgewood. Serpentine is the California State Rock.

There are over 160 acres of serpentine derived soils at Edgewood. Typically serpentine soils are low in calcium and nitrogen and high in magnesium and heavy metals. This combination of chemical constituents can be inhospitable to most plants, and most species introduced during European settlement cannot live in serpentine soil. However, certain native plants have adapted to the harsh chemical components over time and Edgewood represents the way this part of California looked before European settlement.

Soils have an important influence on plant distribution and some can survive only on specific soil types (endemics) and are genetically and physiologically adapted to them. Edgewood has 7 serpentine endemic species:

Acanthomintha duttonii	San Mateo thornmint
Allium falcifolium	Brewer's onion / sickle leaved onion
Hesperolinon congestum	dwarf flax
Linanthus ambiguus	serpentine linanthus
Linanthus liniflorus	flax-flowered linanthus
Quercus durata	leather oak
Sidalcea diploscypha	fringed checkerbloom

Reader's Guide

Included Taxa

Native and nonnative vascular plant taxa are included. Noninvasive garden plants are not described within the text but that list can be seen on page 2.

Identification Keys

Dichotomous identification keys are provided for taxa recognized to occur at Edgewood Natural Preserve. Dichotomous keys are composed of a series of consecutively numbered, paired, comparative statements of couplets. The first phrase of a couplet begins with a number followed by a period; the alternate, second phrase begins with the same number followed by a prime symbol.

Names of Taxa

Scientific names and abbreviation of authors are those considered to be the most correct, based on the names published in *The Jepson Manual* (1993) and using the addendum published in the *Jepson Globe*. There have also been new name changes since the first edition of the Edgewood flora. These are published on the Jepson Online Interchange web page:

http://ucjeps.berkeley.edu/interchange.html

Common names were used as in *The Jepson Manual*. If there is no common name indicated in *The Jepson Manual*. then the common name from *The Flora of the Santa Cruz Mountains* was used.

An example of scientific nomenclature:

Family: Portulacaceae — Purslane Family

GENUS	SPECIFIC EPITHET	AUTHOR	SUBSPECIES (SSP.)
Claytonia	*perfoliata*	Torrey & A. Gray	ssp. *perfoliata*

Common Name: miner's lettuce

Native Versus Nonnative

These are indicated. If nonnative then the place of origin is given.

Time of Flowering

The time during which plants produce spores, cones, or flowers is given as a range from earliest to latest month.

Descriptions

Descriptions are brief and provide a summary of characteristics easily seen using a hand-lens and without injuring the plant. Plants were measured in the field and their characteristics described within the descriptions. Specimens housed at The Sharsmith Herbarium at San Jose State, and the Teaching Herbarium at Jasper Ridge, Stanford University were also used to describe the plants and to construct the keys.

Morphological descriptions of the family and genera are inclusive for their worldwide distribution. More complete descriptions may be found in Abrams, Hickman, and Munz and Keck. See the bibliography. Definitions of botanical terms may be found in the glossary.

Measurements

Measurements indicate length or height unless otherwise indicated.

Name Derivation

The genus derivation used is from *The Jepson Manual* when available. The specific epithet derivation used is from *The Names of Plants* by D. Gledhill and other texts indicated in the bibliography as well as the web page:

http://www.calflora.net/botanicalnames/index.html

Notes

These are useful for interpretive information and other information about the plant.

Uses Past and Present

These notes pertain to economic use, especially by Native Americans, as well as toxicity, and other information gathered from the various texts listed in the bibliography. **Warning:** No plants can be gathered from Edgewood as the park is a natural preserve and the natural resources are protected. When using this information for interpretive purposes be sure to indicate that although this information is given for past and present use of plants, it is provided for educational purposes only. Some plants can be useful in one quantity but lethal in another and some people may have an allergic reaction to the plant. Be sure to give this warning. Preserving habitats is essential and saving plants for their ecological value should be the first consideration.

Illustrations

All plants are illustrated when possible. When possible one habitat is illustrated for each taxa, and diagnostic characters are illustrated. Illustrations are designed to complement identification keys and highlight morphological structures such as flowers, fruit and other structures. When appropriate, labels were used to identify individual structures. Original illustrations are by Judy Mason and Linda Bea Miller. Illustrations for most of the sunflower and grass family and others unable to be drawn before publication, were used by permission from *Illustrated Flora of the Pacific States, Washington, Oregon and California* by L. Abrams and R. S. Ferris.

Abbreviations Used

cm = centimeter

dm = decimeter

e.g. = for example

etc. = and so on

m = meter

Medit. = Mediterranean

mm = millimeter

ssp. = subspecies

var. = variety

Symbols Used

< less than or up to

= equal to

> greater than

Identification verifications

• *Seen elsewhere in S.F. Bay area*

√ *Seen in Edgewood Natural Preserve*
   or elsewhere in San Carlos

   E   Seen in Edgewood

   SC Seen in San Carlos
      (mostly in Eaton or Big Canyon Parks)

Key to Major Taxonomic Groups

1. Plants reproducing by means of spores; large woody cones, flowers, and seeds not produced
   Group 1 — Pteridophytes — Ferns and Fern Allies
1´ Plants reproducing by seeds and pollen; seeds either enclosed in ovaries of flowers or naked and borne on woody cones
   2. Plants woody, either trees, small trees, large shrubs, shrubs or woody vines (this key will get you to plant species)
      Group 2— Woody Plants
   2´ Plants herbaceous, nonwoody, either annuals or herbaceous perennials (this key will get you to plant family)
      Group 3 — Herbaceous Flowering Plant Families

Group 1. Pteridophytes — Ferns and Fern Allies

Ferns do not have flowers or seeds but have specialized structures on their leaves called *sporangia*. These are often clustered, forming sori. The sori may be protected by flaps or disks called indusia, or the sori may be covered by the in-rolled margin of the leaflets. The sporangium produce microscopic spores, which are released and scattered by the wind.

Key to Ferns and Fern Allies
1. Leaves with well developed blades, not whorled
   2. Sori located along the margin of the leaflets or lobes, often covered by the in-rolled margin
      3. Leaflets fan-shaped, thin, margin lobed or toothed .... *Adiantum jordanii,* (Pteridaceae), CALIFORNIA MAIDEN-HAIR
      3´ Leaflets narrow, thick .... *Pellaea andromedifolia,* (Pteridaceae), COFFEE FERN
   2´ Sori not located along the margin of the leaflets or lobes
      4. Indusia absent
         5. Lower leaf surfaces powdery, golden .... *Pentagramma triangularis,* (Pteridaceae), GOLDBACK FERN
         5´ Lower leaf not powdery .... *Polypodium californicum,* (Polypodiaceae), CALIFORNIA POLYPODY
      4´ Indusia present
         6. Leaves 1-pinnate, base of each leaflet with an enlarged one-sided lobe...*Polystichum munitum,* (Dryopteridaceae), WESTERN SWORD FERN

6′ Leaves 1-2-pinnate, base of leaflet not as above ....
.... *Dryopteris arguta,* (Dryopteridaceae), COASTAL WOOD FERN
1′ Leaves whorled, fused into a toothed sheath at each internode ....
.... *Equisetum telmateia,* (Equisetaceae), GIANT HORSETAIL

Group 2. Woody Plants — Trees, Large Shrubs, or Small Trees, Shrubs, Ground Covers, Woody Vines

Woody plants are perennial and woody at the base; most are long lived and evidence of their presence would be obvious year round. This section is grouped into four categories: (A) Vine (Woody or Herbaceous Perennial); (B) Shrub (Obvious), or Woody Ground Cover; (C) Large Shrub or Small Tree; (D) Tree.

A. Vine (Woody or Herbaceous Perennial)

1. Leaves simple
2. Leaves alternate
3. Plant with tendrils ....
.... *Marah fabaceus,* (Cucurbitaceae), CALIFORNIA MAN-ROOT
3′ Plant without tendrils
4. Leaves (mature) entire .... *Hedera helix,* (Araliaceae), ENGLISH IVY
4′ Leaves lobed
5. Leaves with 2 lobes at the base
6. Plants hairy at least around leaf sinus or top of peduncle ....
.... *Calystegia occidentalis,* (Convolvulaceae),
CHAPARRAL MORNING-GLORY
6′ Plants not at all hairy ....
...... *Calystegia purpurata,* (Convolvulaceae), SMOOTH WESTERN
MORNING GLORY
5′ Leaves mostly equally lobed ....
.... *Delairea odorata,* (Asteraceae), CAPE IVY
2′ Leaves opposite .. *Lonicera hispidula,* (Caprifoliaceae), HAIRY HONEYSUCKLE
1′ Leaves compound
7. Plant with spines
8. Plant with 3 leaflets; prickles straight, slender all along stem ....
.... *Rubus ursinus,* (Rosaceae), CALIFORNIA BLACKBERRY
8′ Plant with (usually) more than 3 leaflets; prickles curved,
stout, widely spaced along stem ....
.... *Rubus discolor,* (Rosaceae), HIMALAYAN BLACKBERRY
7′ Plant without spines ....
.... *Clematis lasiantha,* (Ranunculaceae), VIRGIN'S BOWER

B. Shrub (obvious), or Woody Ground Cover

1. Plant growing in trees, green, parasitic ....
    .... *Phoradendron villosum,* (Viscaceae), OAK MISTLETOE
1´ Plant terrestrial
   2. Leaves simple
      3. Leaves or leaf clusters alternate
         4. Leaves in clusters
            5. Leaf narrow-linear (thread-like)
               6. Leaf bright green, without hairs ....
                  .... *Adenostoma fasciculatum,* (Rosaceae), CHAMISE
              6´ Leaf gray-green
                 7. Most leaves > 2 cm, threadlike, with a strong odor ....
                  ..... *Artemisia californica,* (Asteraceae), CALIFORNIA SAGEBRUSH
                 7´ Most leaves < 2 cm ....
                  .... *Eriogonum fasciculatum,* (Polygonaceae),
                  CALIFORNIA BUCKWHEAT
            5´ Leaf not narrow-linear
              8. Plant with spines or spine-tipped branches
                 9. Leaf margin lobed and toothed
                    10. Lower leaf surface with glandular hairs ....
                     ... *Ribes menziesii,* (Grossulariaceae), CANYON GOOSEBERRY
                    10´ Lower leaf surface not glandular hairy ....
                     Ribes californicum, (Grossulariaceae), HILLSIDE GOOSEBERRY
                 9´ Leaf margin smooth or toothed
                    11. Leaf length < 2 cm ....
                     .... *Rhamnus crocea,*[1] (Rhamnaceae), SPINY REDBERRY
                    11´ Leaf length > 2 cm ....
                     .... *Pyracantha angustifolia,*[1] (Rosaceae), FIRETHORN
               8´ Plant without spines..
                12. Leaf margin entire (smooth)
                   13. Branches flexible and with obvious white spots ....
                     .... *Dirca occidentalis,*[1] (Thymelaeaceae),
                     WESTERN LEATHERWOOD
                   13´ Branches not flexible, brown without obvious spots ......
                     .... *Oemleria cerasiformis,*[1] (Rosaceae), OSO BERRY
                12´ Leaf margin lobed and toothed ....
                ... *Ribes malvaceum,*[1] (Grossulariaceae), CHAPARRAL CURRENT
         4´ Leaves not in clusters
            14. Leaf margin entire (smooth)
               15. Stem (new growth) with long hairs
                 16. Leaf base lobed, sessile or very short petiole ....
                  ....*Arctostaphylos regismontana,*[1] (Ericaceae),
                  KINGS MOUNTAIN MANZANITA

16′ Leaf with a definite petiole ....
.... *Arctostaphylos tomentosa,*[1] (Ericaceae), HAIRY MANZANITA
15′ Stem without long hairs
  17. Plant with spines .... *Pyracantha angustifolia,*[2] (Rosaceae), FIRETHORN
  17′ Plant without spines
    18. Leaf white hairy on undersurface
      19. Upper surface of leaf dark green, stamens 5 ....
.... *Rhamnus tomentella,*[1] (Rhamnaceae), HOARY COFFEEBERRY
      19′ Upper surface of leaf dull green, stamens > 10 ....
.... *Cotoneaster pannosa,* (Rosaceae), COTONEASTER
    18′ Leaf not white-hairy on undersurface
      20. Leaves narrow, linear ....
.... *Helianthemum scoparium,* (Cistaceae), PEAK RUSH-ROSE
      20′ Leaves not linear, narrow
        21. Mature leaves < 4 cm, soft-hairy, stems green, hairy
          22. Leaves > 1 cm wide ....
.... *Solanum umbelliferum,* (Solanaceae), BLUE WITCH
          22′ Leaves < 1 cm wide
.... *Spartium junceum,* (Fabaceae), SPANISH BROOM
        21′ Mature leaves > 4 cm
          23. Most leaves longer than wide
            24. Upper and undersurface of leaf different colors ....
.... *Rhamnus californica,*[1] (Rhamnaceae),
CALIFORNIA COFFEEBERRY
            24′ Upper and undersurface of leaf the same color ....
.... *Oemleria cerasiformis,*[2] (Rosaceae), OSO BERRY
          23′ Most leaves roundish ....
Dirca occidentalis,[2] (Thymelaeaceae), WESTERN LEATHERWOOD
14′ Leaf margin toothed or lobed
  25. Leaf margin toothed
    26. Bark red to dark brown
      27. Leaf base lobed, sessile or very short petiole ....
Arctostaphylos regismontana,[2] (Ericaceae), KINGS MOUNTAIN MANZANITA
      27′ Leaf with a definite petiole ....
....................*Arctostaphylos tomentosa,*[2] (Ericaceae), HAIRY MANZANITA
    26′ Bark not red to dark brown
      28. Lower leaf with veins equally raised, leaf fan-shaped ....
.... *Holodiscus discolor,* (Rosaceae), OCEANSPRAY
      28′ Lower leaf with only main vein strongly raised
        29. Leaf > 4 cm
          30. Lower leaf surface hairy, not shiny ....
...... *Rhamnus tomentella,*[2] (Rhamnaceae), HOARY COFFEEBERRY
          30′ Lower leaf surface not hairy

31. Plant with black sooty mold, new leaves sticky ....
.... *Eriodictyon californicum,* (Hydrophyllaceae), YERBA SANTA
31′ Plant not as above
    32. Leaf margin finely toothed ....
.... *Rhamnus californica,*[2] (Rhamnaceae),
CALIFORNIA COFFEEBERRY
    32′ Leaf margin sharply toothed ....
.... *Heteromeles arbutifolia,* (Rosaceae), CHRISTMAS BERRY
29′ Leaf < 4 cm
    33. Leaf with a definite petiole ....
.... *Rhamnus crocea,*[2] (Rhamnaceae), SPINY REDBERRY
    33′ Leaf without a definite petiole ....
.... *Baccharis pilularis,* (Asteraceae), COYOTE BRUSH
25′ Leaf margins lobed, lobes may be toothed
    34. Leaf deeply cut appearing almost compound ....
.... *Eriophyllum confertiflorum,* (Asteraceae), GOLDEN-YARROW
    34′ Leaf palmately lobed
        35. Upper and lower leaf very hairy; leaf gray-green ....
.... *Malacothamnus fasciculatus,* (Malvaceae), CHAPARRAL MALLOW
        35′ Upper and lower leaf finely hairy; leaf light-green
            36. Plant with glandular hairs ....
.... *Ribes malvaceum,*[2] (Grossulariaceae), CHAPARRAL CURRANT
            36′ Plant without glandular hairs ....
.... *Physocarpus capitatus,* (Rosaceae), PACIFIC NINEBARK
3′ Leaves opposite
    37. Plant a low-growing groundcover, less than 6 dm
        38. Leaves soft-hairy ....
.... *Symphoricarpos mollis,* (Caprifoliaceae), CREEPING SNOWBERRY
        38′ Leaves not hairy ....
.... *Vinca major,* (Apocynaceae), GREATER PERIWINKLE
    37′ Plant an upright shrub taller than 6 dm
        39. Leaves sticky (look at new leaves), or with a strong odor
            40. Leaves gray-green, with a strong odor ....
.... *Lepechinia calycina,* (Lamiaceae), PITCHER SAGE
            40′ Leaves dark green, edges rolled under .... *Mimulus aurantiacus,*
(Scrophulariaceae), STICKY MONKEYFLOWER
        39′ Leaves not sticky
            41. Leaves soft-hairy
                42. Leaves in clusters .... *Cistus creticus,* (Cistaceae), ROCK-ROSE
                42′ Leaves not in clusters ....
.... *Symphoricarpos albus,* (Caprifoliaceae), SNOWBERRY
            41′ Leaves thick, leathery ....
.... *Ceanothus cuneatus,* (Rhamnaceae), BUCK BRUSH

2′ Leaves compound
    43. Plant with spines
       44. With stout, generally curved spines ....
           .... *Rosa californica,* (Rosaceae), CALIFORNIA ROSE
       44′ With slender spines
           45. Plant low-growing, less than 5 dm ....
               .... *Rosa spithamea,* (Rosaceae), GROUND ROSE
           45′ Plant taller, up to > 5 dm ....
               .... *Rosa gymnocarpa,* (Rosaceae), WOOD ROSE
    43′ Plant not as above (but may have spines at the ends of branches)
       46. With 3 leaflets (mostly) (watch out—poison oak is in this group)
          47. Leaflets broad, > 2 cm wide
             48. Upright shrub, can also be vine-like ....
                 Toxicodendron diversilobum, (Anacardiaceae), WESTERN POISON OAK
             48′ Low-growing, trailing shrub less than 5 dm ....
                 .... *Rupertia physodes,* (Fabaceae), CALIFORNIA TEA
          47′ Leaflets narrower
             49. Low-growing shrub to 5 dm, with shiny green stems ....
                 .... *Lotus scoparius,* (Fabaceae), CALIFORNIA BROOM
             49′ Larger shrub
                50. Leaves soft-hairy; flowers yellow ....
                    .... *Genista monspessulana,* (Fabaceae), FRENCH BROOM
                50′ Leaves leathery; flowers rose-purple ....
                    .... *Pickeringia montana,* (Fabaceae), CHAPARRAL PEA
       46′ Leaflets more than 3..
           .... *Lupinus albifrons,* (Fabaceae), SILVER BUSH LUPINE

[1] First time this species appears in the key.
[2] Second time this species appears in the key.

C. Large Shrub or Small Tree

(If you don't find the plant here look at the Shrub (B) or Tree (D) key)
1. Leaves simple
    2. Leaves alternate
       3. Leaf margin entire to irregularly toothed ....
           .... *Salix lasiolepis,* (Salicaceae), ARROYO WILLOW
       3′ Leaf margin lobed and/or toothed
          4. Leaf margin lobed and toothed ....
              .... *Crataegus monogyna,* (Rosaceae), ENGLISH HAWTHORN
          4′ Leaf margin toothed
             5. Leaf margin finely toothed
                6. Leaves round, oval ....
                    ....*Prunus subcordata,* (Rosaceae), PACIFIC PLUM

      6′ Leaves long-narrow ....
      .... *Morella californica,* (Myricaceae), WAX MYRTLE
    5′ Leaf margin sharply toothed
      7. Upper and/or lower leaf surface hairy
        8. Leaf curving under (convex) ....
        .... *Quercus durata,* (Fagaceae), LEATHER OAK
        8′ Leaf flat or wavy not convex ....
        .... *Quercus berberidifolia,* (Fagaceae), SCRUB OAK
      7′ Leaf surface not hairy ....
      .... *Prunus ilicifolia,* (Rosaceae), HOLLY-LEAVED CHERRY
  2′ Leaves opposite
    9. Leaf margins wavy, leaf leathery, lower leaf with soft felty hairs ....
    .... *Garrya elliptica,* (Garryaceae), COAST SILK TASSEL
    9′ Leaf margins not wavy
      10. Leaves with 3-4 pairs of veins ....
      .... *Cornus glabrata,* (Cornaceae), BROWN DOGWOOD
      10′ Leaves with 4-7 pairs of veins ....
      .... *Cornus sericea,* (Cornaceae), AMERICAN DOGWOOD
1′ Leaves compound
  11. Leaves palmately compound ....
  .... *Aesculus californica,* (Hippocastanaceae), CALIFORNIA BUCKEYE
  11′ Leaves odd-pinnately compound ....
  .... *Sambucus mexicana,* (Caprifoliaceae), BLUE ELDERBERRY

D. Tree

(If you don't find the plant here look at the Large Shrub or Small Tree (C) key)
1. Leaves needle-like or scale-like
  2. Leaves scale-like ....
  .... *Cupressus macrocarpa,* (Cupressaceae), MONTEREY CYPRESS
  2′ Leaves needle-like
    3. Needles > 4 cm .... *Pinus radiata,* (Pinaceae), MONTEREY PINE
    3′ Needles < 4 cm
      4. Most needles < 1.5 mm wide, newer stems with round raised
         structures where needles have fallen off, cone > 3 cm long ....
        .... *Pseudotsuga menziesii,* (Pinaceae), DOUGLAS FIR
      4′ Most needles > 1.5 mm wide, needle-like scales appressed
         to the stem, cone < 3 cm long ....
        .... *Sequoia sempervirens,* (Taxodiaceae), COAST REDWOOD
1′ Leaves not needle-like
  5. Leaves simple
    6. Leaf margin entire (smooth)
      7. Outer bark shredding in obvious strips

8. Bark red-brown...*Arbutus menziesii,*[1] (Ericaceae), PACIFIC MADRONE
8´ Bark gray-white
   9. All leaves similar, alternate ....
      .... *Eucalyptus globulus,* (Myrtaceae), BLUE GUM
   9´ Immature leaves opposite, mature leaves alternate ....
      .... *Eucalyptus pulverulenta,* (Myrtaceae), SILVER-LEAVED GUM
7´ Outer bark not shredding in obvious strips
   10. Leaves of two kinds, mature simple, juvenile compound ....
      .... *Acacia melanoxylon,*[1] (Fabaceae), BLACKWOOD ACACIA
   10´ All leaves simple
      11. Leaves aromatic, dark green above, lighter green beneath ....
         .... *Umbellularia californica,* (Lauraceae), CALIFORNIA BAY
      11´ Leaves olive green above, white beneath ....
         .... *Olea europaea,* (Oleaceae), OLIVE
6´ Leaf margin lobed or toothed
   12. Leaf margin lobed
      13. Leaf palmately lobed .... *Platanus* sp., (Platanaceae), SYCAMORE
      13´ Leaf shallowly lobed .... *Quercus douglasii,* (Fagaceae), BLUE OAK
      13´´ Leaf more deeply lobed .... *Quercus lobata,* (Fagaceae), VALLEY OAK
   12´ Leaf margin toothed
      14. Leaf fan-shaped .... *Washingtonia* sp., (Arecaceae), FAN PALM
      14´ Leaf not fan-shaped
         15. Leaf margin spine-tipped, most leaves rolled under ....
            .... *Quercus agrifolia,* (Fagaceae), COAST LIVE OAK
         15´ Leaf margin toothed
            16. Bark red-brown, shredding ....
            .... *Arbutus menziesii,*[2] (Ericaceae), PACIFIC MADRONE
            16´ Bark not shredding in large strips ....
            ....*Prunus* sp., (Rosaceae), ORNAMENTAL PLUM
5´ Leaves compound
   17. Leaves 1-pinnate
      18. Leaflets mostly > 10 ....
         .... *Juglans californica,* (Juglandaceae), CALIFORNIA BLACK WALNUT
      18´ Leaflets mostly < 10 .... *Juglans regia,* (Juglandaceae), ENGLISH WALNUT
   17´ Leaves 2-pinnate
      19. Plant with 2 kinds of leaves, juvenile compound, mature simple.............
         .... *Acacia melanoxylon,*[2] (Fabaceae), BLACKWOOD ACACIA
      19´ Plant with only compound leaves
         20. Leaves ≯ 10 cm ≤10cm..... *Acacia baileyana,* (Fabaceae), BAILEY ACACIA
         20´ Leaves ≮ 10 cm ≥10cm..... *Acacia dealbata,* (Fabaceae), SILVER WATTLE

[1] First time this species appears in the key.
[2] Second time this species appears in the key.

Group 3. Herbaceous Flowering Plant Families — Annuals, Biennials, Herbaceous Perennials (nonwoody)

1. Leaf venation usually parallel; perianth parts usually in multiples of 3
    .... Monocotyledons
    2. Perianth either absent or composed of greenish to brown, scale-like bristly parts
        3. Perianth parts 6, scale-like; fruit a capsule with many seeds ....
            .... Juncaceae *(Juncus, Luzula)*
        3´ Perianth parts absent, or if present, bristle-like; fruit usually with one seed
            4. Inflorescence a dense, elongated, cylindrical spike ....
                .... Typhaceae *(Typha)*
            4´ Inflorescences of various types (raceme, spike, panicle) but not dense and cylindrical
                5. Stems usually sharply or obtusely 3-angled, usually with solid internodes; leaves in 3 ranks; stamens and pistil usually subtended by 1 bract; fruit 3-angled .... Cyperaceae *(Carex, Eleocharis)*
                5´ Stems circular, usually with hollow internodes; leaves in 2 ranks; stamens and pistil usually subtended by 2 bracts; fruit usually elliptic or oblong, not angled .... Poaceae (All Grasses)
    2´ Perianth present, brightly colored
        6. Ovary superior ...*in all species present in Edgewood*... Liliaceae (All)
        6´ Ovary inferior
            7. Flowers irregular .... Orchidaceae (All)
            7´ Flowers regular .... Iridaceae (All)
1´ Leaf venation pinnate or palmate; perianth parts usually in multiples of 4 or 5 .... Dicotyledons
    Key 1 — Perianth small, or 0, green, brown or reddish   *this page*
    Key 2 — Petals separate to base, most petals falling off individually *p. 20*
    Key 3 — Petals fused at least at the base into a ring or tube, petals *p. 21* falling off all together

Key 1 — Perianth small, or 0, green, brown or reddish
1. Stems and leaves densely hairy
    2. Stems and leaves with stinging hairs, inflorescence a long, loose spike-like raceme ...*in many species in this family*........... Urticaceae[1] *(Urtica)*
    2´ Stems and leaves with soft or bristly hairs, not stinging
        3. Stems and leaves with soft hairs, leaf hairs stellate, leaves yellow-green ...
            .... Euphorbiaceae[1] *(Croton)*
        3´ Stems and leaves bristly hairy, leaves darker green ....
            .... Urticaceae[2] *(Parietaria)*

1′ Stems and leaves smooth, or sparsely hairy   *species*
    4. Plant succulent, small *perianth tiny only in our* ..... Crassulaceae (*Crassula*)
    4′ Plant not succulent
        5. Leaves opposite .... Polygonaceae[1] (*Pterostegia*)
        5′ Leaves alternate or basal
            6. Inflorescence open, many flowered .... Polygonaceae[2] (*Rumex*)
            6′ Inflorescence axillary, head-like or in a terminal spike
                7. Inflorescence axillary .... Euphorbiaceae[2] (*Euphorbia*)
                7′ Inflorescence head-like, axillary or in a terminal spike
                    8. Inflorescence head-like .... Rosaceae[1] (*Aphanes, Sanguisorba*)
                    8′ Inflorescence axillary and/or in a terminal spike ....
                     .... Chenopodiaceae (*Chenopodium*)

Key 2 — Petals separate to base, most petals falling off individually

1. Stamens numerous, > 10 per flower
    2. Ovary inferior .... Rosaceae[2] (*Potentilla*)
    2′ Ovary superior
        3. Stamens united into a tube .... Malvaceae (*Sidalcea*)
        3′ Stamens separate from each other
            4. Pistil 1 per flower .... Papaveraceae (All)
            4′ Pistils 2 to many per flower .... Ranunculaceae (All)
1′ Stamens 10 or fewer per flower
    5. Corolla with 4 petals, flowers regular
        6. Ovary superior .... Brassicaceae (All)
        6′ Ovary inferior .... Onagraceae (All)
    5′ Corolla with 5 or more than 5 petals
        7. Flowers irregular, pea shaped .... Fabaceae (All)
        7′ Flowers regular (maybe slightly irregular, but not pea shaped)
            8. Inflorescence an umbel or umbel-like
                9. Ovary inferior .... Apiaceae (All)
                9′ Ovary superior
                    10. Leaves compound, leaflets 3 .... Oxalidaceae (*Oxalis*)
                    10′ Leaves simple or compound ....
                     .... Geraniaceae (*Erodium, Geranium*)
            8′ Inflorescence in other arrangements
                11. Sepals 2 .... Portulacaceae[1] (*Calandrinia, Claytonia*)
                11′ Sepals > 2
                    12. Leaves mostly in a basal rosette
                      13. Petals 5 .... Saxifragaceae (*Lithophragma, Saxifraga*)
                      13′ Petals more than 5 .... Portulacaceae[2] (*Lewisia*)
                  12′ Leaves alternate, opposite or whorled
                    14. Leaves alternate .... Linaceae (*Hesperolinon, Linum*)

14′ Leaves opposite or whorled
    15. Leaves whorled .... Primulaceae *(Trientalis)*
    15′ Leaves opposite
        16. Petals notched or fringed ....
           .... Caryophyllaceae *(Silene, Cerastium, Stellaria)*
        16′ Petals entire
           17. Stigma and style 1 .... Primulaceae *(Anagallis)*
           17′ Stigma and style more than 1 ....
           ....Caryophyllaceae *(Minuartia, Spergularia)*

Key 3 — Petals fused at least at the base into a ring or tube, petals falling off all together
1. Inflorescence in heads; fruit an achene, ovary inferior
    2. Calyx never green but modified as a white to brownish pappus (sometimes absent); heads with either or both ray and disk flowers .... Asteraceae (All)
    2′ Calyx of 4-5 green sepals; petals pale pink .... Dipsacaceae *(Dipsacus)*
1′ Inflorescence in various arrangements
    3. Leaves mostly in a basal rosette
        4. Inflorescence a simple umbel .... Primulaceae[2] *(Dodecatheon)*
        4′ Inflorescence in other arrangements
           5. Inflorescence open, branched .... Polygonaceae[3] *(Eriogonum)*
           5′ Inflorescence a dense spike .... Plantaginaceae *(Plantago)*
    3′ Leaves alternate, opposite or whorled, mostly along the stem
        6. Flowers irregular
           7. Plants without chlorophyll .... Orobanchaceae *(Orobanche)*
           7′ Plants green, photosynthetic
               8. Herbage with a minty aroma; fruit of 4 nutlets .. Lamiaceae (All)
               8′ Herbage not mint-scented; fruit a capsule...Scrophulariaceae (All)
        6′ Flowers regular
           9. Plants without chlorophyll .... Cuscutaceae *(Cuscuta)*
           9′ Plants green, photosynthetic..
              10. Inflorescence in coiled clusters
                  11. Fruit a capsule .... Hydrophyllaceae[1] *(Phacelia)*
                  11′ Fruit 1-4 nutlets .... Boraginaceae (All)
              10′ Inflorescence in other arrangements
                  12. Ovary inferior
                      13. Corolla spurred .... Valerianaceae *(Plectritis)* flowers irregular
                      13′ Corolla not spurred
                          14. Calyx absent .... Rubiaceae (All)
                        14′ Calyx present .... Lythraceae *(Lythrum)*
                12′ Ovary superior
                  15. Leaves opposite or whorled
                      16. Leaves opposite

17. Inflorescence an elongated spike .... Verbenaceae *(Verbena)*
17´ Inflorescence in other arrangements
    18. Style not divided, stamens 5, twisting ... Gentianaceae *(Centaurium)*
    18´ Style divided
        19. Style 3-parted .... Polemoniaceae[1] *(Linanthus, Phlox)*
        19´ Style 2-parted.................................... Hydrophyllaceae[2] *(Nemophila)*
16´ Leaves whorled or appearing whorled
    20. Petals reflexed ....Asclepiadaceae *(Asclepias)*
    20´ Petals not reflexed .... Polemoniaceae[2] *(Linanthus)*
15´ Leaves alternate
    21. Inflorescence axillary
        22. Flowers large, showy .... Convolvulaceae *(Calystegia)*
        22´ Flowers smaller, < 3 mm............................. Polygonaceae[4] *(Polygonum)*
    21´ Inflorescence in other arrangements
        23. Style 3-parted .... Polemoniaceae[4]
        (Collomia, Eriastrum, Gilia, Navarretia)
        23´ Style 2-parted .... Hydrophyllaceae[3] *(Phacelia)*

[1] First time this family appears in the key.
[2] Second time this family appears in the key.
[3] Third time this family appears in the key.
[4] Fourth time this family appears in the key.

Pteridophytes

Fern and Fern Allies

Characteristics

Herbaceous perennials from rhizomes; reproducing from spores. Leaves compound, 1–4 pinnate. Sorus round, oblong, elongate, or J-shaped; arranged in rows or along veins or marginal or aggregated in terminal, cone-like structures; indusia linear, oblong, reniform or 0. Spores microscopic.

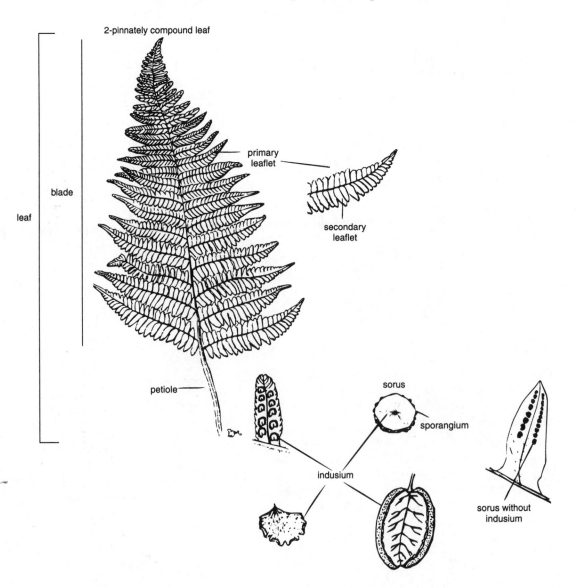

Dryopteridaceae — Wood Fern Family

Leaf blades mostly 2–4-pinnately compound, often scaly or hairy. Sori usually round, borne on midvein or at tips of veins; indusia reniform, peltate or hood-like. (*Dryopteris arguta, Polystichum munitum*).

For key to Ferns and Fern Allies *see* Group 1. Pteridophytes — Ferns and Fern Allies.

Dryopteris arguta (Kaulf.) Maxon

COASTAL WOOD FERN   Native

Flowering Time: N/A

Habitat: woodland

Description: Herbaceous fern to 6 dm. Leaves compound, 1–2 pinnate, blades to 6 dm; leaflets toothed and lobed; lower primary leaflets to 30 cm, upper reduced; secondary leaflets to 2 cm. Sori round to reniform to 1 mm, in two rows except on upper leaflets may be more than two rows; indusium reniform.

Genus & Specific Name Derivation: Greek: oak-fern, referring to habitat / sharply toothed or notched, referring to the leaflets

leaflet with sori

Ht. to 0.6m

Polystichum munitum (Kaulf.) C. Presl

WESTERN SWORD FERN   Native

Flowering Time: N/A

Habitat: woodland

Description: Herbaceous fern to 14 dm. Leaves compound, blade to 12 dm, 1-pinnate; leaflets toothed, lower with a larger lobe at the base. Sori round, produced in two rows along both sides of the main leaflet vein.

Genus & Specific Name Derivation: Greek: many rows, referring to the rows of sori / armed or fortified

Notes: At the base of each leaflet is a larger lobe, which looks like the hilt of a sword.

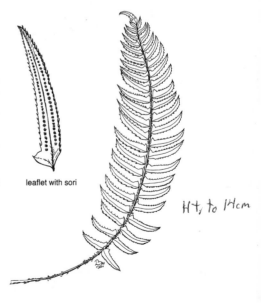

leaflet with sori

Ht, to 14cm

Equisetaceae — Horsetail Family

Herbaceous perennials; aerial stems erect, jointed, green, with silica, internodes hollow. Leaves whorled, small, fused into a sheath, not green, tips usually free, tooth-like, deciduous or persistent. Cones terminal, scale-like. Sporangia on lower surfaces of peltate sporophyll; spores green. Natives used the abrasive stems for polishing wooden items.

For key to Ferns and Fern Allies *see* Group 1. Pteridophytes — Ferns and Fern Allies.

√*Equisetum telmateia* Ehrh. ssp. *braunii* (Milde) R. L. Hauke

GIANT HORSETAIL   Native

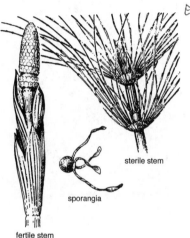

sterile stem

sporangia

fertile stem

Flowering Time: N/A

Habitat: riparian woodland, seeps

Description: Herbaceous perennial from rhizomes. Stem erect, ridged lengthwise, hollow except at nodes, 2 kinds, sterile and fertile. Sterile stem to 60 cm, light green; sheath to 18 mm with 14–28 teeth; branch with 4–5 grooved ridges, solid. Fertile stem to 45 cm, unbranched, fleshy, brown; sheath to 4 cm, teeth 20–30. Sporangia several on inner surfaces of scale-like rims of terminal cone.

Genus & Specific Name Derivation: Latin: horse, bristle, referring to the roots / from marshes

Notes: Illustration from *Illustrated Flora of the Pacific States.*

Uses Past and Present: Some species were eaten by the Romans in the seventh century. The young heads were boiled like asparagus, or mixed with flour and fried. Natives used the stems as a diuretic. The outer layer of the stem contains silica useful in scouring tools and cooking supplies.

Polypodiaceae — Polypody Family

Leaf blades simple to 1-pinnately compound; petioles often glabrous. Sori round to oblong, along veins or scattered over lower surfaces, not near margins; indusia absent. *(Polypodium californicum.)*

For key to Ferns and Fern Allies *see* Group 1. Pteridophytes — Ferns and Fern Allies.

√ *Polypodium californicum* Kaulf.

E CALIFORNIA POLYPODY   Native

SC *Flowering Time:* N/A

Habitat: woodland

Description: Herbaceous fern to 4 dm, from rhizomes. Leaves compound, blade to 25 cm, 1-pinnate, margins toothed. Sori roundish to 3.5 mm, in one row on each side of leaflet main vein.

Genus & Specific Name Derivation: Latin: many feet, from rhizome / from California

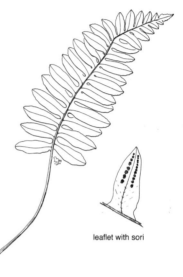

Ht. to 0.4m

leaflet with sori

Pteridaceae — Brake or Maiden-Hair Family

Leaf blades often 2–5-pinnately compound or palmately-pinnate. Sori borne at or near leaf margins, sometimes along veins, often covered by recurved blade margin; indusia absent. *(Adiantum jordanii, Pellaea andromedifolia, Pentagramma triangularis.)*

For key to Ferns and Fern Allies *see* Group 1. Pteridophytes — Ferns and Fern Allies.

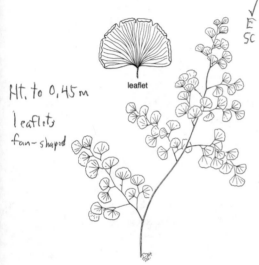

Ht. to 0.45 m

leaflets
fan-shaped

leaflet

Adiantum jordanii C. Mueller

CALIFORNIA MAIDEN-HAIR   Native

Flowering Time: N/A

Habitat: woodland

Description: Herbaceous fern, stem dark brown to black, wiry. Frond to 45 cm including stem. Leaves 2–3-pinnate to palmately compound, leaflets rounded, margins toothed and lobed. Leaflet margins rolled under; spores are produced there.

Genus & Specific Name Derivation: Greek: unwettable / derivation unknown

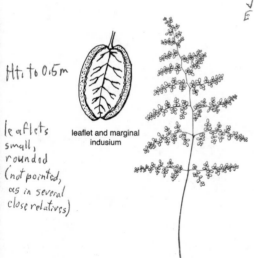

Ht. to 0.5 m

leaflets
small,
rounded
(not pointed,
as in several
close relatives)

leaflet and marginal
indusium

Pellaea andromedifolia (Kaulf.) Fee

COFFEE FERN   Native

Flowering Time: N/A

Habitat: chaparral

Description: Herbaceous fern from creeping rhizomes. Frond to 50 cm. Leaves compound, 3-pinnate, leaflets to 15 mm, rounded, green to purplish. Sporangia in a continuous marginal band on the undersurface of leaflet where the spores are produced.

Genus & Specific Name Derivation: Greek: dusky, from bluish gray leaves / after Andromeda, the daughter of Cepheus and Cassiope, rescued by Perseus from the sea monster

Pentagramma triangularis (Kaulf.) G. Yatskievych, M. D. Windham & E. Wollenweber ssp. *triangularis*

GOLDBACK FERN   Native

Flowering Time: N/A

Habitat: woodland

Description: Herbaceous perennial from a short-creeping rhizome. Frond to 15 cm, triangular; petiole dark brown to black. Leaves compound, 3–4-pinnate, undersurface with a yellow exudate. Sporangia produced along veins and throughout undersurface.

Genus & Specific Name Derivation: Five lines or stripes / shaped like a triangle, referring to the shape of frond

Notes: The yellow powdery exudate on the leaf undersurface are not the spores. Frond includes the petiole.

Ht. to 15 cm

Gymnosperms

Cupressaceae — Cypress Family

Evergreen, monoecious trees. Leaves scale-like. Pollen on short, terminal cones; ovules and seeds naked, borne on woody, scale-like cones. Seeds 2–many per scale, flat, winged. Many species are cultivated and the wood of some is used commercially.

For key to woody plants *see* Group 2. Woody Plants

Evergreen
Large
tree

Cupressus macrocarpa Gordon

MONTEREY CYPRESS   Native / Planted

Flowering Time: N/A

Habitat: planted at Day Camp

Description: Large tree to 25 m. Leaves scale-like, overlapping, bright green. Flowers unisexual, male called the pollen cone, female called the seed cone. Fruit a cone to 25 mm wide, spherical, brown.

Genus & Specific Name Derivation: Latin: cypress / large fruit, referring to the cone

Notes: This tree is rare where it occurs naturally on the Monterey Peninsula. It has been planted and has become naturalized outside of its natural range. Illustration from *Illustrated Flora of the Pacific States.*

Pinaceae — Pine Family

Trees or shrubs, monoecious, evergreen. Leaves simple, generally alternate, sometimes in bundles, linear or awl-like. Pollen cone not woody, deciduous. Seed cone woody; bracts, scales persistent. Seeds 2 on upper side of scale base. Many of great commercial value, supplying more than half of the world's timber.

For key to woody plants *see* Group 2. Woody Plants

Pinus radiata D. Don

MONTEREY PINE   Native / Planted

Flowering Time: February–March

Habitat: planted at Day Camp

Description: Evergreen tree to 40 m. Leaves in bundles of 3, to 15 cm, needle-like, gray-green, fragrant. Flowers are unisexual cones; pollen cone to 6 cm, not woody, deciduous; seed cone becomes woody, with bracts and scales. Fruit a cone to 15 cm, asymmetric.

Genus & Specific Name Derivation: Latin: pine / arrangement of seed cones in whorls around branches

Notes: This tree is rare where is occurs naturally, it was planted here and is extensively planted throughout our area where it has become naturalized. In New Zealand it is planted as a major timber tree.

Uses Past and Present: Seeds were roasted and eaten, strung on thread to decorate dresses; soft centers of green cones were roasted and eaten; pitch used as glue, also smeared on burns and cuts and chewed. Twigs and rootlets used for sewing baskets.

Evergreen
Large
tree

Evergreen
Large
tree

√ **_Pseudotsuga menziesii_** (Mirbel) Franco
E var. **_menziesii_**

DOUGLAS FIR   Native

Flowering Time: N/A

Habitat: woodland, ridges

Description: Evergreen tree to 70 m. Leaves flat to 4 cm, needle-like, with 2 whitish bands on lower surface. Flowers are unisexual cones, pollen cone not woody, deciduous; seed cone pendent to 9 cm, with exserted bracts. Fruit a cone to 9 cm, ripens in fall.

Genus & Specific Name Derivation: Latin and Japanese: false hemlock / for Archibald Menzies (1754–1842), English naturalist on the ship *Discovery*

Notes: Bracts at the base of each scale said to look like a mouse tail.

Uses Past and Present: Used extensively by natives for lumber, harpoon shafts and other tools. The roots were used in weaving baskets. A tea was made from the fresh needles.

Taxodiaceae — Bald Cypress Family

Trees or shrubs, monoecious, evergreen. Leaves simple, alternate, not in bundles, linear or awl-like; tip pointed. Seed cone generally woody; scales fused with bracts. Seeds 2–9 per scale; with wings. Many with great commercial value.

For key to woody plants *see* Group 2. Woody Plants

√ *Sequoia sempervirens* (D. Don) Endl.

COAST REDWOOD   Native / Planted

Flowering Time: N/A

Habitat: Day Camp

seed

Evergreen Large tree (handwritten)

Description: Evergreen, monoecious tree to 115 m; bark fibrous, reddish. Leaves alternate, simple to 1.5 cm, linear, needle-like, tip pointed. Male cones minute, yellow; female seed cones with whorled, wrinkled, diamond-shaped scales. Fruit a woody cone to 3 cm, spherical, maturing in 1 year, at first green, turning brown.

Genus & Specific Name Derivation: Sequoyah (1770–1843), Cherokee chief / always green

Notes: Old-growth trees hold the record as the tallest trees in our area and are long-lived to over 1,000 years. The coast redwood once dominated the forests across North America when our climate was moister and cooler. Now native stands are restricted to coastal areas. Because of the dark, shaded areas under redwoods and the persistent dampness, natives did not make their homes in redwood forests. Because of the high tannin content in the bark, wood and leaves, there is very little understory vegetation in a natural redwood forest.

Angiosperms

Flowering Plants — Dicotyledons

Anacardiaceae — Sumac Family

Shrubs or trees, often dioecious. Leaves alternate, simple to compound, deciduous or evergreen. Inflorescence in racemes or panicles. Flowers bisexual or unisexual, regular. Sepals 5, fused; petals 5, free; stamens 5 or 10; pistil 1, ovary superior, styles 1–3. Fruit drupe-like. Some species used for wood and food (cashew, mango, pistachio). Contact with sap of some can cause severe dermatitis in humans.

For key to woody plants *see* Group 2. Woody Plants

PETALS
PALE GREEN
small

fruit

Shrub
or
Woody
vine

Toxicodendron diversilobum (Torrey & A. Gray) E. Greene

WESTERN POISON OAK   Native

Flowering Time: March–May

Habitat: woodland, chaparral, disturbed areas

Description: Deciduous shrub or vine to 25 m; usually dioecious. Leaves alternate, compound, 1-pinnate. Leaflets usually 3 sometimes up to 5, to 13 cm, "leaves of 3 leave it be." Petiole to 10 cm. Inflorescence a raceme. Flowers unisexual, regular. Sepals 5, fused; petals 5, separate, pale green, fragrant, attracting many pollinators. Stamens 5; ovary superior, stigma 3 parted. Fruit a drupe-like berry, to 6 mm wide, cream-colored with black vertical striations.

Genus & Specific Name Derivation: Latin: toxic tree / diverse lobes, referring to the leaves

Notes: Resin on leaves, stems, fruits can cause a severe rash. In its deciduous form, this plant can be identified by long upright main branches with short, stubby side branches. Individual plants vary as to size, shape and growth form. The leaves turn red before falling, making it one of our few fall color plants. It is one of the most widely distributed plants in California. Illustration from *Illustrated Flora of the Pacific States.*

Uses Past and Present: Natives are said to have been immune and used the fresh juice, which produces a black stain, to ornament their utensils, cure warts and ringworm. The stems were used in their baskets.

Apiaceae — Carrot Family

Annuals, biennials, or herbaceous perennials, often aromatic; stems hollow and usually ribbed. Leaves basal, alternate or opposite, usually compound; petiole base often sheathing. Inflorescence a simple or compound umbel. Flowers mostly bisexual, older may be unisexual; mostly regular, some may be slightly irregular; sepals 5, separate, usually minute, may not even be visible; petals 5, separate; stamens 5, exserted; pistil 1, ovary inferior, style and stigma 2-lobed. Fruit splits in 2, often with wings, prickles or hooks on the margins, seeds 2. Many species are cultivated for food and culinary herbs (e.g., anise, caraway, carrots, celery, coriander, cumin, dill, fennel, parsley). Some species (e.g., hemlock) are highly toxic. Synonym Umbelliferae.

Family Characteristics

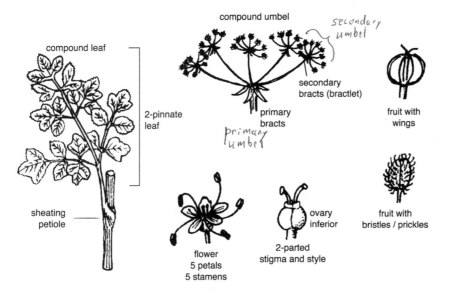

compound umbel

secondary umbel

compound leaf

2-pinnate leaf

secondary bracts (bractlet)

primary bracts

primary umbel

fruit with wings

sheating petiole

flower
5 petals
5 stamens

2-parted stigma and style

ovary inferior

fruit with bristles / prickles

For key to families *see* Group 3. Herbaceous Flowering Plant Families

1. Umbels head-like
    2. Leaves simple
        3. Leaves opposite .... *Bowlesia incana* (BOWLESIA)
        3´ Leaves variously arranged
            4. Bracts spiny, sharp to the touch ....
                .... *Eryngium aristulatum* (JEPSON ERYNGO/COYOTE THISTLE)
            4´ Bracts not spine-tipped
                5. Leaves lobed, rounded .... *Sanicula crassicaulis* (PACIFIC SANICLE)
                5´ Leaves deeply 3-lobed, sharply toothed ....
                    .... *Sanicula laciniata* (COAST SANICLE)
    2´ Leaves compound
        6. Corolla purple .... *Sanicula bipinnatifida* (PURPLE SANICLE)
        6´ Corolla yellow or white
            7. Corolla yellow
                8. Fruit with bristles .... *Sanicula bipinnata* (POISON SANICLE)
                8' Fruit with wart-like tubercles ...... *Sanicula tuberosa* (TURKEY PEA)
            7´ Corolla white .... *Torilis nodosa* (KNOTTED HEDGE PARSLEY)
1´ Umbels open
    9. Mature plant > 5 dm
        10. Leaflets thread-like
            11. Plant anise-scented .... *Foeniculum vulgare* (FENNEL)
            11´ Plant not anise-scented ...... *Perideridia kelloggii* (KELLOGG'S YAMPAH)
        10´ Leaflets not thread-like
            12. Leaflets 1-pinnate .... *Heracleum lanatum* (COW PARSNIP)
            12´ Leaflets 2–3-pinnate
                13. Stems with reddish-brown blotches ....
                    .... *Conium maculatum* (POISON HEMLOCK)
                13´ Stems more or less green
                    14. Leaves hairy
                        15. Some leaflets longer than 10 cm ..fruit..oblong........................
                            .... *Angelica tomentosa* (WOOD ANGELICA)
                        15´ Most leaflets shorter than 10 cm ..fruit elongate (very)........
                            ....*Osmorhiza berteroi* (WOOD SWEET CICELY)
                    14´ Leaves without hairs ....
                        .... *Lomatium californicum* (CALIFORNIA LOMATIUM)
    9´ Mature plant mostly < 5 dm
        16. Plant low-growing, spreading
            17. Bracts longer than the inflorescence ....
                .... *Daucus pusillus* (RATTLESNAKE WEED)
            17´ Bracts shorter than the inflorescence
                18. Petals hairy ....
                    .... *Lomatium dasycarpum* (WOOLLY-FRUITED LOMATIUM)
                18´ Petals hairless
                    19. Leaflet segments linear, some thread-like ....

.... *Lomatium caruifolium* (CARAWAY-LEAVED LOMATIUM)
  19´ Leaflet segments not thread-like
    20. Bractlets one-sided, linear-lanceolate ....
.... *Lomatium macrocarpum* (LARGE-FRUITED LOMATIUM)
    20´ Bractlets spreading, ovate to rounded ....
Lomatium utriculatum (COMMON LOMATIUM / BLADDER PARSNIP)
 16´ Plant upright, branched above
  21. Fruit elongated, longer than 1 cm ....
....*Scandix pecten-veneris* (VENUS' NEEDLE)
  21´ Fruit less than 1 cm
    22. Fruit with an obvious beak, tip pointed ...~~fruit with prickles~~.....
.... *Anthriscus caucalis* (BUR-CHERVIL)
    22´ Fruit without a beak, tip rounded
      23. Fruit smooth .... *Tauschia hartwegii* (HARTWEG'S TAUSCHIA)
      23´ Fruit roughened or with prickles
        24. Bracts leaf-like...
.... *Yabea microcarpa* (CALIFORNIA HEDGE PARSLEY)
        24´ Bracts 0 or inconspicuous
          25. Fruit with prickles ....
....*Torilis arvensis* (HEDGE PARSLEY)
          25´ Fruit roughened ....
...........................*Apiastrum angustifolium* (WILD CELERY)

Angelica tomentosa S. Watson

WOOD ANGELICA   Native / CALIF. ANGELICA

Flowering Time: June–September

Habitat: woodland

Description: Upright, glaucous (whitish waxy coating), herbaceous perennial to 20 dm. Leaves basal and alternate, compound, 2–3-pinnate, blade to 1 dm, reduced upward; upper surface sparsely hairy, lower surface paler, hairy; leaflets to 12 cm, margin toothed. Petiole to 30 cm, base sheathing. Inflorescence a compound, open umbel; individual umbels to 10 cm wide; bracts 0. Sepals minute; petals white; stamens exserted; ovary inferior, style and stigma 2-parted. Fruit to 10 mm, oblong.

Genus & Specific Name Derivation: Latin: angelic, for cordial and medicinal properties / thickly matted hairs, referring to the hairs on the inflorescence and lower surface of the leaves

Notes: The species name "tomentosa" refers to the hairs on the plant, however the closely related species "A. hendersonii" is much more tomentose or hairy. Although individual flowers are small the whole umbel is quite large and showy.

Uses Past and Present: European species used medicinally and as a herb.

Compare to Osmorhiza berteroi

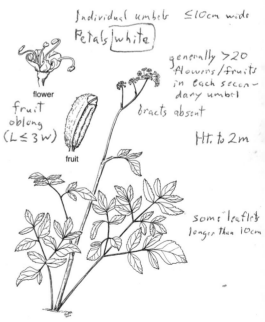

Individual umbels ≤10cm wide
Petals white
generally >20 flowers/fruits in each secondary umbel
bracts absent
Ht. to 2m
flower
fruit oblong (L ≤ 3 w)
fruit
some leaflets longer than 10cm

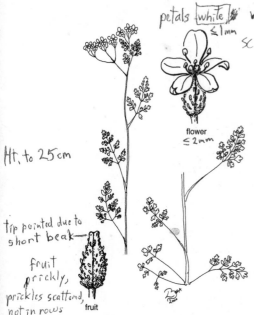

petals white ≤1mm

flower ≤2mm

Ht. to 25cm

tip pointed due to short beak—

fruit prickly, prickles scattered, not in rows

fruit

✓ *Anthriscus caucalis* M. Bieb.

BUR-CHERVIL   Nonnative / Eurasia

Flowering Time: April–June

Habitat: woodland

Description: Annual to 25 cm. Leaves alternate, compound, 2-pinnate then deeply toothed; blade to 4 cm. Petiole to 4 cm, sheathing at the base. Inflorescence a compound umbel; peduncle to 1.5 cm; pedicel to 5 mm; bracts to 3 mm, green. Flowers to 2 mm wide. Sepals minute; petals white to 1 mm; ovary inferior; style and stigma 2-parted. Fruit to 4 mm, with upward-turned prickles on surface and a short beak.

Genus & Specific Name Derivation: Ancient Greek name / ancient Greek name for umbelliferous plant

Notes: Beak separates it from *Torilis*.

Compare to Torilis spp. and Yabea

Apiastrum angustifolium Nutt.

WILD CELERY   Native

Flowering Time: February–May

Habitat: grassland

Description: Annual to 50 cm, much-branched. Leaves mostly opposite some alternate, compound finely dissected; blade to 5 cm; petiole to 4 cm. Inflorescence a compound umbel; from axils of leaves; bracts 0. Sepals 0; petals minute, white. Fruit to 2 mm, roundish, roughened.

Genus & Specific Name Derivation: Latin for wild celery / narrow foliage

Notes: Illustration from *Illustrated Flora of the Pacific States.*

petals white

minute (<1mm)

leaves finely dissected plant much branched

Ht. to 0.5m

flower

fruit cross section

fruit roughened but without prickles, heart-shaped due to cleft at base

fruit   J

Bowlesia incana Ruiz Lopez & Pavon

BOWLESIA   Native

Flowering Time: March–May

Habitat: open woodland

Description: Annual, trailing to 20 cm, whole plant bristly-hairy. Leaves opposite, simple to 3 cm, margin lobed. Petiole to 12 cm. Inflorescence a simple, axillary umbel; bracts small. Sepals 0 or minute; petals minute, yellowish-white. Fruit to 2 mm, roundish, prickly.

Genus & Specific Name Derivation: For William Bowles (1705–1780), Irish writer on Spanish natural history / grayish-white

Notes: Illustration from *Illustrated Flora of the Pacific States.*

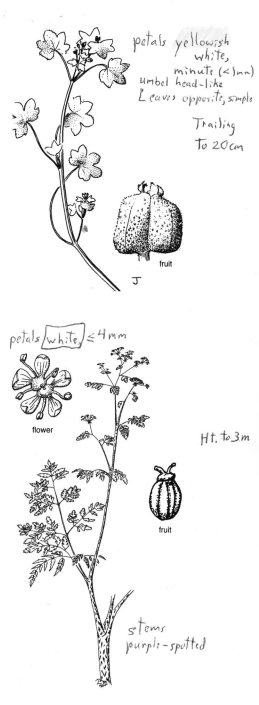

petals yellowish white,
minute (<1mm)
umbel head-like
Leaves opposite, simple

Trailing
To 20 cm

fruit

J

*Conium maculatum* L.

E
Sc

POISON HEMLOCK   Nonnative / Europe

Flowering Time: May–June

Habitat: disturbed areas

Description: Herbaceous biennial or herbaceous perennial to 30 dm. Stems purple-spotted or streaked. Leaves alternate, compound, 2–3-pinnate; blade to 3 dm. Inflorescence a compound umbel; peduncle to 8 cm. Sepal lobes 0, petals white to 4 mm. Fruit to 3 mm wide, roundish.

Genus & Specific Name Derivation: Greek name used by Dioscorides / Latin: spotted, referring to the spots on the stems

Notes: Invasive. Introduced to the U.S. as a garden plant sometime in the 1800s. First collected in California in 1893. Socrates was said to have taken this to end his life, and the red-purple spots are said to be reminders of the blood of Socrates. The plant contains highly toxic alkaloids used in ancient Greece for capital punishment.

Uses Past and Present: All plant parts highly toxic.

petals white, ≤4mm

flower

Ht. to 3m

fruit

stems
purple-spotted

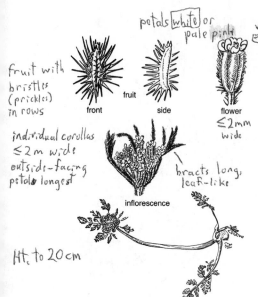

petals white or pale pink

fruit with bristles (prickles) in rows

fruit

front   side   flower

≤2mm wide

individual corollas ≤2m wide outside-facing petals longest

bracts long, leaf-like

inflorescence

Ht. to 20 cm

√ *Daucus pusillus* Michaux

RATTLESNAKE WEED   Native

Flowering Time: April–May

Habitat: chaparral

Description: Low-growing, spreading herbaceous biennial to 20 cm, whole plant soft-hairy. Leaves basal and alternate, compound, fern-like; blade to 10 cm. Petiole to 5 cm, clasping. Inflorescence a compound umbel; bracts leaf-like, longer than the inflorescence; peduncle to 1 cm. Sepals minute; individual flowers to 2 mm wide, white to light pink. Fruit to 5 mm with bristly hairs.

Genus & Specific Name Derivation: Greek: carrot / Latin: very small, referring to the small flowers

Notes: Foliage smells like carrots.

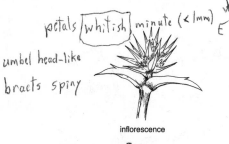

petals whitish minute (< 1mm)

umbel head-like

bracts spiny

inflorescence

Ht. to 0.4 m

✗ *Eryngium aristulatum* Jepson var. *aristulatum*

JEPSON ERYNGO / COYOTE THISTLE   Native /

BUTTON CELERY

Flowering Time: June–August

Habitat: grassland

Description: Low-growing, spiny biennial or herbaceous perennial to 4 dm tall. Leaves basal, simple; blade to 10 cm; margin irregularly cut and lobed with coarse teeth. Inflorescence a spiny bracted head-like umbel. Sepals to 3 mm; petals minute, whitish. Fruit to 2 mm, roughened.

Genus & Specific Name Derivation: Ancient Greek name used by Theophrastus / Latin: an awn or bristle, referring to the spines on the plant

√ *Foeniculum vulgare* Miller

SC
E

FENNEL   Nonnative / Europe

Flowering Time: June–August

Habitat: disturbed areas

Description: Upright herbaceous perennial to 20 dm. Leaves alternate, pinnately compound and finely dissected, blade to 4 dm; leaflets thread-like. Petiole to 14 cm, sheathing. Inflorescence a compound umbel; individual umbel to 4 cm wide. Sepals minute; petals yellow, minute. Fruit to 4 mm, ribbed.

Genus & Specific Name Derivation: Latin: fennel / common

Notes: Fennel is incorrectly called anise (true anise is related but grows only in cultivation). The foliage and seeds are anise or licorice scented. Plant is used by the swallow-tail butterfly as a host.

Uses Past and Present: Worldwide this herb has been and continues to be used in cooking and flavoring. It's said that the missionary fathers of old California spread fennel seeds on the mission floors and when stepped on a pleasant aroma would fill the rooms.

Heracleum lanatum Michaux

COW PARSNIP   Native

Flowering Time: April–July

Habitat: woodland

Description: Stout, upright, hairy, herbaceous perennial to 30 dm; strongly scented. Leaves alternate, compound, 1-pinnate; blade to 5 dm; leaflets usually 3, margins lobed and toothed. Petioles with large sheaths. Inflorescence a large, compound umbel. Flowers mostly regular although outer may be slightly irregular. Petals white. Fruit to 12 mm.

Genus & Specific Name Derivation: Hercules, presumably from large stature of this plant / Latin: wool, referring the hairiness of the plant

Uses Past and Present: Natives mashed and soaked the seeds and roots in water to treat toothache and to stimulate nerve growth after injury. They also burned the leaves and used the ash as a salt substitute.

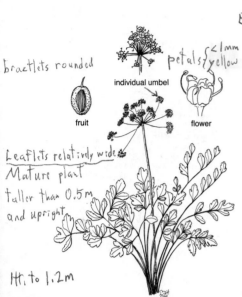

bractlets rounded

petals <1mm yellow

individual umbel

fruit

flower

Leaflets relatively wide
Mature plant
taller than 0.5 m
and upright.

Ht. to 1.2m

Lomatium californicum (Torrey & A. Gray) Mathias & Constance

CALIFORNIA LOMATIUM   Native / CHUCHUPATE

Flowering Time: April–May

Habitat: serpentine grassland, woodland

Description: Upright herbaceous perennial to 12 dm. Leaves basal and alternate, compound, 2-pinnate; blade to 30 cm, bluish green; leaflet margins divided or deeply lobed. Petiole to 20 cm with a sheathing base. Inflorescence a compound umbel to 12 cm wide. Flowers mostly bisexual, older flowers sometimes unisexual, mostly regular, outer may be slightly irregular. Sepals inconspicuous or 0; petals < 1 mm, yellow. Fruit to 15 mm, wings narrower than the body, ribs barely raised.

Genus & Specific Name Derivation: Greek: bordered, from marginal fruit wing / from California

Uses Past and Present: Roots of some *Lomatium* species were used by natives and early settlers for lung problems, fevers, and other illnesses. The milky sap that oozes from spring roots was used as a skin-moisturizing agent. Natives are said to have baked the roots for food.

Lomatiums other than L. californicum shorter than 0.5 m, spreading

compound
umbel

petals yellow,
minute (<1mm)

bractlets rounded

leaves
essentially
basal*

Ht. to 0.4m

fruit

Lomatium caruifolium (Hook. & Arn.) J. Coulter & Rose var. caruifolium

CARAWAY-LEAVED LOMATIUM   Native

Flowering Time: April–May

Habitat: serpentine grassland

Description: Low-growing herbaceous perennial from a tuber, to 40 cm. Leaves basal, compound, 3-pinnate; blade to 10 cm; leaflet segments linear, pointed. Petiole to 7 cm with bladder-like sheathing bases. Inflorescence a compound umbel to 12 cm wide; bractlet to 5 mm, off to one side. Flowers bisexual, older flowers sometimes unisexual, regular, outer may be slightly irregular. Sepals inconspicuous or 0; petals < 1 mm, yellow. Fruit to 13 mm, wings thin, wide. The 2 seeds split from the base lengthwise and can be seen this way in the late summer to fall.

Genus & Specific Name Derivation: Greek: bordered, from marginal fruit wing / caraway foliage

Uses Past and Present: See *L. californicum.*

*No more than one leaf along the stem, and usually entirely basal. All the other Lomatiums have some leaves along the stem.
Other lomatiums have linear leaflet segments also, but none of them have such thread-like leaflet segments.

Lomatium dasycarpum (Torrey & A. Gray) J. Coulter & Rose ssp. *dasycarpum*

WOOLLY-FRUITED LOMATIUM Native / *HOG-FENNEL*

Flowering Time: March–April

Habitat: serpentine grassland and chaparral

Description: Low-growing herbaceous perennial from a tuber, to 50 cm. Whole plant densely hairy. Leaves mostly basal, some alternate, compound; blade to 15 cm, repeatedly lobed; leaflet segments linear. Petiole to 12 cm, generally sheathing. Inflorescence a compound umbel to 9 cm wide; bractlet often fused. Sepals inconspicuous; petals < 1 mm, greenish-white, hairy. Fruit to 20 mm, body hairy, wings wider than the body. The 2 seeds split from the base lengthwise and can be seen this way in the late summer to fall.

Genus & Specific Name Derivation: Greek: bordered, from marginal fruit wing / hairy fruit

Notes: Other species don't have hairy petals.

Uses Past and Present: See *L. californicum.*

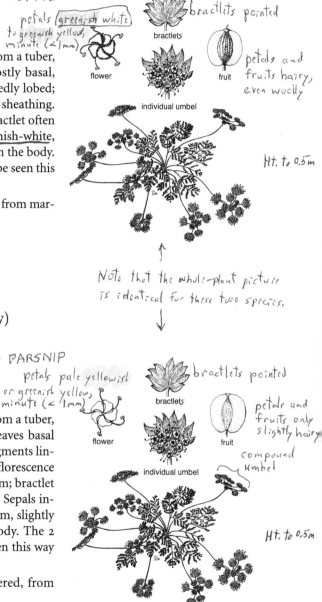

petals greenish white to greenish yellow, minute (<1mm)

flower

bractlets

bractlets pointed

fruit

petals and fruits hairy, even woolly

individual umbel

Ht. to 0.5m

Note that the whole-plant picture is identical for these two species.

Lomatium macrocarpum (Torrey & A. Gray) J. Coulter & Rose

LARGE-FRUITED LOMATIUM Native / *SHEEP PARSNIP*

Flowering Time: March–April

Habitat: serpentine grassland and chaparral

Description: Low-growing herbaceous perennial from a tuber, to 50 cm. Herbage gray, usually densely hairy. Leaves basal and alternate, compound; blade to 15 cm; leaflet segments linear to oblong, repeatedly lobed. Petiole to 7 cm. Inflorescence a compound umbel to 8 cm wide; peduncle to 30 cm; bractlet linear-lanceolate to ovate, tip pointed, some fused. Sepals inconspicuous; petals < 1 mm, yellow.* Fruit to 20 mm, slightly hairy or not, wings mostly narrower than the body. The 2 seeds split from the base lengthwise and can be seen this way in the late summer to fall.

Genus & Specific Name Derivation: Greek: bordered, from marginal fruit wing / large fruit

Notes: Like other species except the bracts in this species are more lanceolate.

Uses Past and Present: See *L. californicum.*

petals pale yellowish or greenish yellow, minute (< 1mm)

flower

bractlets

bractlets pointed

fruit

petals and fruits only slightly hairy

compound umbel

individual umbel

Ht. to 0.5m

*However, the yellow is pale, whitish, or greenish according to Koxloff & Beidleman

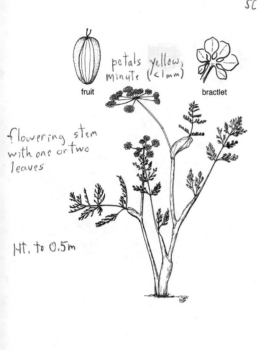

petals yellow, minute (<1mm)

fruit

bractlet

flowering stem with one or two leaves

Ht. to 0.5m

Lomatium utriculatum (Torrey & A. Gray) J. Coulter & Rose

SC

COMMON LOMATIUM / BLADDER PARSNIP / Native

SPRING-GOLD

Flowering Time: March–April

Habitat: serpentine grassland

Description: Low-growing herbaceous perennial from a tuber, to 50 cm. Leaves alternate, compound; blade to 15 cm, repeatedly lobed; leaflet segments linear. Petiole to 10 cm with bladder-like sheaths, upper leaves mostly wholly sheathing. Inflorescence a compound umbel to 12 cm wide; peduncle to 11 cm; bractlet 3–4 mm, ovate, rounded with a pointed tip. Flowers bisexual, older flowers sometimes unisexual, regular, outer may be slightly irregular. Sepals inconspicuous or 0; petals < 1 mm, bright yellow. Fruit to 15 mm, wings sometimes pinkish. The 2 seeds split from the base lengthwise and can be seen this way in the late summer to fall.

Genus & Specific Name Derivation: Greek: bordered, from marginal fruit wing / having a bladder-like structure, referring to the large basal sheath at the base of the petiole

Notes: Leaves may not be available when plant is in fruit.

Uses Past and Present: See *L. californicum*.

*Usually with 2–3 leaves along the stem

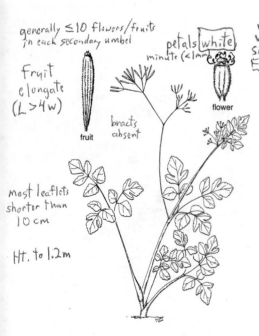

generally ≤10 flowers/fruits in each secondary umbel

Fruit elongate (L>4w)

fruit

petals white, minute (<1mm

flower

bracts absent

most leaflets shorter than 10cm

Ht. to 1.2m

Osmorhiza berteroi DC. formerly O. chilensis

SC

WOOD SWEET CICELY   Native

Flowering Time: May

Habitat: woodland

Description: Herbaceous perennial to 12 dm. Leaves alternate, compound, 2–3-pinnate; blade to 20 cm, soft hairy, leaflets to 8 cm. Petiole to 10 cm. Inflorescence a compound umbel, to 12 cm wide; peduncle to 20 cm; pedicel to 15 mm. Sepals inconspicuous, petals white, < 1 mm. Fruit 12–15 cm, linear, with hairs and ribs, silvery

Genus & Specific Name Derivation: Greek: sweet root / for Carlo Giuseppe Bertero (1789–1831), an Italian physician.

Notes: Seeds are anise scented. New name accepted by *Jepson Manual* staff, name in *The Jepson Manual* (1993) *Osmorhiza chilensis*.

Uses Past and Present: Roots used medicinally.

Compare to Angelica tomentosa

photo in K & B plate 5

✓ *Perideridia kelloggii* (A. Gray) Mathias

E
SC

KELLOGG'S YAMPAH   Native

Flowering Time: June–July

Habitat: nonserpentine grassland

Description: Herbaceous perennial to 15 dm. Leaves alternate, compound; blade to 20 cm, gray-green; leaflets long linear. Petiole to 10 cm, sheathing. Inflorescence a compound umbel to 7 cm wide; primary and secondary bracts small, linear. Sepals inconspicuous; petals green-white, to 2 mm. Fruit to 5 mm, ribs thread-like.

Genus & Specific Name Derivation: Greek: around the neck, referring to the involucre / for A. Kellogg (1813–1887), a San Francisco physician and botanist; a founder of the California Academy of Sciences

Uses Past and Present: A very important food for the natives. The roots were dried and ground into flour, or baked and cooked as a vegetable. Seeds were used medicinally for colds and indigestion, and a poultice made of powdered seeds was used for eyes and bruises.

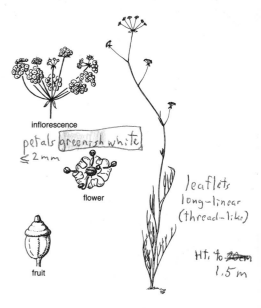

inflorescence

petals greenish white ≤2mm

flower

fruit

leaflets long-linear (thread-like)

Ht. to 1.5 m

Genus *Sanicula*: Umbels dense, head-like (i.e., the secondary umbels, not the primary ones)

✗ *Sanicula bipinnata* Hook. & Arn.

E

POISON SANICLE   Native

Flowering Time: March–May

Habitat: serpentine grassland, woodland

Description: Herbaceous perennial to 60 cm; stem ribbed. Leaves basal and alternate, compound, 1–2-pinnate; blade to 15 cm, margin lobed and toothed. Petiole to 1.5 cm, sheathing. Inflorescence an umbel-like head; bracts to 12 mm, green-yellow. Sepals minute, green; petals yellow, < 1 mm. Fruit to 2 mm with hooked prickles over the whole surface.

Genus & Specific Name Derivation: Latin: to heal / two, divided, referring to the leaves

Notes: Plant smells like cilantro, however this species is poisonous.

Uses Past and Present: Although the scientific name means "to heal," no mention of the healing properties are given in the references used.

Compare to *S. laciniata*

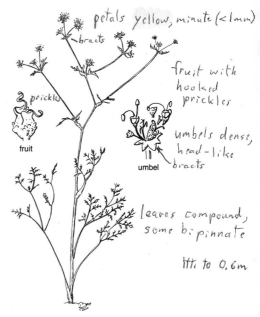

petals yellow, minute (<1mm)

bracts

prickly

fruit

umbel

fruit with hooked prickles

umbels dense, head-like bracts

leaves compound, some bipinnate

Ht. to 0.6m

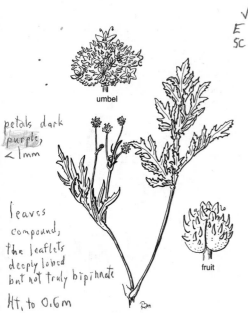

umbel

petals dark
purple,
<1mm

leaves
compound,
the leaflets
deeply lobed
but not truly bipinnate

Ht. to 0.6m

fruit

✓ *Sanicula bipinnatifida* Hook.

E
SC

PURPLE SANICLE   Native

Flowering Time: February–May

Habitat: grassland

Description: Herbaceous perennial to 60 cm. Leaves basal and alternate, compound, 1-pinnate; blade to 12 cm, purplish-green, margin deeply lobed and toothed. Petiole to 3 cm with a sheathing base, upper leaves almost sessile. Inflorescence an umbel-like head; bracts to 5 mm. Sepals minute, green; petals purple, < 1 mm. Fruit to 6 mm, with stout, curved prickles.

Genus & Specific Name Derivation: Latin: to heal / two-winged, divided, referring to the leaves

Notes: This plant is easy to distinguish from other sanicles by its purple flowers or inflorescence. Another common name for it is satellite plant, because of the ball-like inflorescence with exserted stamens.

Uses Past and Present: See *S. bipinnata.*

~~Compare to S. tuberosa~~

✓ *Sanicula crassicaulis* DC.

E
SC

PACIFIC SANICLE   Native / SNAKE ROOT

Flowering Time: March–May

Habitat: all plant communities

Description: Herbaceous perennial to 10 dm. Leaves basal and alternate, simple, to 7 cm, margins toothed and lobed. Petiole to 20 cm with a sheathing base, upper leaves almost sessile. Inflorescence an umbel-like head, each head to 4 mm wide; bracts to 12 mm, deeply divided, green. Sepals minute, green; petals yellow, < 1 mm. Fruit to 5 mm, nearly round with curved prickles.

Genus & Specific Name Derivation: Latin: to heal / thick, fleshy stem

Notes: This plant is variable; some plants get very tall and open, others can be smaller and more compact. The prickles on the fruit make it easily dispersed by animals.

Uses Past and Present: See *S. bipinnata.*

Compare to S. laciniata
photo in K & B plate 5

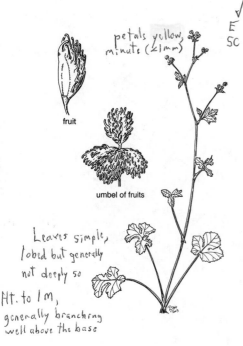

petals yellow,
minute (<1mm)

fruit

umbel of fruits

Leaves simple,
lobed but generally
not deeply so

Ht. to 1m,
generally branching
well above the base

Sanicula laciniata Hook. & Arn.

COAST SANICLE   Native

Flowering Time: April–May

Habitat: woodland

Description: Upright, herbaceous perennial to 30 cm. Leaves basal and alternate, simple, deeply 3 lobed and sharply toothed; blade to 4 cm. Inflorescence an umbel-like head; peduncle to 8 cm. Sepal lobes minute, petals yellow to 2 mm. Fruit to 4 mm, prickles slender, curved.

Genus & Specific Name Derivation: Latin: to heal / jagged, unevenly cut, slashed, referring to the leaf margins

Notes: So far only one plant has been found.

Uses Past and Present: See *S. bipinnata*.

Compare to S. crassicaulis

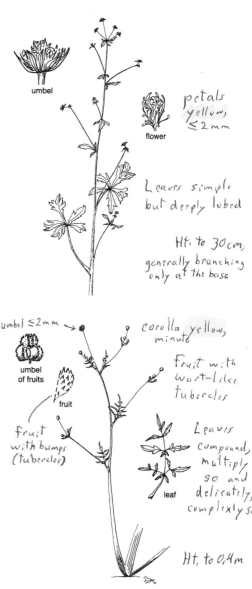

umbel

flower

petals yellow, ≤ 2 mm

Leaves simple but deeply lobed

Ht. to 30 cm, generally branching only at the base

Sanicula tuberosa Torrey

TURKEY PEA   Native / TUBEROUS SANICLE

Flowering Time: March–May

Habitat: serpentine grassland

Description: Herbaceous perennial from a tuber, to 40 cm. Leaves basal and alternate, compound, 3–4-pinnate; blade to 5 cm, margin toothed, green turning reddish with sheathing red petioles. Inflorescence an umbel-like head; bracts below the individual umbel to 2 mm, fused, light green with darker streaks. Flowers minute, bright yellow. Fruit to 2 mm, with wart-like tubercles.

Genus & Specific Name Derivation: Latin: to heal / swollen, tuberous, referring to the tuber-like root

Uses Past and Present: See *S. bipinnata*.

Compare to S. bipinnata

umbel ≤ 2 mm

umbel of fruits

fruit

fruit with bumps (tubercles)

leaf

corolla yellow, minute

Fruit with wart-like tubercles

Leaves compound, multiply so and delicately, complexly so

Ht. to 0.4 m

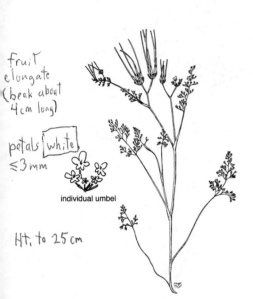

fruit
elongate
(beak about
4 cm long)

petals white
≤3 mm

individual umbel

Ht. to 25 cm

Scandix pecten-veneris L.

VENUS' NEEDLE   Nonnative / Mediterranean

Flowering Time: March–April

Habitat: grassland

Description: Annual to 25 cm, whole plant somewhat bristly-hairy. Leaves alternate, compound, 2-pinnate then lobed; blade to 6 cm. Petiole to 8 cm. Inflorescence a compound umbel; individual umbel to 5 cm wide; peduncle to 6 cm. Sepals minute; petals white, to 3 mm, outer somewhat larger; some stamens may be missing in full flower; ovary continues to elongate as petals fall off; styles and stigmas 2, sitting on a reddish nectary. Fruit to 5 cm, linear, bristly.

Genus & Specific Name Derivation: Greek: chervil / Venus' comb

Notes: Ovary and stigma elongate as petals fall.

photo in K+B plate 5

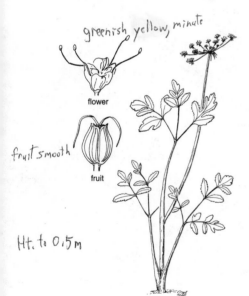

greenish yellow, minute

flower

fruit smooth

fruit

Ht. to 0.5 m

Tauschia hartwegii (A. Gray) J. F. Macbr.

HARTWEG'S TAUSCHIA   Native

Flowering Time: March–April

Habitat: woodland

Description: Upright herbaceous perennial to 50 cm. Leaves mostly basal, compound, 2-pinnate; blade to 20 cm; leaflets to 6 cm, margins lobed and toothed. Petiole to 15 cm, base sheathing. Inflorescence a compound umbel; bracts below the umbel to 1.5 cm, deeply divided, linear. Flowers greenish yellow. Fruit to 5 mm, oblong, smooth.

Genus & Specific Name Derivation: I. F. Tausch (1793–1848), Czech botanist / for Karl T. Hartweg (1812–1871), a German collector sent to Mexico by the London Horticultural Society, and later to California.

√ *Torilis arvensis* (Hudson) Link

SC
E

HEDGE PARSLEY   Nonnative / Europe

Flowering Time: June–July

Habitat: woodland

Description: Annual to 50 cm. Leaves alternate, compound, 2–3-pinnate; blade to 9 cm. Petiole to 3 cm. Inflorescence a compound open umbel; peduncle to 12 cm, pedicel to 4 mm. Flowers minute, petals white. Fruit to 5 mm, oblong with prickles on both halves.

Genus & Specific Name Derivation: Name used by Adanson in 1793, meaning obscure / of the field

Notes: No beak on tip of fruit separates it from *Anthriscus*.

Compare to Yabea microcarpa
and Torilis nodosa

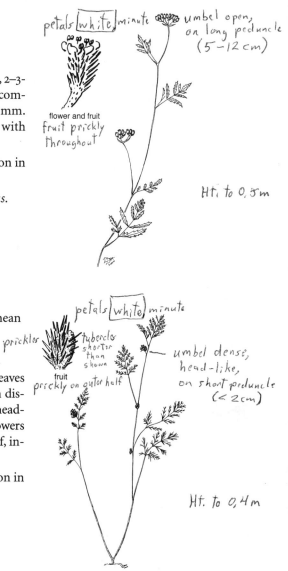

petals white minute

flower and fruit
fruit prickly
throughout

umbel open,
on long peduncle
(5–12 cm)

Ht. to 0.5m

√ *Torilis nodosa* (L.) Gaertner

SC

KNOTTED HEDGE PARSLEY   Nonnative / Mediterranean

Flowering Time: May–June

Habitat: woodland

Description: Annual to 40 cm, whole plant soft-hairy. Leaves alternate, compound, 1–2-pinnate; blade to 9 cm, margin dissected. Petiole to 3 cm. Inflorescence a dense compound head-like umbel; peduncle to 3 mm, pedicel very short or 0. Flowers minute, petals white. Fruit to 3 mm, prickles on outer half, inner tubercled.

Genus & Specific Name Derivation: Name used by Adanson in 1793, meaning obscure / many-jointed

Notes: See *T. arvensis*.

Compare to T. arvensis

prickles

fruit
prickly on outer half

petals white minute

tubercles
shorter
than
shown

umbel dense,
head-like,
on short peduncle
(< 2cm)

Ht. to 0.4m

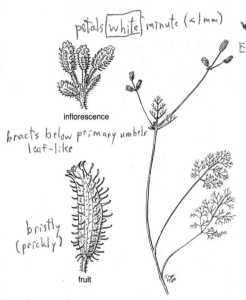

petals white minute (<1mm)

inflorescence

bracts below primary umbels leaf-like

bristly (prickly)

fruit

HT. to 30cm

Yabea microcarpa (Hook. & Arn.) Koso-Polj.

CALIFORNIA HEDGE PARSLEY   Native

Flowering Time: March–April

Habitat: chaparral, woodland

Description: Soft-hairy upright annual to 30 cm. Leaves basal and alternate, compound, 1-pinnate; blade to 2.5 cm; leaflets to 1 cm, margin lobed. Petiole clasping the stem. Inflorescence a simple to compound umbel; bracts leaf-like. Flowers more or less regular, some slightly irregular, to 3 mm wide. Sepals minute; petals white, to 1 mm; stamens barely visible; stigma 2 parted, barely visible. Ovary inferior, white bristly. Fruit white bristly, globose, not beaked.

Genus & Specific Name Derivation: H. Yabe (1876–1931), Japanese botanist / small fruit

Compare to Torilis spp.
and Daucus spp.

Apocynaceae — Dogbane Family

Annuals, herbaceous perennials or shrubs. Leaves alternate or opposite, simple. Inflorescence axillary, or cymose. Flowers bisexual, regular. Sepals 5, fused; petals 5, fused; stamens 5; pistils 2, ovary superior, styles and stigmas fused into 1 structure. Fruit a follicle, usually 2 per flower. Some species cultivated as ornamentals (oleander). Some species highly poisonous.

For key to woody plants *see* Group 2. Woody Plants

√ *Vinca major* L.

GREATER PERIWINKLE   Nonnative / Europe

Flowering Time: all year

Habitat: woodland

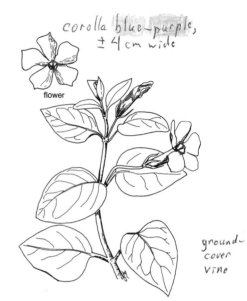

corolla blue-purple, ± 4 cm wide

flower

ground cover vine

Description: Low-growing, trailing, vine-like shrub or ground cover that forms mats to 5 dm. Leaves opposite, simple, to 7 cm, entire, glossy dark green. Petiole to 1 cm. Stem exudes milky juice when broken. Inflorescence solitary in axils of leaves. Flowers regular to 5 cm wide. Sepals 5, fused, triangular to 9 mm; petals fused, 5, blue-purple. Stamens 5; ovary superior. Fruit a follicle to 5 cm. Fruit does not usually develop on our plants.

Genus & Specific Name Derivation: Latin: to bind, refers to its use in wreaths / larger

Notes: This was probably planted in the park along with many other ornamental plants that can be found along the lower part of the Sylvan Trail. Vinca does not reproduce from seed but spreads by rooting at the new growing tips and can continue to spread in this way taking over large areas and forming dense mats. Since the leaves can be toxic to grazers that otherwise would hold it in check, it continues to invade areas and can form an understory monoculture in an otherwise native area.

Uses Past and Present: The leaves are used by herbalists for internal and external bleeding. However, the plant contains alkaloids and tannins which are toxic.

Araliaceae — Ginseng Family

Shrubs, woody vines. Leaves alternate, simple or compound. Inflorescence an umbel. Flowers bisexual, regular. Sepals 5, fused, inconspicuous; petals 5, free; stamens 5; ovary inferior. Fruit a berry or drupe. Some medicinal, e.g., ginseng, sarsaparilla (*Aralia*); some ornamental, e.g., ivy, which can become invasive.

For key to woody plants *see* Group 2. Woody Plants

petals white to green, minute

Evergreen
woody
vine

√ *Hedera helix* L.

5C   ENGLISH IVY   Nonnative / Europe

Flowering Time: N / A

Habitat: woodland

Description: Woody evergreen ground cover and climbing vine. Leaves alternate, simple, to 20 cm, margin lobed to entire. Petiole to 7 cm. Inflorescence an umbel. Flowers, regular. Sepals 5, fused; petals 5, free, white to green. Stamens 5; ovary inferior. Fruit a berry, black, to 7 mm wide.

Genus & Specific Name Derivation: Latin: sacred plant of Bacchus, god of wine / ancient Greek name for twining plants

Notes: The strong branches can choke the plant they are growing on causing it to die. Only mature plants flower. Juice can cause contact dermatitis, berries and leaves toxic. The ivy at Edgewood was planted in the Day Camp area.

Asclepiadaceae — Milkweed Family

Annuals or herbaceous perennials; sap milky. Leaves opposite or whorled, simple. Inflorescence in racemes or umbels. Flowers bisexual, regular. Sepals 5, often strongly reflexed; petals 5, fused; stamens 5, anthers fused to style and stigma to form a columnar structure; pistils 2, ovaries superior, styles and stigmas fused with anthers above ovaries. Fruit a follicle; seeds with tufts of hairs. Cardiac glycosides produced by some, used in medicine and by insects for defense.

For key to families *see* Group 3. Herbaceous Flowering Plant Families

⅄ *Asclepias fascicularis* Decne.

Ε NARROW-LEAF MILKWEED   Native

Flowering Time: May–October

Habitat: grassland

Description: Erect herbaceous perennial to 50 cm. Leaves whorled, simple, to 10 cm, lanceolate; sessile. Inflorescence umbel-like. Bracts to 3 mm, pink, falling off in flower. Sepals 5, to 6 mm, fused, pinkish white, folded back; petals 5, to 2 mm, fused, white, folded back. Stamens 5, fused to form a filament column, also 5 appendages outside of the filament column; pistils 2, ovary superior, style tip fused into a head-like pistil surrounded by the anther head. Fruit a follicle. The seeds have tufts of silky hairs that aid in wind dispersal.

Genus & Specific Name Derivation: Asklepios, ancient Greek physician / clustered in bundles referring to the leaves

Notes: Monarch butterflies and caterpillars use some species as a food source, accumulating the plant poisons which make them undesirable as a food for birds.

Uses Past and Present: Some plants of this genus produce glycosides used as cardiac medicine, as an arrow poison, and the Monarch butterfly for defense. Natives used this genus medicinally, applying fresh sap to remove warts, and for treatment of ringworm. Some species were used for the strong fibers in the stems. One species was entered in the U.S. Pharmacopoeia for treatment of various chest and lung ailments in the early 1900s. Generally the narrow-leafed milkweeds have been shown to be toxic.

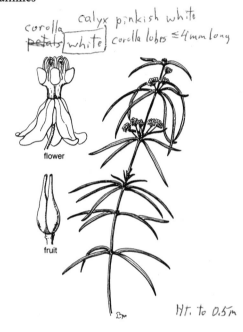

corolla
petals [white]

calyx pinkish white
corolla lobes ≤ 4mm long

flower

fruit

Ht. to 0.5m

photo in K & B plate 6

Asteraceae — Sunflower Family

Annuals or perennials. Inflorescence a head, composed of 1–many flowers, surrounded by an involucre of bracts called phyllaries. Heads of 3 kinds, heads with ray flowers only, heads with disk flowers only, heads with both ray and disk flowers. Ray flowers are strap shaped and often 1–5 lobed, these are actually several fused petals; disk flowers are fused, tubular and usually 5 lobed. Ray flowers are often unisexual or sterile; disk flowers are usually bisexual. Calyx is absent or modified into a pappus, composed of scales or bristles. Stamens 5, anthers fused into a tube surrounding the style; pistil 1, ovary inferior, style branches 2. Fruit an achene.

Family Characteristics

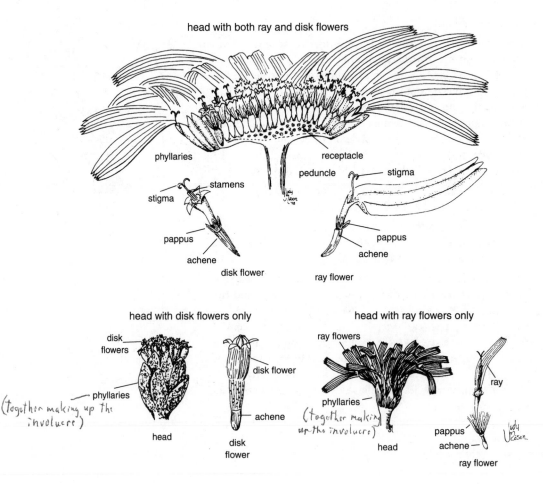

head with both ray and disk flowers

phyllaries

receptacle

peduncle — stigma

stamens

stigma

pappus

achene

disk flower

pappus

achene

ray flower

head with disk flowers only

disk flowers

phyllaries

(together making up the involucre)

head

disk flower

achene

disk flower

head with ray flowers only

ray flowers

ray

phyllaries

(together making up the involucre)

head

pappus

achene

ray flower

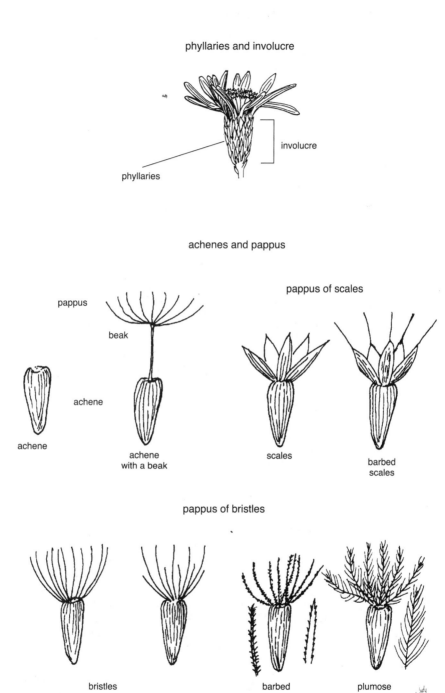

phyllaries and involucre

involucre

phyllaries

achenes and pappus

pappus of scales

pappus

beak

achene

achene

achene
with a beak

scales

barbed
scales

pappus of bristles

bristles

barbed

plumose

For key to woody plants *see* Group 2. Woody Plants

For key to families *see* Group 3. Herbaceous Flowering Plant Families

for Key 2, based on pappus, see p.64

Key to Herbaceous Plants — Key 1, based on characteristics other than the pappus:

1. Heads small, covered with hairs or phyllaries covering the flowers so cannot easily tell if flowers are ray or disk; *flowers all of disk type except as noted*
   2. Plants densely white-or gray-hairy
      3. Plants low-growing, branched at the base, *< 10 cm*
         4. Heads bristly-angular in the center of leafy bracts ....
         ....*heads solitary*............... *Hesperevax sparsiflora* (ERECT EVAX)
         4´ Heads round, head-like ....*leaves opposite*..............................
         ....*Psilocarphus brevissimus* (DWARF WOOLLY-HEADS)
      3´ Plants upright, mostly branched above the middle *(if branched at all)*
         5. Heads rounded
            6. Plants usually < 10 cm *bracts not extending beyond head clusters*
            .... *Micropus californicus* (SLENDER COTTONWEED)
            6´ Plants usually > 10 cm...*both ray and disk flowers*.....................
            .... *Lagophylla ramosissima* (COMMON HARELEAF)
         bracts extending beyond head clusters → 5´ Heads pointed .... *Filago gallica* (NARROW-LEAVED FILAGO)
   2´ Plants green, may be glandular but not white-hairy; *both ray and disk flowers*
      7. Plants < 10 cm .... *Madia exigua*[1] (THREADSTEM MADIA)
      7´ Plants > 10 cm
         8. Stems glandular in upper half only ....
         ....*Madia gracilis*[1] (SLENDER TARWEED)
         8´ Stems glandular throughout .... *Madia sativa*[1] (COAST TARWEED)
1´ Flowers in heads with either or both ray and disk flowers
   ray flowers only
   9. Heads with ray flowers only; usually with milky sap
      10. Ray flowers yellow
         11. Ray flowers bright yellow
            12. Leaves mostly basal
               13. Inflorescence scapose, arising from a basal rosette of leaves
                  14. Phyllaries very hairy
                     15. Annual < 4 dm; pappus of bristles, body of achene strongly ribbed and winged; grassland ....
                     ....*Agoseris heterophylla* (ANNUAL AGOSERIS)
                     15´ Perennial > 4 dm; pappus of bristles, body of achene ribbed but not winged; woodland ....
                     .... *Agoseris grandiflora* (CALIFORNIA DANDELION)
                  14´ Phyllaries glabrous to slightly hairy
                     16. Leaves bristly-hairy, some leaf margins deeply lobed; pappus of bristles, achene beaked ....
                     .... *Hypochaeris radicata* (ROUGH CAT'S-EAR)
                     16´ Leaves not bristly-hairy, may be slightly hairy on leaf margins

        17. Leaf margins slightly lobed; pappus of bristles, outer achene beakless, inner beaked .... *Hypochaeris glabra* (SMOOTH CAT'S-EAR)

        17´ Leaf margins deeply lobed

            18. Pappus scales entire at the tip, awn coming from the tip .. *Microseris douglasii* (DOUGLAS' MICROSERIS)

            18´ Pappus scales notched at the tip, awn coming from the notch .... *Stebbinsoseris heterocarpa* (DERIVED MICROSERIS)

    13´ Inflorescence open .... *Crepis vesicaria* ssp. *taraxacifolia* (HAWK'S BEARD)

  12´ Leaves along the stem

        19. Heads with an row of bracts below the phyllaries .... *Picris echioides* (BRISTLY OX-TONGUE)

        19´ Heads with overlapping phyllaries, without bracts at base of phyllaries

            20. Stem leaves toothed and spiny .... *Sonchus asper* (PRICKLY SOW THISTLE)

            20´ Stem leaves entire, toothed or lobed, not spiny

                21. Inflorescence mostly solitary, heads on a long peduncle .... *Urospermum picroides* (PRICKLY GOLDENFLEECE)

                21´ Inflorescence open many flowered .... *Sonchus oleraceus* (COMMON SOW THISTLE)

 11´ Ray flowers pale yellow

        22. Inflorescence narrow, leaves narrow, basal lobes narrow .... *Lactuca saligna* (WILLOW LETTUCE)

        22´ Inflorescence open, leaves wider, basal lobes rounded .... *Lactuca serriola* (PRICKLY LETTUCE)

 10´ Ray flowers white, blue, purple or pink

    23. Ray flowers white to pink

        24. Inflorescence open .... *Rafinesquia californica* (CALIFORNIA CHICORY)

        24´ Inflorescence clustered .... *Stephanomeria virgata* (VIRGATE STEPHANOMERIA)

    23´ Ray flowers purple or blue

        25. Ray flowers purple .... *Tragopogon porrifolius* (SALSIFY/OYSTER PLANT)

        25´ Ray flowers blue .... *Cichorium intybus*[2] (CHICORY)

9´ Heads with disk flowers

  26. Heads with disk flowers only   *disk flowers only*

    27. Phyllaries bristly or spiny

      28. Flowers yellow

        29. Central spines of main phyllaries > 1 cm .... *Centaurea solstitialis* (YELLOW STAR-THISTLE)

        29´ Central spines of main phyllaries < 1 cm, spine base purple .... *Centaurea melitensis* (TOCALOTE)

28′ Flowers white, pink, purple
  30. Phyllaries < 2 cm ....
  .... *Carduus pycnocephalus* (ITALIAN THISTLE)
  30′ Phyllaries > 2 cm
    31. Leaves large, dark green blotched with white ....
    .... *Silybum marianum* (MILK THISTLE)
    31′ Leaves not blotched with white
      32. Phyllaries reflexed
        33. Stems spiny-winged .... *Cirsium vulgare* (BULL THISTLE)
        33′ Stems not spiny-winged ....
        .... *Cirsium fontinale* (FOUNTAIN THISTLE)
      32′ Phyllaries not reflexed ....
      .... *Cirsium brevistylum* (INDIAN THISTLE)
27′ Phyllaries not bristly or spiny
  34. Phyllaries thin, dry, white, straw-colored, pink, some opaque
    35. Leaves green
      36. Larger stem leaves to 1 cm wide, fragrant; heads spheric;
      phyllaries generally white ....
      .... *Gnaphalium californicum* (CALIFORNIA CUDWEED)
      36′ Larger stem leaves ≤ 1 cm wide, not fragrant;
      phyllaries dull white to greenish or pinkish ....
      ....*Gnaphalium ramosissimum* (PINK EVERLASTING)
    35′ Leaves gray because of dense hairs
      37. Inflorescence open ....*Gnaphalium canescens* ssp. *beneolens*
      (FRAGRANT EVERLASTING)
      37′ Inflorescence in a dense terminal cluster
        38. Phyllaries brown to purple ....
        .... *Gnaphalium purpureum* (PURPLE CUDWEED)
        38′ Phyllaries white at least at tips ....
        .... *Gnaphalium stramineum* (COTTON-BATTING PLANT)
34′ Phyllaries green
  39. Some flowers yellow
    40. Flower head conical, phyllaries much shorter than the
    flower head .... *Chamomilla suaveolens* (PINEAPPLE WEED)
    40′ Phyllaries more than half the length of the flower head
      41. Phyllaries soft-hairy or glandular
        42. Phyllaries soft-hairy
          43. Phyllaries purple-tinged ....
          .... *Conyza bonariensis* (HORSEWEED)
          43′ Phyllaries gray-hairy, margin transparent ....
          .... *Artemisia douglasiana* (MUGWORT)
        42′ Phyllaries glandular, long-hairy ....
        .... *Arnica discoidea* (RAYLESS ARNICA)
      41′ Phyllaries not hairy, some black-tipped
        44. Most leaves < 10 cm ....
        .... *Senecio vulgaris* (COMMON GROUNDSEL)

44´ Lower leaves > 10 cm .... *Senecio aronicoides*
(CALIFORNIA BUTTERWEED/ GROUNDSEL)
39´ Flowers lavender-purple, yellow-reddish, or white
45. Flowers lavender-purple ....
.... *Lessingia hololeuca* (WOOLLY-HEADED LESSINGIA)
45´ Flowers yellow-reddish or white
46. Flowers yellow-reddish ... *Erigeron petrophilus* (ROCK DAISY)
46´ Flowers whitish .... *Baccharis douglasii* (MARSH BACCHARIS)
26´ Heads with both ray and disk flowers   both ray and disk flowers
47. Ray flowers all white, pink or purple
48. Ray flowers white
49. Leaves compound .... *Achillea millefolium* (YARROW)
49´ Leaves simple ....
.... *Hemizonia congesta* ssp. *luzulifolia* (HAYFIELD TARWEED)
48´ Ray flowers pink or purple
50. Small annual < 3 dm ....
.... *Pentachaeta bellidiflora* (WHITE-RAYED PENTACHAETA)
50´ Herbaceous perennial > 3 dm
51. Leaves < 1.5 cm wide; margin finely toothed ....
.... *Symphyotrichum chilense* (COMMON CALIFORNIA ASTER)
51´ Leaves > 1.5 cm wide; margin sharply toothed ....
.... *Eurybia radulinus* (rough-leaved aster)
47´ Ray flowers yellow, brown, orange or two-colored
52. Heads open
53. Ray flowers two-colored
54. Ray flowers yellow with white tips ....
.... *Layia platyglossa* (TIDY-TIPS)
54´ Ray flowers not white-tipped
55. Ray flowers yellow with maroon base ....
.... *Madia elegans* (COMMON MADIA)
55´ Ray flowers two-tone colored yellow-orange ....
.... *Gazania linearis* (GAZANIA)
53´ Ray flowers all one color
56. Ray flowers blue/lavender .... *Erigeron foliosus* (LEAFY DAISY)
56´ Ray flowers yellow
57. Flower buds white-gummy, phyllaries coiled or spreading
58. Stems not hairy, appearing varnished ....
.... *Grindelia camporum* (GREAT VALLEY GRINDELIA)
58´ Stems hairy ...... *Grindelia hirsutula* (HIRSUTE GRINDELIA)
57´ Flower buds not white-gummy
59. Ray flowers < 1.5 cm
60. Phyllaries in 1 row
61. Leaves deeply lobed ....
.... *Deinandra corymbosa* (COAST TARWEED)
61´ Leaves entire or toothed-lobed

62. Ray flowers equally 3-lobed ....
.... *Monolopia major* (CUPPED MONOLOPIA)
62′ Ray flowers entire or unevenly lobed ....
.... *Monolopia gracilens* (WOODLAND MONOLOPIA)
60′ Phyllaries in 2-5 rows
   63. Stems winged .... *Helenium puberulum* (SNEEZEWEED)
   63′ Stems not winged
      64. Ray flowers pale yellow, often purple-tinged ....
      .... *Rigiopappus leptocladus* (RIGIOPAPPUS)
      64′ Ray flowers bright yellow
         65. Leaves opposite .... *Lasthenia californica* (GOLDFIELDS)
         65′ Leaves alternate
            66. Leaves hairy, not glandular ....
            .... *Solidago californica* (CALIFORNIA GOLDENROD)
            66′ Leaves hairy, glandular or resin-dotted
               67. Leaves hairy and glandular ....
               .... *Heterotheca sessiliflora* ssp. *echioides*
               (GOLDENASTER)
               67′ Leaves resin-dotted ....
               .... *Euthamia occidentalis* (WESTERN GOLDENROD)
59′ Ray flowers > 1.5 cm
   68. Phyllaries > 2 cm; leaves not deeply lobed
      69. Leaves < 5 cm wide, linear ....
      ....*Wyethia angustifolia* (NARROW-LEAVED MULE EARS)
      69′ Leaves > 5 cm wide, lanceolate to oblong
         70. Some phyllaries > 4 cm ....*Wyethia glabra* (MULE EARS)
         70′ Phyllaries < 4 cm ....
         .... *Helianthus californicus* (CALIFORNIA SUNFLOWER)
   68′ Phyllaries < 2 cm; leaves deeply lobed ....
   .... *Packera breweri* (BREWER'S BUTTERWEED)
52′ Heads tightly closed
   71. Heads cup-shaped
      72. Plants < 10 cm .... *Madia exigua*[2] (THREADSTEM MADIA)
      72′ Plants > 10 cm
         73. Plants white-hairy, may be glandular ....
         .... *Lagophylla ramosissima* (COMMON HARELEAF)
         73′ Plant not white-hairy
            74. Plant glandular on upper half only ....
            .... *Madia gracilis*[2] (SLENDER TARWEED)
            74′ Plant glandular throughout .... *Madia sativa*[2] (COAST TARWEED)
   71′ Head tubular, barely opening .... *Achyrachaena mollis* (BLOW-WIVES)

Key based on pappus

Key to Herbaceous Plants — Key 2, based on pappus:

1. Heads small, covered with hairs or phyllaries covering the flowers so cannot easily tell if flowers are ray or disk
2. Plants densely white-or gray-hairy

3. Plants low-growing, branched at the base
    4. Heads bristly-angular in the center of leafy bracts ....
    .... *Hesperevax sparsiflora* (ERECT EVAX)
    4´ Heads round, head-like ....
    .... *Psilocarphus brevissimus* (DWARF WOOLLY-HEADS)
3´ Plants upright, mostly branched above the middle
    5. Heads rounded
      6. Plants usually < 15 cm ....
      .... *Micropus californicus* (SLENDER COTTONWEED)
      6´ Plants usually > 1.5 cm ....
      .... *Lagophylla ramosissima* (COMMON HARELEAF)
    5´ Heads pointed .... *Filago gallica* (NARROW-LEAVED FILAGO)
2´ Plants green, may be glandular but not white-hairy
    7. Plants < 10 cm .... *Madia exigua*[1] (THREADSTEM MADIA)
    7´ Plants > 10 cm
      8. Stems glandular in upper half only ....
      .... *Madia gracilis*[1] (SLENDER TARWEED)
      8. Stems glandular throughout .... *Madia sativa*[1] (COAST TARWEED)
1´ Flowers in heads with either or both ray and disk flowers
    9. Heads with ray flowers only
      10. Pappus 0 or minute .... *Cichorium intybus*[1] (CHICORY)
      10´ Pappus present on some flowers
        11. Pappus of bristles
          12. Ray flowers yellow
            13. Inflorescence mostly solitary or scapose; leaves mostly basal
              14. Phyllaries ≥ 2 cm
                15. Annual, plant to 4 dm; body of achene strongly ribbed
                and winged ...... *Agoseris heterophylla* (ANNUAL AGOSERIS)
                15´ Perennial, plant to 8 dm; achene ribbed but not winged
                .... *Agoseris grandiflora* (CALIFORNIA DANDELION)
              14´ Phyllaries < 2 cm
                16. Annual, much branched, hairy ....
                .... *Crepis vesicaria* ssp. *taraxacifolia* (HAWK'S BEARD)
                16´ Annual or perennial
                  17. Annual; leaves glabrous ....
                  .... *Hypochaeris glabra* (SMOOTH CAT'S-EAR)
                  17´ Perennial, leaves rough-hairy ....
                  .... *Hypochaeris radicata* (ROUGH CAT'S-EAR)
            13´ Inflorescence of various other arrangements
              18. Phyllaries smooth (may be a few hairs)
                19. Achene with a beak
                  20. Inflorescence open
                    21. Leaves narrow, basal lobes narrow, pointed ....
                    .... *Lactuca saligna* (WILLOW LETTUCE)

21´ Leaves wider, basal lobes rounded ....
.... *Lactuca serriola* (prickly lettuce)
20´ Inflorescence mostly solitary, head with on a
long peduncle ....
.... *Urospermum picroides* (PRICKLY GOLDENFLEECE)
19´ Achene without a beak
22. Stem leaves toothed and spiny ....
.... *Sonchus asper* (PRICKLY SOW THISTLE)
22´ Stem leaves toothed, not spiny ....
.... *Sonchus oleraceus* (COMMON SOW THISTLE)
18´ Phyllaries prickly .... *Picris echioides* (BRISTLY OX-TONGUE)
12´ Ray flowers white, pink or purple
23. Flowers purple .... *Tragopogon porrifolius* (SALSIFY/OYSTER PLANT)
23´ Flowers white to pink
24. Achene with a beak ....
.... *Rafinesquia californica* (CALIFORNIA CHICORY)
24´ Achene without a beak ....
.... *Stephanomeria virgata* (VIRGATE STEPHANOMERIA)
11´ Pappus of scales
25. Ray flowers blue .... *Cichorium intybus*[2] (CHICORY)
25´ Ray flowers yellow or white
26. Scale entire, awn coming from tip ....
.... *Microseris douglasii* (DOUGLAS' MICROSERIS)
26´ Scale tip notched, awn coming from the notch ....
.... *Stebbinsoseris heterocarpa* (DERIVED MICROSERIS)
9´ Heads with disk flowers
27. Heads with disk flowers only
28. Pappus 0
29. Plant > 3 dm .... *Artemisia douglasiana*[1] (MUGWORT)
29´ Plant < 3 dm .... *Chamomilla suaveolens* (PINEAPPLE WEED)
28´ Pappus present on some flowers
30. Pappus of bristles
31. Phyllaries bristly or spiny
32. Flowers yellow
33. Central spines of main phyllaries > 1 cm ....
.... *Centaurea solstitialis* (YELLOW STAR-THISTLE)
33´ Central spines of main phyllaries < 1 cm, spine base purple
.... *Centaurea melitensis* (TOCALOTE)
32' Flowers white, pink, purple
34. Phyllaries < 2 cm ... *Carduus pycnocephalus* (ITALIAN THISTLE)
34´ Phyllaries > 2 cm
35. Leaves dark green blotched with white ....
.... *Silybum marianum* (MILK THISTLE)
35' Leaves not blotched with white
36. Phyllaries reflexed

37. Stems spiny-winged .... *Cirsium vulgare* (BULL THISTLE)

37′ Stems not spiny-winged .. *Cirsium fontinale* (FOUNTAIN THISTLE)

36′ Phyllaries not reflexed .... *Cirsium brevistylum* (INDIAN THISTLE)

31′ Phyllaries not bristly or spiny

38. Phyllaries thin, dry, white, straw-colored, pink, some opaque

39. Leaves green ~~5-7 mm~~ 10-15 mm

40. Larger stem leaves to 1 cm wide, fragrant; heads spheric; phyllaries generally white ....
.... *Gnaphalium californicum* (CALIFORNIA CUDWEED)

40′ Larger stem leaves ≤ 1 cm wide, not fragrant; phyllaries *heads elongate* dull white to greenish or pinkish ....
.... *Gnaphalium ramosissimum* (PINK EVERLASTING)

39′ Leaves gray because of dense hairs *on one or both surfaces*

41. Inflorescence open .... *phyllaries white to tan,* ....
...... *Gnaphalium canescens* ssp. *beneolens* (FRAGRANT EVERLASTING)

41′ Inflorescence in a dense terminal cluster

42. Phyllaries brown to purple .... *upper surface of leaves green, scarcely hairy (at least when mature)*
bronzed .... *Gnaphalium purpureum* (PURPLE CUDWEED)

42′ Phyllaries white at least at tips .... *stems, leaves, and phyllaries pale greenish yellow (straw-colored)*
.... *Gnaphalium stramineum* (COTTON-BATTING PLANT)

38′ Phyllaries green

43. Some flowers yellow

44. Phyllaries soft-hairy or glandular

45. Phyllaries soft-hairy, purple-tinged ....
....*Conyza bonariensis* (HORSEWEED)

45′ Phyllaries glandular, long-hairy ....
.... *Arnica discoidea* (RAYLESS ARNICA)

44′ Phyllaries not hairy, black-tipped

46. Most leaves < 10 cm .... *Senecio vulgaris* (COMMON GROUNDSEL)

46′ Lower leaves > 10 cm ....
.... *Senecio aronicoides* (CALIFORNIA BUTTERWEED/ GROUNDSEL)

43′ Flowers lavender-purple or white

47. Flowers lavender-purple ....
.... *Lessingia hololeuca* (WOOLLY-HEADED LESSINGIA)

47′ Flowers whitish .... *Baccharis douglasii* (MARSH BACCHARIS)

30′ Pappus of scales .... *Artemisia douglasiana*[2] (MUGWORT)

27′ Heads with both ray and disk flowers

48. Pappus 0

49. Some flowers white

50. Leaves compound .... *Achillea millefolium* (YARROW)

50′ Leaves simple ...*Hemizonia congesta* ssp. *luzulifolia* (HAYFIELD TARWEED)

49′ Some flowers yellow

51. Heads open

52. Ray flowers yellow with maroon base ....
.... *Madia elegans* (COMMON MADIA)

52′ Ray flowers yellow
  53. Some leaves deeply lobed ....
      .... *Deinandra corymbosa* (COAST TARWEED)
  53′ Leaves not deeply lobed
    54. Ray flowers equally 3-lobed ....
      .... *Monolopia major* (CUPPED MONOLOPIA)
    54′ Ray flowers entire or unevenly lobed ....
      .... *Monolopia gracilens* (WOODLAND MONOLOPIA)
51′ Heads tightly closed
  55. Plants < 10 cm .... *Madia exigua*[2] (THREADSTEM MADIA)
  55′ Plants > 10 cm
    56. Plant glandular on upper half only ....
      .... *Madia gracilis*[2] (SLENDER TARWEED)
    56′ Plant glandular throughout .... *Madia sativa*[2] (COAST TARWEED)
48′ Pappus present on some flowers
  57. Pappus of bristles
    58. Ray flowers yellow
      59. Ray flowers yellow with white tips .... *Layia platyglossa* (TIDY-TIPS)
      59′ Ray flowers all yellow
        60. Flower buds white-gummy, phyllaries coiled or spreading
          61. Stems not hairy, appearing varnished ....
            .... *Grindelia camporum* (GREAT VALLEY GRINDELIA)
          61′ Stems hairy .... *Grindelia hirsutula* (HIRSUTE GRINDELIA)
        60′ Flower buds not white-gummy
          62. Phyllaries in one series (may be several reduced at base) ....
            .... *Packera breweri* (BREWER'S BUTTERWEED)
          62′ Phyllaries in 3–5 series, overlapping
            63. Upper plant and phyllaries glandular
              64. Leaves and plant with glandular hairs ....
                .... *Heterotheca sessiliflora* ssp. *echioides* (GOLDENASTER)
              64′ Leaves resin-dotted ....
                .... *Euthamia occidentalis* (WESTERN GOLDENROD)
            63′ Plant hairy, not glandular ....
            .... *Solidago californica* (CALIFORNIA GOLDENROD)
    58′ Ray flowers pink or purple
      65. Phyllaries glandular; leaves linear .... *Erigeron foliosus* (LEAFY DAISY)
      65′ Phyllaries not glandular
        66. Small annual < 3 dm ....
          .... *Pentachaeta bellidiflora* (WHITE-RAYED PENTACHAETA)
        66′ Herbaceous perennial > 3 dm
          67. Leaves < 1.5 cm wide; margin finely toothed ....
            .... *Symphyotrichum chilensis* (COMMON CALIFORNIA ASTER)
          67′ Leaves > 1.5 cm wide; margin sharply toothed ....
            .... *Eurybia radulinus* (ROUGH-LEAVED ASTER)
  57′ Pappus of scales

68. Head tubular, barely opening .... *Achyrachaena mollis* (BLOW-WIVES)
68′ Heads open
   69. Ray flowers < 1 cm
     70. Stems winged .... *Helenium puberulum* (SNEEZEWEED)
     70′ Stems not winged
       71. Ray flowers pale yellow, often purple-tinged ....
       .... *Rigiopappus leptocladus* (RIGIOPAPPUS)
       71′ Ray flowers bright yellow .... *Lasthenia californica* (GOLDFIELDS)
   69′ Ray flowers > 1 cm
     72. Ray flowers with two colors .... *Gazania linearis* (GAZANIA)
     72′ Ray flowers evenly colored yellow
       73. Ray flowers fruiting, style present
         74. Leaves narrow, linear ....
         .... *Wyethia angustifolia* (NARROW-LEAVED MULE EARS)
         74′ Leaves wide .... *Wyethia glabra* (MULE EARS)
       73′ Ray flowers sterile, style 0 ....
       .... *Helianthus californicus* (CALIFORNIA SUNFLOWER)

[1] First time this species occurs in the key
[2] Second time this species occurs in the key
> greater than
< less than
≥ greater than or equal to

Rays & disks both [white]

rays ≈ 4mm long

Ht. to 1 m

✓ *Achillea millefolium* L.

YARROW   Native

Flowering Time: April–July

Habitat: grassland, open woodland

Description: Herbaceous perennial to 10 dm. Leaves alternate, compound, 3-pinnate, fern-like, to 10 cm, aromatic. Inflorescence a flat top cluster, heads with both ray and disk flowers; phyllaries in 3–4 rows; ray flowers to 4 mm, white; disk corollas to 3 mm, white. Fruit an achene to 2 mm; pappus 0.

Genus & Specific Name Derivation: Greek: Achilles of ancient mythology / thousand-leaves, referring to the fern-like divisions of the leaves

Notes: This species is circumpolar, occurring on all continents in the northern hemisphere. The strong oils in the leaves discourage insect damage, and can make livestock sick. Illustration from *Illustrated Flora of the Pacific States*.

Uses Past and Present: Leaves have been used medicinally since ancient times to heal wounds. Achilles is said to have used it to heal the wounds of his soldiers.

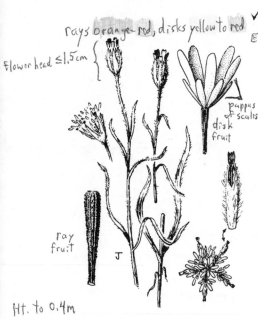

rays orange-red, disks yellow to red

Flower head ≤1.5cm

pappus & scales

disk fruit

ray fruit

Ht. to 0.4m

✓ *Achyrachaena mollis* Schauer

BLOW-WIVES   Native

Flowering Time: April–May

Habitat: grassland

Description: Soft-hairy annual to 4 dm. Leaves simple, sessile, lower opposite, upper alternate. Inflorescence a head with both ray and disk flowers, head not expanding until fruit matures; ray flowers orange-red; disk flowers yellow to red. Fruit an achene to 8 mm; ray achene pappus 0, disk achene pappus of white, shiny scales in 2 series, which form a showy round head in fruit.

Genus & Specific Name Derivation: Greek: chaffy achene, referring to the fruit / soft-hairy, referring to the hairs on the whole plant

Notes: This plant is most noticeable when it is in fruit when the flower head becomes round and papery-white with the showy pappus. Illustration from *Illustrated Flora of the Pacific States*.

photo in K & B plate 6

✓*Agoseris grandiflora* (Nutt.) E. Green

E
5C

CALIFORNIA DANDELION   Native

Flowering Time: April–September

Habitat: woodland

Description: Herbaceous perennial to 8 dm. Leaves basal, entire to deeply lobed. Inflorescence scapose, heads with ray flowers only; phyllaries to 3 cm, soft-hairy; ray flowers to 1 cm, yellow. Fruit an achene to 7 mm, beak longer than body of fruit; pappus of bristles.

Genus & Specific Name Derivation: Greek: goat chicory / grand or large

Notes: Illustration from *Illustrated Flora of the Pacific States.*

photo in K & B plate 7

Agoseris heterophylla (Nutt.) E. Greene

ANNUAL AGOSERIS   Native

Flowering Time: January–June

Habitat: grassland, woodland

Description: Annual to 4 dm, whole plant white-hairy. Leaves basal, simple, margins entire to toothed or lobed. Inflorescence solitary, upright; heads with ray flowers only; involucre to 2.5 cm; phyllaries in 2–4 rows; ray flowers yellow. Fruit an achene to 7 mm, beak to 25 mm; pappus of white bristles.

Genus & Specific Name Derivation: Greek: goat chicory / diverse leaves

Notes: Illustration from *Illustrated Flora of the Pacific States.*

Compare to Microseris

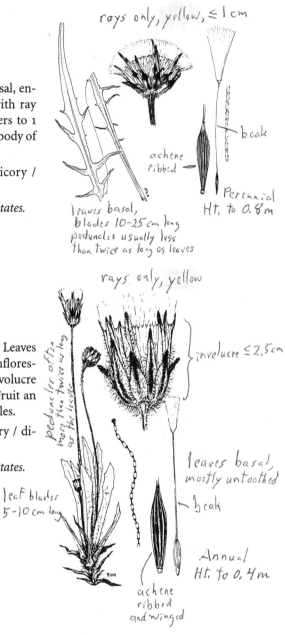

rays only, yellow, ≤ 1 cm

beak

achene ribbed

leaves basal, blades 10-25 cm long
peduncles usually less than twice as long as leaves

Perennial Ht. to 0.8 m

rays only, yellow

involucre ≤ 2.5 cm

peduncles often more than twice as long as the leaves

leaves basal, mostly untoothed

beak

leaf blades 5-10 cm long

achene ribbed and winged

Annual Ht. to 0.4 m

disks only, yellow

involucre
10-17mm

plant
glandular
and long-hairy

leaves
opposite,
toothed but
not lobed

Ht. to 0.6m   J

disks only, yellow-green

involucre
2-3 mm

Evergreen
Shrub to 2.5m

X *Arnica discoidea* Benth.

SC RAYLESS ARNICA   Native

Flowering Time: May–July *(into Sept.*

Habitat: chaparral, edge of woodland *opposite*

Description: Herbaceous perennial to 6 dm, glandular and long-hairy. Leaves basal and stem, blade to 12 cm, margin toothed. Inflorescence open; heads with disk flowers only; phyllaries glandular, long-hairy. Disk flowers yellow, soft-hairy, glandular. Fruit an achene to 8 mm, glandular, hairy; pappus of bristles, strongly short-barbed.

Genus & Specific Name Derivation: Latin or Greek: ancient name / disk flowers only

Notes: Illustration from *Illustrated Flora of the Pacific States.*

photo in K + B plate 7

√ *Artemisia californica* Less.

E
SC CALIFORNIA SAGEBRUSH   Native

Flowering Time: August–November

Habitat: chaparral, open woodland

Description: Gray, rounded, much-branched evergreen shrub with slender, flexible branches to 2.5 m. Leaves alternate, simple, to 10 cm, threadlike, some deeply lobed, gray-green, aromatic. Inflorescence arranged in elongate, narrow racemes at the ends of branches. Flowers yellow-green, arranged in heads of small disk flowers only. Fruit an achene.

Genus & Specific Name Derivation: Greek: Artemis, goddess of the hunt and herbalist, Queen of Anatolia / from California

Notes: Rub your fingers along the leafy branches and the aroma will stick to your fingers. Some have said it smells like turpentine. This is not the true sage used in cooking which is in the genus *Salvia* in the Mint family. Illustration from *Illustrated Flora of the Pacific States.*

Uses Past and Present: Natives brewed the leaves to make a tea for colds and as a strong wash for wounds and swellings. Early pioneers spread branches around their beds to keep fleas away.

√ *Artemisia douglasiana* Besser

MUGWORT   Native

Flowering Time: June–November

Habitat: chaparral, woodland

Description: Erect, herbaceous perennial to 25 dm. Leaves simple, lobed, hairy above, densely white-hairy below; aromatic. Inflorescence a dense spike; heads with disk flowers only; phyllaries gray-hairy, margins transparent; corolla yellow. Fruit an achene to 1 mm; pappus 0 or a minute crown of scales.

Genus & Specific Name Derivation: Greek: Artemis, goddess of the hunt, and noted herbalist, Queen of Anatolia / David Douglas (1798–1834), a Scottish collector in northwestern America. He collected nearly 500 specimens of California plants for the Royal Horticultural Society in England.

Notes: The common name "mug" means "midge" (a small flying insect) and "wort" means "herb." May have been used to either attract or repel these small insects. Illustration from *Illustrated Flora of the Pacific States.*

Uses Past and Present: Used by some to prevent or alleviate poison oak.

disks only, yellow

involucre ~2-3mm

Ht. to 2.5m

photo in K & B plate 7

√ *Baccharis douglasii* DC.

MARSH BACCHARIS   Native

Flowering Time: April–December

Habitat: moist areas

Description: Plant dioecious, upright herbaceous perennial to 2 m. Leaves simple, to 13 cm, entire to toothed; petiole to 10 mm, winged. Inflorescence flat-topped clusters; heads of disk flowers only; phyllaries in 2–3 rows, generally sticky; staminate corollas to 5 mm; pistillate corollas to 3 mm. Fruit an achene to 1.5 mm; pappus of bristles to 4 mm.

Genus & Specific Name Derivation: Latin: Bacchus, god of wine / for David Douglas (1798–1834), collector in American Northwest for the Royal Horticultural Society

Notes: Has separate (dioecious) male and female plants. Illustration from *Illustrated Flora of the Pacific States*

slightly woody near base

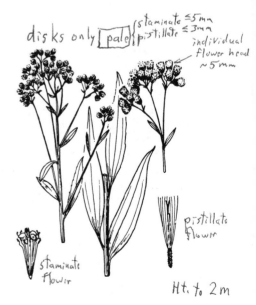

disks only [pale] staminate ≤5mm pistillate ≤3mm

individual flower head ~5mm

pistillate flower

staminate flower

Ht. to 2m

disks only, creamy (anthers showy yellow)

flower head ~5mm

Flower head ~5mm

male flowers (staminate)

female flowers (pistillate)

Evergreen Shrub Ht. to 3m

Baccharis pilularis DC.

COYOTE BRUSH   Native

Flowering Time: August–November

Habitat: chaparral, woodland, disturbed areas

Description: Evergreen dioecious shrub up to 3 m. Leaves alternate, simple, sessile, shiny green, to 4 cm, usually with 3 main veins; margins with coarse teeth. Inflorescence in a leafy panicle. Flowers unisexual; male and female flowers are on different plants (dioecious). The male plant has heads of small disk flowers with showy yellow anthers. The female plant has heads of small cream-colored disk flowers. The female plant is most showy in the fall – winter when the white tuft of pappus on top of the seeds is open, giving the flowers a fluffy appearance. Fruit an achene with fluffy pappus that allows the seeds to be dispersed by the wind.

Genus & Specific Name Derivation: Latin: Bacchus, god of wine / bearing small balls or globular structures, referring to the insect galls that can usually be found at the end of the stems

Notes: The common name may refer to the female flowers in seed, when the pappus looks hairy, as if a coyote had walked by and left its fur on the bush. The female bush produces a great quantity of seeds that are blown in the wind to many different areas. This is one of the first plants to become established in a disturbed area, therefore it can be called a pioneer plant.

disks only, pink to purple, ≤ 14mm

involucre 1.5-2.0 cm

Ht. to 2m

fruit

Carduus pycnocephalus L.

ITALIAN THISTLE

Nonnative / Mediterranean and North Africa

Flowering Time: May–September

Habitat: grassland, disturbed areas

Description: Annual or biennial to 20 dm, stem winged, spiny. Leaves simple, alternate to 15 cm, lobed, spine-tipped. Inflorescence a head of disk flowers only; phyllaries hairy, spiny; corolla to 14 mm, pink to purple. Fruit an achene to 6 mm; pappus of bristles to 15 mm.

Genus & Specific Name Derivation: Latin: ancient name / thick-spiked

Notes: Invasive. Accidentally introduced into California in 1912. A single plant can produce 20,000 seeds in one season. Bumblebees and butterflies are the primary pollinators of thistles. Illustration from *Illustrated Flora of the Pacific States.*

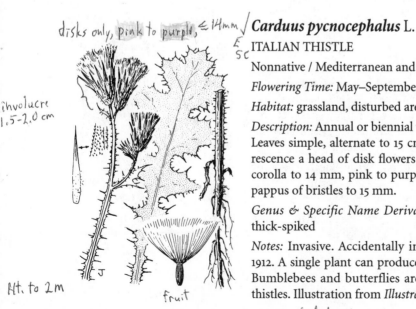

2008 Addendum
Bellis perennis ENGLISH DAISY nonnative
in day-camp lawn   Both ray and disk flowers
ray flowers white to purple
in lawns

√ *Centaurea melitensis* L.

TOCALOTE   Nonnative / Europe

Flowering Time: May–September

Habitat: grassland, disturbed areas

Description: Annual to 10 dm. Leaves simple, alternate to 15 cm. Inflorescence a head of disk flowers only; phyllaries straw-colored, base spine-fringed, tip with long slender spines; disk corolla to 12 mm, yellow. Fruit an achene to 2.5 mm; pappus of bristles to 3 mm.

Genus & Specific Name Derivation: Greek: ancient name / from Malta

Notes: Invasive. Brought to California during the Spanish period, earliest record of seed occurrence found in adobe bricks dating from 1797 in San Fernando. See *C. solstitialis*. Illustration from *Illustrated Flora of the Pacific States*.

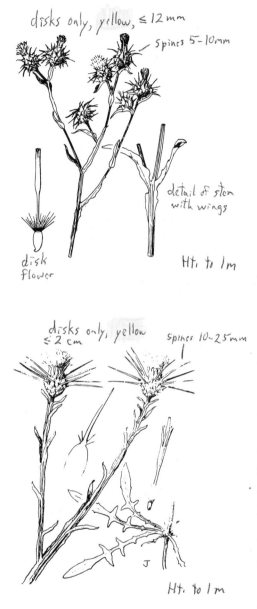

√ *Centaurea solstitialis* L.

YELLOW STAR-THISTLE   Nonnative / Europe

Flowering Time: June–December

Habitat: grassland, disturbed areas

Description: Annual to 10 dm. Leaves simple, alternate to 15 cm, lower lobed. Inflorescence a head of disk flowers only; phyllaries spiny; disk corolla to 20 mm, yellow. Fruit an achene to 3 mm; pappus 0 or of bristles to 4 mm.

Genus & Specific Name Derivation: Greek: ancient name / midsummer, referring to the flowering time

Notes: Invasive. Introduced after 1848 as a contaminant with alfalfa seeds. Large plants can produce as many as 75,000 seeds. Has become a major problem to grazing livestock, containing a poison that sickens and can kill them. A major effort by volunteers is underway to try to eradicate this plant at Edgewood. Illustration from *Illustrated Flora of the Pacific States*.

disks only, yellow

flower head {
6-9 mm

Ht. to 30 cm

J

fruit
(achene)

√ *Chamomilla suaveolens* (Pursh) Rydb.

PINEAPPLE WEED   Nonnative / Asia

Flowering Time: March–June

Habitat: disturbed areas along trails and roads

Description: Branched, aromatic annual to 30 cm. Leaves simple, alternate to 5 cm; margin deeply lobed. Inflorescence a head of disk flowers only; phyllaries in 2–3 unequal rows; disk corolla yellow, to 2 mm. Fruit an achene; pappus 0.

Genus & Specific Name Derivation: Derivation of name not known / sweet-scented

Notes: Fresh flower heads smell like pineapple. Illustration from *Illustrated Flora of the Pacific States.*

rays only, blue

flower head
≥ 3 cm wide

Ht. to 1m

J

Cichorium intybus L.

CHICORY   Nonnative / Europe and Africa

Flowering Time: all year

Habitat: disturbed areas, edge of trails

Description: Herbaceous perennial to 1 m, from a deep woody taproot. Leaves basal and stem, reduced upward; lower to 2 cm, margin toothed; middle stem leaves sessile, upper reduced. Inflorescence axillary; heads with ray flowers only; phyllaries in 2 rows; flowers blue. Fruit an achene to 2.5 mm; pappus of scales to 0.5 mm.

Genus & Specific Name Derivation: Old Arabic name / from Virgil, a name for wild chicory or endive

Notes: Illustration from *Illustrated Flora of the Pacific States.*

Uses Past and Present: In the Mediterranean region the leaves have long been used for bitter greens and its roots roasted as a coffee additive.

photo in K & B plate 9

Genus Cirsium: Flowers all of disk type; phyllaries and plant as a whole spiny; spines straight; pappus with feathery bristles; leaves spiny, lobed or curved

ASTERACEAE 77

Cirsium brevistylum Cronq.

INDIAN THISTLE   Native

Flowering Time: April–July

Habitat: woodland

Description: Annual or biennial to 20 cm. Leaves simple, alternate to 25 cm; margin lobed to toothed, spiny; upper leaves clasping. Inflorescence with 1–3 heads, with disk flowers only; phyllaries to 5 rows, spiny; corollas to 24 mm, white to purple. Fruit an achene to 4 mm; pappus bristles to 20 mm.

Genus & Specific Name Derivation: Greek: thistle / short-styled

Notes: One species of *Cirsium* was a lifesaving plant to Truman Everts, who was lost for a month in Yosemite Park in the late 1800s; he survived by eating the roots. Illustration from *Illustrated Flora of the Pacific States.*

Uses Past and Present: Roots, young leaves, and stalks are boiled and eaten. These are related to artichokes and the flower heads are eaten like artichokes.

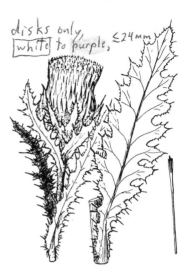

disks only, white to purple, ≤24mm

Ht. to 20cm

Cirsium fontinale E. Greene var. *fontinale*   No longer present

FOUNTAIN THISTLE   Native

Flowering Time: May–October

Habitat: serpentine seeps

Description: Herbaceous perennial to 20 dm. Basal leaves to 7 dm, wavy; petiole spiny-lobed or toothed, margin spiny; stem leaves reduced upward; petiole clasping. Inflorescence nodding; heads of disk flowers only; phyllaries to 2 cm in several rows, reddish, recurved, spine-tipped; disk corolla pink to lavender, tube to 10 mm, throat to 6 mm, lobes to 6 mm. Fruit an achene to 4 mm; pappus of bristles to 15 mm.

Genus & Specific Name Derivation: Greek: thistle / flowers nodding

Notes: State and federally listed as endangered. Extirpated from Edgewood, last seen in 1980s. Illustration from *Illustrated Flora of the Pacific States.*

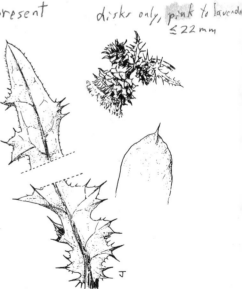

disks only, pink to lavender ≤22mm

Ht. to 2m

2008 Addendum

• *Cirsium quercetorum*   BROWNIE THISTLE native

Flowers all of disk type; phyllaries and plant as a whole spiny; spines straight; pappus with feathery bristles; leaves mostly (but not totally) basal; not more than 30cm tall; phyllaries with lighter margins; corollas purple to white

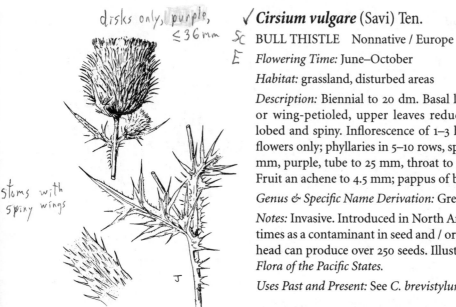

disks only, purple, ≤36mm SC E

Cirsium vulgare (Savi) Ten.

BULL THISTLE Nonnative / Europe

Flowering Time: June–October

Habitat: grassland, disturbed areas

Description: Biennial to 20 dm. Basal leaves to 40 cm, sessile or wing-petioled, upper leaves reduced, clasping; margin lobed and spiny. Inflorescence of 1–3 heads; heads with disk flowers only; phyllaries in 5–10 rows, spiny; disk corollas to 35 mm, purple, tube to 25 mm, throat to 6 mm, lobes to 6 mm. Fruit an achene to 4.5 mm; pappus of bristles to 30 mm.

Genus & Specific Name Derivation: Greek: thistle / common

Notes: Invasive. Introduced in North America during colonial times as a contaminant in seed and / or ballast. A single flower head can produce over 250 seeds. Illustration from *Illustrated Flora of the Pacific States.*

Uses Past and Present: See *C. brevistylum.*

stems with spiny wings

Ht. to 2 m

SOUTH-AMERICAN

Conyza bonariensis (L.) Cronq.

HORSEWEED Nonnative / South America

Flowering Time: June–September

Habitat: grassland, disturbed areas

disks only, greenish-yellow, ≤4mm; phyllaries often purple-tipped

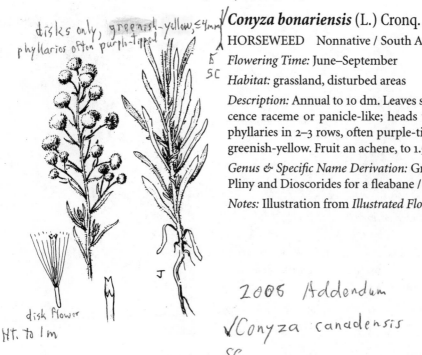

Description: Annual to 10 dm. Leaves simple to 8 cm. Inflorescence raceme or panicle-like; heads with disk flowers only; phyllaries in 2–3 rows, often purple-tipped; flowers to 4 mm, greenish-yellow. Fruit an achene, to 1.5 mm; pappus to 4 mm.

Genus & Specific Name Derivation: Greek: flea; name used by Pliny and Dioscorides for a fleabane / from Buenos Aires

Notes: Illustration from *Illustrated Flora of the Pacific States.*

disk flower *Ht. to 1m*

2008 Addendum
Conyza canadensis HORSEWEED native
SC E

Crepis vesicaria L. ssp. *taraxacifolia* (Thuill.) Thell.

HAWKSBEARD Nonnative / Europe

Flowering Time: April–July

Habitat: grassland

Description: Annual or biennial to 8 dm. Leaves simple to 10 cm, lobed and toothed. Inflorescence a cyme; each head with ray flowers only; phyllaries in 2 rows; ray flowers yellow. Fruit an achene to 8 mm including beak; pappus of white bristles.

Genus & Specific Name Derivation: Greek: sandal, for unknown reason / inflated, bladder-like

Notes: Illustration from *Illustrated Flora of the Pacific States.*

rays only, yellow

beak

fruit

J

Ht. to 0.8m

This species not in Kozloff and Beidleman
Key in Jepson Manual: Fruit tapered to a distinct
slender beak; beak slightly shorter than or similar
in length to fruiting body; involucre and stems with
a few blackish bristles, in addition to hairs

Deinandra corymbosa (DC.) B. G. Baldwin ssp. *corymbosa*   (former genus Hemizonia)

COAST TARWEED Native called Coast Spikeweed in K+B

Flowering Time: May–November

Habitat: grassland

Description: Annual to 10 dm; stems bristly-hairy. Leaves alternate, simple to 8 cm, lower deeply lobed almost appearing compound, soft-hairy, glandular. Inflorescence open; heads with both ray and disk flowers; phyllaries partially enclosing ray fruits, glandular; ray flowers to 7 mm, bright yellow; disk corollas yellow; anthers black. Fruit an achene to 2.5 mm, beaked; pappus 0.

Genus & Specific Name Derivation: Derivation unknown / flowers arranged in a corymb (a flat-topped raceme)

Notes: Illustration from *Illustrated Flora of the Pacific States.* New name accepted by *Jepson Manual* staff, name in *The Jepson Manual* (1993) *Hemizonia corymbosa* ssp. *corymbosa.*

rays yellow, disks yellow ≤ 7mm (anthers black)

phyllaries in one row, partially enclosing ray fruits

leaves deeply lobed

disk flower

ray flower

Ht. to 1m

Resembles Hemizonia congesta ssp. congesta (yellow hayfield tarweed) except for lobed leaves.

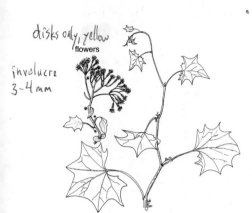

disks only, yellow
flowers

involucre
3-4 mm

Vine

Delairea odorata Lem. formerly Senecio mikansoides

GERMAN-IVY / CAPE IVY   Nonnative / South Africa

Flowering Time: December–March

Habitat: woodland, riparian

Description: Perennial vine that trails along the ground and scrambles up surrounding vegetation. Leaves alternate, simple to 8 cm, palmately 5–9 lobed. Petiole to 9 cm. Inflorescence a head of 20–40 disk flowers. Each flower bright yellow. Fruit an achene.

Genus & Specific Name Derivation: For Eugene Delaire, head gardener at the botanical gardens in Orleans from 1837 to 1856 / fragrant or sweet smelling

Notes: Introduced in eastern U.S. in 1850s as an ornamental plant, in California in the 1950s. By the 1960s it became naturalized in Golden Gate Park. There are plants in the creek below the bridge at the Day Camp. This is a very invasive plant in the riparian areas. It can choke out other plants and kill them. New name accepted by *Jepson Manual* staff, name in *The Jepson Manual* (1993) *Senecio mikanioides*.

or blue
rays purple, disks yellow
≤12 mm

ray flower

disk flower

Ht. to 1 m

Erigeron foliosus Nutt. var. *foliosus*

LEAFY DAISY   Native

Flowering Time: June–September

Habitat: grassland

Description: Herbaceous perennial to 10 dm. Leaves simple to 5 cm. Inflorescence flat topped, heads with both ray and disk flowers; phyllaries in 3–5 unequal rows, hairy, margin scarious; ray flowers to 12 mm, purple; disk corollas yellow. Fruit an achene; pappus of bristles.

Genus & Specific Name Derivation: Greek: early old age / leafy

Notes: Illustration from *Illustrated Flora of the Pacific States.*

Erigeron petrophilus E. Greene var. *petrophilus*

ROCK DAISY   Native

Flowering Time: June–August

Habitat: edge of woodland

Description: Herbaceous perennial to 30 cm. Leaves simple to 25 mm. Inflorescence in flat-topped clusters, heads with ~~both ray and~~ *only* disk flowers; phyllaries in 3–5 rows, glandular; disk corollas to 6.5 mm, yellow to reddish. Fruit an achene to 3 mm; pappus of bristles.

Genus & Specific Name Derivation: Greek: early old age / rock lover, referring to the preferred habitat

Notes: Illustration from *Illustrated Flora of the Pacific States.*

photo in K & B plate 10

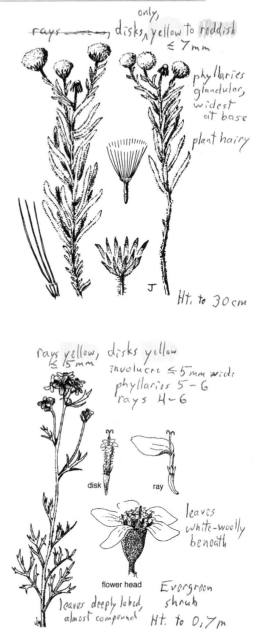

rays ~~——~~ only, disks, yellow to reddish ≤ 7mm

phyllaries glandular, widest at base

plant hairy

J   Ht. to 30cm

rays yellow, disks yellow
≤ 15mm   involucre ≤ 5mm wide
phyllaries 5 – 6
rays 4 – 6

disk   ray

leaves white-woolly beneath

flower head

leaves deeply lobed, almost compound

Evergreen shrub
Ht. to 0.7m

✓ *Eriophyllum confertiflorum* (DC.) A. Gray var. *confertiflorum*

E
Sc

GOLDEN-YARROW   Native

Flowering Time: March–November

Habitat: grassland, edge of chaparral

Description: Evergreen shrub to 7 dm. Leaves alternate, simple to almost compound, to 5 cm, deeply 3–5 lobed. Leaves green above, white woolly beneath, margin rolled under. Inflorescence a clustered head with up to 30 flowers. Flowers with both ray and disk flowers. Petals bright golden-yellow. Fruit an achene.

Genus & Specific Name Derivation: Greek: woolly leaf, referring to the white hairs on the under surface of the leaf / crowded flowers

photo in K & B plate 10

Eriophyllum staechadifolium

LIZARD TAIL / SEASIDE WOOLLY SUNFLOWER Native, no longer present
both rays and disks, yellow. Leaves lobed, alternate, woolly on undersides;
plants woody (shrubs), involucre ≤ 5mm wide; phyllaries 8–11; rays 6–9;
evergreen   mostly on coastal bluffs

[handwritten annotations around illustration:]
rays white to pale violet, ≤ 13 mm
disks ____

leaves broad (only 2-3 times as long as wide), toothed

disk flower

Ht. to 0.7 m

ray flower

rays and disks both yellow
rays ≤ 2.5 mm
disks ≤ 4 mm

inflorescence broad

leaves resin-dotted (dark, glandular pits), linear

ray

disk

involucre

Ht. to 2 m

Eurybia radulina (A. Gray) G. L. Nesom /Aster r.

ROUGH-LEAVED ASTER   Native

Flowering Time: July–December

Habitat: woodland

Description: Herbaceous perennial to 7 dm. Leaves mainly stem, broad, sharply toothed. Inflorescence a flat-topped panicle, each head with both ray and disk flowers; phyllaries in 3–5 rows with dark midvein, margin often purple; ray flowers to 13 mm, white to pale violet. Fruit an achene; pappus of tawny bristles.

Genus & Specific Name Derivation: Derivation unknown / a scraper, referring to the firm, rough leaves

Notes: Illustration from *Illustrated Flora of the Pacific States.* New name accepted by *Jepson Manual* staff, name in *The Jepson Manual* (1993) *Aster radulinus*.

Euthamia occidentalis Nutt.

WESTERN GOLDENROD   Native

Flowering Time: August–November

Habitat: edges of wet meadows

Description: Herbaceous perennial to 2 m. Leaves alternate, sessile, to 10 cm, linear, resin-dotted. Inflorescence panicle-like; heads with both ray and disk flowers; phyllaries in 3–4 series. Ray flowers to 2.5 mm, yellow; disk flowers to 4 mm, yellow. Fruit an achene to 1 mm; pappus of bristles.

Genus & Specific Name Derivation: Greek: well-crowded, from dense inflorescence / western

Notes: Illustration from *Illustrated Flora of the Pacific States.*

[handwritten:] Compare to Solidago californica

√ *Filago gallica* L. / Logfia gallica is new name

SC
E   NARROW-LEAVED FILAGO   Nonnative / Mediterranean/
                              FLUFFWEED

Flowering Time: April–May

Habitat: grassland

Description: Annual to 1.5 dm, grayish, cobwebby-hairy. Leaves simple, alternate to 3 cm, grayish-cobwebby hairy, sessile. Inflorescence loose heads with disk flowers only; chaff-like phyllaries below each pistillate flower; pistillate flowers in 4–8 series; each flower subtended by a chaff scale; disk flowers 5–11, to 3 mm, brown to yellow. Fruit an achene, outer enfolded by a chaff scale; pappus 0; inner fruit not enfolded by a chaff scale; pappus of bristles.

Genus & Specific Name Derivation: Latin: with threads, referring to the woolly hairs / from France

Notes: Illustration from *Illustrated Flora of the Pacific States.*

Compare to Micropus and Lagophylla

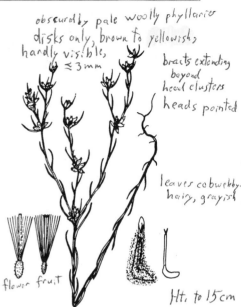

obscured by pale woolly phyllaries
disks only, brown to yellowish,
hardly visible,
≲ 3 mm

bracts extending
beyond
head clusters
heads pointed

leaves cobwebby-
hairy, grayish

flower fruit

Ht. to 15 cm

√ *Gazania linearis* (Thunb.) Druce

SC   GAZANIA   Nonnative / South Africa

Flowering Time: N/A

Habitat: grassland, disturbed areas

Description: Herbaceous perennial. Leaves in a basal rosette; petioles long, winged. Inflorescence a scapose head with both ray and disk flowers; phyllaries in 2 or more series; ray flowers to 5 cm, yellow or orange; disk corollas to 8 mm, reddish orange. Fruit an achene to 2 mm; pappus scales to 4 mm.

Genus & Specific Name Derivation: Theodorus of Gaza, died in 1478, translator of works of Theophrastus / narrow, referring to the leaves

Notes: May have been introduced in seed mix for erosion control. Illustration from *Illustrated Flora of the Pacific States.*

two-toned
rays yellow & orange, disks reddish orange
≲ 5cm

J

Genus Gnaphalium: Disk flowers only

Phyllaries thin, dry, often translucent, pale-colored

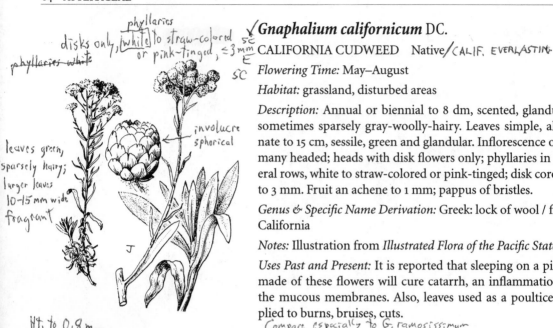

phyllaries white

disks only, white to straw-colored or pink-tinged, ≤3 mm

SC
E

SC

leaves green, sparsely hairy; larger leaves 10-15 mm wide fragrant

involucre spherical

Ht. to 0.8 m

√ *Gnaphalium californicum* DC.

CALIFORNIA CUDWEED   Native/*CALIF. EVERLASTING*

Flowering Time: May–August

Habitat: grassland, disturbed areas

Description: Annual or biennial to 8 dm, scented, glandular, sometimes sparsely gray-woolly-hairy. Leaves simple, alternate to 15 cm, sessile, green and glandular. Inflorescence open many headed; heads with disk flowers only; phyllaries in several rows, white to straw-colored or pink-tinged; disk corollas to 3 mm. Fruit an achene to 1 mm; pappus of bristles.

Genus & Specific Name Derivation: Greek: lock of wool / from California

Notes: Illustration from *Illustrated Flora of the Pacific States.*

Uses Past and Present: It is reported that sleeping on a pillow made of these flowers will cure catarrh, an inflammation of the mucous membranes. Also, leaves used as a poultice applied to burns, bruises, cuts.

Compare especially to G. ramosissimum photo in K & B plate 11

disks only, white to straw-colored ≤4 mm

phyllaries white

SC

inflorescence open branched

Fragrant stems and leaves whitish gray

leaves 4-10 mm wide

involucre

Ht. to 1 m

√ *Gnaphalium canescens* DC. ssp. *beneolens*
SC (Davidson) Stebb. & Keil

FRAGRANT EVERLASTING   Native

Flowering Time: July–September

Habitat: chaparral

Description: Biennial or short-lived perennial to 10 dm; scented. Leaves simple, alternate to 5 cm, linear, sessile, gray. Inflorescence open; heads with disk flowers only; phyllaries in several rows, white or pale straw-colored; disk corollas to 4 mm. Fruit an achene to 1 mm; pappus of bristles.

Genus & Specific Name Derivation: Greek: lock of wool / white-hairy

Notes: Illustration from *Illustrated Flora of the Pacific States.*

Uses Past and Present: See *G. californicum.*

Compare especially to G. purpureum, etc. other Gnaphaliums

2008 Addendum

√ *Gnaphalium luteo-album*   WEEDY CUDWEED   nonnative

SC
E

stems and leaves pale grayish

similar to G. canescens but smaller, phyllaries brownish leaves < 4 mm wide, < 4 cm long

Gnaphalium purpureum L.

PURPLE CUDWEED   Native

Flowering Time: April–June

Habitat: grassland, disturbed areas

Description: Annual or biennial to 6 dm; unscented. Leaves simple, alternate to 10 cm, sessile, hairy below. Inflorescence dense, spike-like; heads with disk flowers only; phyllaries in several rows, brown to purplish above; disk corollas to 2.5 mm. Fruit an achene to 1 mm; pappus of bristles.

Genus & Specific Name Derivation: Greek: lock of wool / reddish purple, referring to the phyllaries

Notes: Illustration from *Illustrated Flora of the Pacific States.*

Uses Past and Present: See *G. californicum.*

Compare to other Gnaphaliums

photo in K & B plate 11

Gnaphalium ramosissimum Nutt.

PINK EVERLASTING   Native

Flowering Time: June–October

Habitat: woodland

Description: Biennial to 12 dm, sweet-scented. Leaves simple, alternate to 8 cm, sessile, green on both surfaces. Inflorescence large, much branched, heads with disk flowers only; phyllaries in several rows, whitish to greenish or pink, opaque; disk corollas to 3.5 mm, pinkish. Fruit an achene to 1 mm; pappus of bristles.

Genus & Specific Name Derivation: Greek: lock of wool / branched, referring to the inflorescence

Notes: Illustration from *Illustrated Flora of the Pacific States.*

Uses Past and Present: See *G. californicum.*

Compare especially to G. californicum

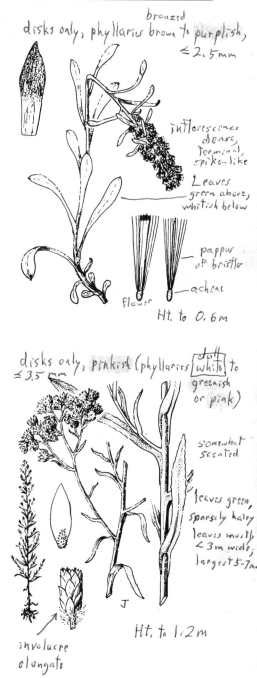

disks only, phyllaries brown to purplish, bronzed ≤ 2.5 mm

inflorescence dense, terminal, spike-like

Leaves green above, whitish below

pappus of bristle

achene

flower

Ht. to 0.6 m

disks only, pinkish (phyllaries dull white to greenish or pink) ≤ 3.5 mm

somewhat scented

leaves green, sparsely hairy

leaves mostly < 3 m wide, largest 5-7m

involucre elongate

Ht. to 1.2 m

disks only, phyllaries white to ≤ 2.5 mm straw-colored

inflorescence dense, terminal, but not spike-like

stems and leaves pale greenish yellow (straw-colored)

Ht. to 0.7 m

involucre 5~6 mm

Gnaphalium stramineum Kunth

COTTON-BATTING PLANT   Native

Flowering Time: all year

Habitat: grassland, disturbed areas

Description: Annual or biennial to 7 dm, hairy throughout; unscented. Leaves simple, alternate to 7 cm, gray. Inflorescence in dense terminal clusters; heads of disk flowers only; phyllaries in several rows, transparent to opaque, white to straw-colored; disk corolla to 2.5 mm. Fruit an achene to 1 mm; pappus of bristles.

Genus & Specific Name Derivation: Greek: lock of wool / straw-colored, referring to color of phyllaries

Notes: Illustration from *Illustrated Flora of the Pacific States.*

Uses Past and Present: See *G. californicum.*

Compare especially to G. lutu-album

rays yellow, disks yellow ≤ 11 mm

tips of outer phyllaries curved (coiled) to straight

stems appearing pale-varnished

disk flower

Ht. to 1 m

Grindelia camporum E. Greene var. *camporum*

GREAT VALLEY GRINDELIA   Native or GUMPLANT

Flowering Time: June–December

Habitat: chaparral

on lower stem to 8 cm

Description: Herbaceous perennial to 10 dm, stems appearing white-varnished. Leaves simple, alternate to 3 cm, entire to toothed. Inflorescence a head with both ray and disk flowers; phyllaries in 6–7 rows, reflexed and coiled; ray flowers to 11 mm, yellow; disk flowers yellow. Fruit an achene to 5 mm; pappus of 2–6 bristles.

Genus & Specific Name Derivation: D. H. Grindel (1776–1836), Latvian botanist / camphor-like scent

Notes: Buds are covered with a whitish protective gum, hence plant also know as gumweed. Illustration from *Illustrated Flora of the Pacific States.*

Uses Past and Present: The upper young branches of some species were used for bronchial conditions, asthma. The resinous tops were used by natives as a wash for poison oak rash.

Compare to G. hirsutula

photo in K&B plate 11

✓ *Grindelia hirsutula* Hook. & Arn.

HIRSUTE GRINDELIA Native *or GUMPLANT*

Flowering Time: May–November

Habitat: edge of woodland

Description: Herbaceous perennial to 12 dm, hairy. Leaves simple, alternate to 10 cm, margin entire to lobed. Inflorescence a head of both ray and disk flowers; phyllaries in 4–5 rows, outer spreading outward; ray flowers to 20 mm, yellow; disk flowers yellow. Fruit an achene to 5 mm; pappus of 2–6 bristles.

Genus & Specific Name Derivation: D. H. Grindel (1776–1836), Latvian botanist / somewhat hairy

Notes: See *G. camporum*. Illustration from *Illustrated Flora of the Pacific States.*

Uses Past and Present: See *G. camporum.*

Compare to G. camporum

• *Helenium puberulum* DC.

SNEEZEWEED Native *called Rosilia in K&B*

Flowering Time: April–November

Habitat: woodland

Description: Annual to herbaceous perennial, stems to 16 dm, winged. Leaves simple, alternate, soft-hairy; wing-petioled. Inflorescence a head of both ray and disk flowers; phyllaries in 1–3 rows; ray flowers to 10 mm, yellow; disk corollas to 3 mm, yellow to brown or purple. Fruit an achene to 2 mm; pappus of scales to 2 mm, awned.

Genus & Specific Name Derivation: Helen of Troy / soft hairy, referring to the leaves

Notes: Illustration from *Illustrated Flora of the Pacific States.*

Uses Past and Present: Flowers are a source of a reddish dye.

photo in K & B plate II

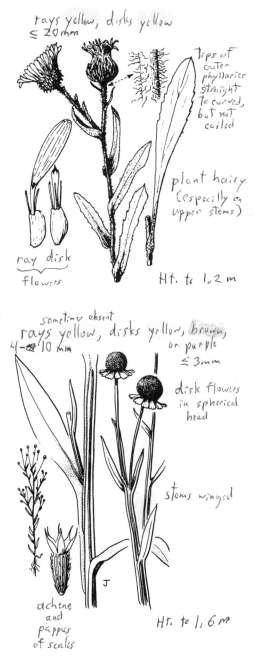

rays yellow, disks yellow ≤ 20 mm

tips of outer phyllaries straight to curved, but not coiled

plant hairy (especially on upper stems)

ray disk flowers

Ht. to 1.2 m

sometimes absent
rays yellow, disks yellow, brown, or purple
4–10 mm ≤ 3mm

disk flowers in spherical head

stems winged

achene and pappus of scales

Ht. to 1.6 m

rays and disks both yellow
rays ≤ /3 cm
disks ≤ 8 mm

Ht. to 2.5 m

Helianthus californicus DC.

CALIFORNIA SUNFLOWER   Native

Flowering Time: August–September

Habitat: woodland

Description: Herbaceous perennial to 25 dm. Leaves simple, alternate; petiole short. Inflorescence a head of both ray and disk flowers; phyllaries to 25 mm, bent back in fruit; ray flowers to 3 cm, yellow; disk corollas to 8 mm, yellow. Fruit an achene to 5 mm; pappus of scales to 4 mm.

Genus & Specific Name Derivation: Greek: sun flower / from California

Notes: The flowering stem turns to follow the sun. Illustration from *Illustrated Flora of the Pacific States.*

Uses Past and Present: Seeds have nutritious value and were eaten by the natives. A useful fiber was taken from the coarse stalks and dye was made from the flowers.

rays [white] often striped red-purple below
disks white to yellow, anthers black
rays ≤ 11 mm

Ht. to 0.8 m

Hemizonia congesta DC.
ssp. luzulifolia (DC.) Babc. & H. M. Hall

HAYFIELD TARWEED   Native

Flowering Time: May–August

Habitat: serpentine grassland

Description: Annual to 8 dm, stem branched and glandular on upper part of the plant. Leaves simple, alternate to 18 cm, lower silky-hairy. Inflorescence open; heads with both ray and disk flowers; phyllaries partially enclosing ray fruits; ray flowers to 11 mm, white, often red-purple-striped below; disk corollas white to yellow; anthers appearing black. Fruit an achene to 2 mm; pappus 0.

Genus & Specific Name Derivation: Greek: half girdle, referring to the partly sheathing phyllaries / arranged close together

Notes: Illustration from *Illustrated Flora of the Pacific States.*

Compare to other tarweeds (Deinandra, Hemizonia, Madia, some Layias)

photo in K & B plate 12

√ ## *Hesperevax sparsiflora* (A. Gray) E. Greene
var. *sparsiflora*

E

ERECT EVAX   Native

Flowering Time: April–May

Habitat: serpentine grassland

Description: Annual to 10 cm, branched at base. Leaves alternate, simple to 3 cm, gray-green, cobwebby-hairy. Inflorescence axillary or terminal; heads with disk flowers only; phyllaries 0, outer structure of chaff scales that appear phyllary-like; pistillate flowers in 1–3 series; staminate corollas to 1.1 mm. Fruit an achene to 1.7 mm; pappus 0.

Genus & Specific Name Derivation: Greek: western Evax / sparsely flowered

Notes: Illustration from *Illustrated Flora of the Pacific States.*

√ ## *Heterotheca sessiliflora* (Nutt.) Shinn.
ssp. *echioides* (Benth.) Semple (A. Gray) Semple

E

GOLDENASTER   Native, *BRISTLY*

Flowering Time: June–September

Habitat: chaparral, grassland

Description: Herbaceous perennial to 13 dm. Leaves alternate, simple, hairy, glandular; upper sessile. Inflorescence open; heads with both ray and disk flowers; phyllaries in 3–5 rows; ray flowers to 10 mm, yellow; disk corollas yellow. Fruit an achene; pappus of bristles.

Genus & Specific Name Derivation: Greek: different cases, referring to ray and disk fruits / individual flowers sessile, without a pedicel

Notes: Also called telegraph weed, probably because of the tall, straight stems, like a telegraph pole; there is also a strong creosote smell to the plant that resembles the smell of telegraph poles. Illustration from *Illustrated Flora of the Pacific States.*

Uses Past and Present: Leaves of some species used as an anti-inflammatory tea.

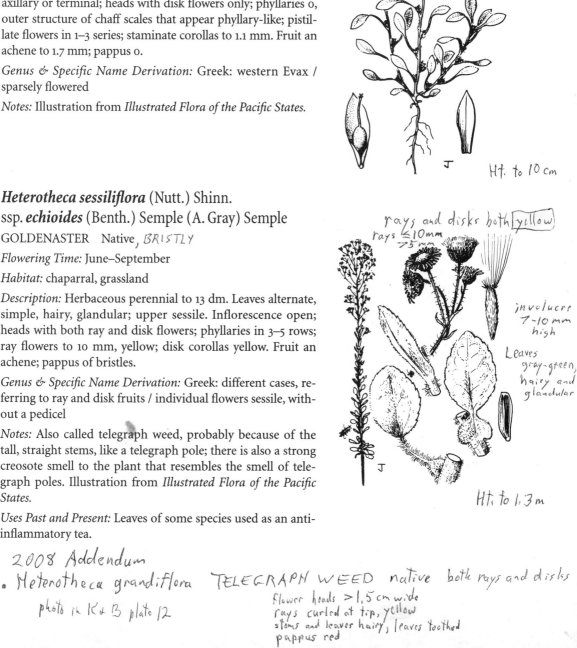

Handwritten annotations (first figure): pale | disks only, hardly visible, ≤1mm | J | Ht. to 10 cm

Handwritten annotations (second figure): rays and disks both yellow | rays ≤10mm >5mm | involucre 7-10 mm high | Leaves gray-green, hairy and glandular | J | Ht. to 1.3 m

Handwritten notes at bottom:
2008 Addendum
• Heterotheca grandiflora TELEGRAPH WEED native both rays and disks
photo in K & B plate 12
flower heads >1.5 cm wide
rays curled at tip, yellow
stems and leaves hairy, leaves toothed
pappus red

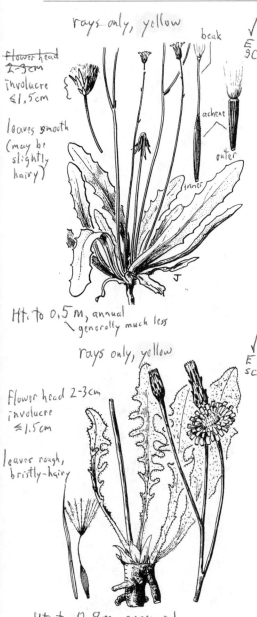

rays only, yellow

beak

Flower head 2-3cm involucre ≤1.5cm

leaves smooth (may be slightly hairy)

achene

outer

inner

J

Ht. to 0,5 m, annual generally much less

rays only, yellow

Flower head 2-3 cm involucre ≤1.5cm

leaves rough, bristly-hairy

Ht. to 0,8m, perennial

Hypochaeris glabra L.

SMOOTH CAT'S-EAR   Nonnative / Europe

Flowering Time: March–September

Habitat: grassland

Description: Annual to 5 dm. Leaves in a basal rosette, simple to 10 cm, shallowly lobed, maybe slightly hairy on leaf and leaf margin. Inflorescence scapose, branched upward; head of ray flowers only; involucre to 1.5 cm; phyllaries in overlapping rows; flowers yellow. Fruit an achene to 4 mm, <u>outer beakless</u>, inner beaked; pappus of bristles.

Genus & Specific Name Derivation: Greek: name from Theophrastus / becoming smooth

Notes: Illustration from *Illustrated Flora of the Pacific States.*

Hypochaeris radicata L.

ROUGH CAT'S-EAR   Nonnative / Europe

Flowering Time: February–August

Habitat: grassland

Description: Herbaceous perennial to 8 dm, rough-hairy. Leaves basal, simple to 14 cm, rough hairy; margin lobed. Inflorescence scapose, branched upward; head of ray flowers only; involucre to 1.5 cm; phyllaries in unequal overlapping rows; flowers yellow. Fruit an achene to 8 mm, including beak; pappus of bristles.   *both outer and inner beaked*

Genus & Specific Name Derivation: Greek: name from Theophrastus / with large roots, referring to the tap root of this plant

Notes: Illustration from *Illustrated Flora of the Pacific States.*

√*Lactuca saligna* L.

WILLOW LETTUCE   Nonnative / Europe

Flowering Time: August–November

Habitat: grassland, disturbed areas

Description: Annual to 1 m. Leaves alternate, simple, clasping; margin lobed. Inflorescence narrow, spike-like; heads with ray flowers only; phyllaries in 2–several rows; flowers pale yellow. Fruit an achene to 9 mm, including beak; pappus of white bristles.

Genus & Specific Name Derivation: Latin: milky, referring to the milky sap in leaves and stem / willow-like

Notes: The milky juice in the leaves and stems makes the plant bitter and prevents them from being eaten. The garden lettuce has been bred so this juice is not produced until late in the life cycle. Illustration from *Illustrated Flora of the Pacific States.*

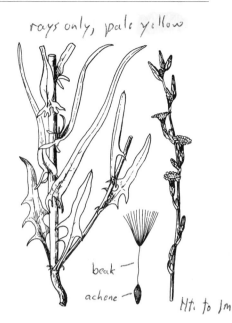

√*Lactuca serriola* L.

PRICKLY LETTUCE   Nonnative / Europe

Flowering Time: July–November

Habitat: grassland, disturbed areas

Description: Annual to 1.5 m. Leaves alternate, simple, bristly, clasping; margin lobed and toothed. Inflorescence open, spreading; heads with ray flowers only; phyllaries in 2–several series; flowers pale yellow. Fruit an achene to 6 mm including beak; pappus of white bristles.

Genus & Specific Name Derivation: Latin: milky, referring to the milky sap in leaves and stem / possibly meaning "in ranks," or an old name for chicory

Notes: See *L. saligna.* Illustration from *Illustrated Flora of the Pacific States.*

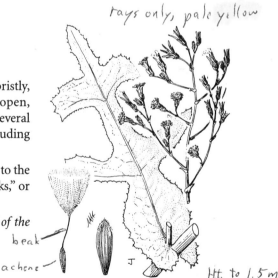

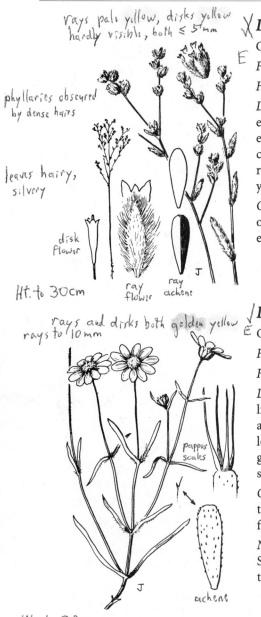

rays pale yellow, disks yellow hardly visible, both ≤ 5 mm

phyllaries obscured by dense hairs

leaves hairy, silvery

disk flower

ray flower

ray achene

J

Ht. to 30cm

rays and disks both golden yellow
rays to 10 mm

pappus scales

J

achene

Ht. to 30cm

Lagophylla ramosissima Nutt. ssp. ramosissima

E

COMMON HARELEAF   Native

Flowering Time: May–October

Habitat: grassland

Description: Annual to 3 dm; soft-hairy. Leaves alternate, linear to 12 cm, silver-hairy. Inflorescence solitary, or a few flowers in a cluster; head with both ray and disk flowers, often closed during the day; phyllaries folded around the ray ovaries. Ray flowers to 5 mm, pale yellow; disk flowers to 4 mm, yellow. Fruit an achene to 4 mm.

Genus & Specific Name Derivation: Greek: hare leaf, because of the hairs on the leaves / branched, referring to the branched form of the plant

Compare to Micropus and Filago

Lasthenia californica Lindley

E

GOLDFIELDS   Native

Flowering Time: March–June

Habitat: serpentine grassland

Description: Annual to 30 cm. Leaves opposite, simple to 7 cm, linear. Inflorescence of solitary heads; heads with both ray and disk flowers; phyllaries in 2 rows, outer scale-like, inner longer; ray flowers to 10 mm, golden-yellow; disk corollas golden-yellow. Fruit an achene to 3 mm; pappus of awned scales or 0.

Genus & Specific Name Derivation: Greek: female pupil of Plato who dressed as a man so she could attend his lectures / from California

Notes: On early Spanish California playing cards, the Jack of Spades always held one of these flowers in his hand. Illustration from *Illustrated Flora of the Pacific States.*

2008 Addendum

Layia hieracioides   TALL LAYIA
                       native

E

both rays and disks; yellow; with glandular hairs
leaves toothed or lobed; phyllaries folded around ray fruits
(as in L. platyglossa); stems with black dots or streaks
rays ~~much more than~~ less than 4 mm long

√ *Layia platyglossa* (Fischer & C. Meyer) A. Gray

E TIDY-TIPS   Native

Flowering Time: March–June

Habitat: serpentine grassland

Description: Annual to 10 dm. Leaves basal and stem, simple, lower lobed. Inflorescence a head of both ray and disk flowers; phyllaries folded around ray fruits; ray flowers to 20 mm, yellow with white tips; disk corollas to 6 mm; anthers generally purple to black. Fruit an achene to 7 mm; pappus of whitish bristles to 6 mm.

Genus & Specific Name Derivation: George T. Lay (1797–1845), an English botanist who visited California in 1827 with Captain Beechey on the ship *Blossom* / broad-tongue-shaped, referring to the ray flowers

Notes: Common name refers to the tidy appearance of the white-tipped ray flowers, although some may be all yellow. The flowers are fragrant. Illustration from *Illustrated Flora of the Pacific States.*

photo in K & B plate 13

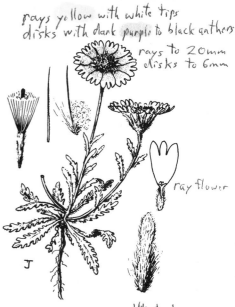

rays yellow with white tips
disks with dark purple to black anthers

rays to 20mm
disks to 6mm

J

ray flower

Ht, to 1 m

Lessingia hololeuca E. Greene

WOOLLY-HEADED LESSINGIA   Native

Flowering Time: June–September or Aug–Oct.

Habitat: serpentine grassland

Description: Annual to 4 dm. Leaves basal and stem, simple to 5 cm, linear. Inflorescence open, heads with disk flowers only; phyllaries in 4–9 rows, woolly, tips purplish tinged; corollas pink to lavender. Fruit an achene to 5 mm; pappus of white to tan bristles.

Genus & Specific Name Derivation: C. F. Lessing (1809–1862), a German specialist in Asteraceae / completely white, referring to the white woolly hairs on the plant

Notes: Listed in *CNPS Inventory of Rare and Endangered Plants of California* on "List 3, plants about which we need more information — a review list."

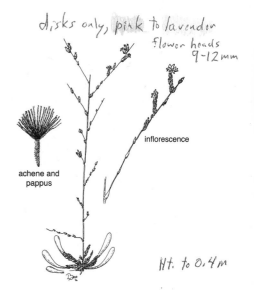

disks only, pink to lavender
flower heads
9–12 mm

inflorescence

achene and
pappus

Ht. to 0.4m

Genus Madia -

Leaves generally opposite on lower part of stem, alternate above
Plants glandular at least in parts, with strong odor
Phyllaries in one row, enclosing ray fruits (and flowers)

rays yellow with maroon base, ≤ 20mm
disks yellow or maroon, ≤ 5mm

Madia elegans Lindley

E COMMON MADIA   Native

Flowering Time: June–November

Habitat: grassland

Description: Annual to 25 dm, strongly scented, glandular on upper branches. Leaves opposite below, alternate above, simple to 20 cm, linear, some toothed, hairy, glandular. Inflorescence an open panicle to cyme; head with both ray and disk flowers; phyllaries enclosing the ray fruits; ray flowers to 20 mm, yellow with a maroon base; disk corollas to 5 mm, yellow or maroon. Fruit an achene to 5 mm; pappus 0.

Genus & Specific Name Derivation: Chilean name / elegant

Notes: Illustration from *Illustrated Flora of the Pacific States.*

ray flower

Ht. to 2.5 m

disk flower

photo in K & B plate 13

rays pale yellow, inconspicuous (≤ 1mm)
disks yellow, inconspicuous, < 2mm

Madia exigua (Smith) A. Gray

E THREADSTEM MADIA   Native

Flowering Time: May–June

Habitat: chaparral, grassland

Description: Annual to 5 cm, aromatic, stems slender, usually glandular. Leaves opposite below, alternate above, simple to 4 cm, hairy. Inflorescence open, panicle-like clusters; heads with both ray and disk flowers; phyllaries enclosing ray fruits, densely glandular; ray flowers to 1 mm, inconspicuous, pale yellow; disk corollas to 1.8 mm; anthers yellow. Fruit an achene to 2.9 mm with a short beak; pappus 0.

Genus & Specific Name Derivation: Chilean name / small

Notes: Peduncles are thread-like. Illustration from *Illustrated Flora of the Pacific States.*

ray

ray

disk flower

ray achene

Ht. to 5 cm

Compare Madia to other tarweeds (Deinandra, Hemizonia, some Layias)

✓ *Madia gracilis* (Smith) Keck

E SLENDER TARWEED Native

Flowering Time: May–July

Habitat: grassland

Description: Annual to 10 dm, fragrant, stems at the upper part of the plant glandular. Leaves opposite below, alternate above, simple to 20 cm, hairy, glandular. Inflorescence axillary; heads with both ray and disk flowers; phyllaries enclosing ray fruits, densely glandular; ray flowers to 8 mm, lemon-yellow; disk corollas to 5 mm; anthers black. Fruit an achene to 5 mm; pappus 0.

Genus & Specific Name Derivation: Chilean name / slender

Notes: Illustration from *Illustrated Flora of the Pacific States.*

photo in K & B plate 13

rays lemon-yellow, disks with black anthers
flowers inconspicuous   rays ≤ 8 mm
disks ≤ 5 mm

plant glandular
on upper half only

ray flower

ray achene

Ht. to 1 m

✓ *Madia sativa* Molina

E COAST TARWEED Native

Flowering Time: May–September

Habitat: grassland

Description: Annual to 25 dm, strongly scented, stems glandular throughout. Leaves opposite below, alternate above, simple to 15 cm, linear, some glandular, hairy. Inflorescence dense clusters or axillary; heads with both ray and disk flowers; phyllaries enclosing ray fruits, hairy or bristly, glandular; ray flowers to 4 mm, yellow; disk corollas to 5 mm; anthers black. Fruit an achene to 5 mm; pappus 0.

Genus & Specific Name Derivation: Chilean name / planted

Notes: Illustration from *Illustrated Flora of the Pacific States.*

rays yellow, disks with black anthers
flowers inconspicuous   rays ≤ 4 mm
disks ≤ 5 mm

plant
glandular
throughout

Ht. to 2.5 m

whitish-woolly
disks only, hardly visible

heads rounded, 2-4mm
bracts not extending
beyond head clusters

leaves cobwebby-
hairy, grayish

Ht. to 10 cm

Micropus californicus Fischer & C. Meyer
var. *californicus*

SLENDER COTTONWEED   Native

Flowering Time: April–June

Habitat: grassland

10 cm

Description: Annual to 1 dm, gray-cobwebby. Leaves simple, alternate. Inflorescence axillary; heads with disk flowers only; phyllaries 4–6, rounded, thin, translucent; pistillate flowers tubular, chaff scales woolly. Fruit an achene to 2.6 mm; pappus 0 or small bristles.

Genus & Specific Name Derivation: Greek: small foot / from California

Notes: Illustration from *Illustrated Flora of the Pacific States.*

Compare to Filago and Lagophylla

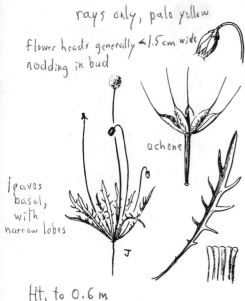

rays only, pale yellow

flower heads generally < 1.5 cm wide
nodding in bud

achene

leaves
basal,
with
narrow lobes

J

Ht. to 0.6 m
(generally much less)

Microseris douglasii (DC.) Schultz-Bip.
ssp. *douglasii*

DOUGLAS' MICROSERIS   Native

Flowering Time: March–May

Habitat: grassland

Description: Annual to 6 dm. Leaves form a basal rosette, simple to 25 cm, deeply lobed. Inflorescence scapose; heads with ray flowers only, nodding in bud; phyllaries in 2–several rows; flowers pale yellow. Fruit an achene to 10 mm; pappus of silvery scales with awns to 8 mm, pappus scales entire.

Genus & Specific Name Derivation: Greek: small chicory / David Douglas (1798–1834), a Scottish collector in northwestern America, collected nearly 500 specimens of California plants for the Royal Horticultural Society in England

Notes: Illustration from *Illustrated Flora of the Pacific States.*

Compare to Stebbinsoseris, Uropappus

X *Monolopia gracilens* A. Gray

WOODLAND MONOLOPIA   Native

Flowering Time: April–June

Habitat: chaparral, woodland

Description: Annual to 8 dm, woolly. Leaves opposite below, alternate above; simple, linear, entire to toothed. Inflorescence open; heads with both ray and disk flowers; phyllaries in 1 row, tips black, hairy; ray flowers to 10 mm, yellow; disk corollas yellow. Fruit an achene to 2 mm; pappus 0.

Genus & Specific Name Derivation: Greek: single husk, referring to the one row of phyllaries / slender, graceful

Notes: Illustration from *Illustrated Flora of the Pacific States.*

Monolopia major DC.

CUPPED MONOLOPIA   Native

Flowering Time: March–May

Habitat: chaparral, woodland

Description: Annual to 6 dm, woolly. Leaves opposite below, alternate above, simple, linear, entire to toothed. Inflorescence open; heads with both ray and disk flowers; phyllaries generally 8, fused into a cup with triangular lobes; ray flowers to 10 mm, 3-lobed, yellow; disk corollas yellow. Fruit an achene to 4 mm; pappus 0.

Genus & Specific Name Derivation: Greek: single husk, referring to the one row of phyllaries / larger

Notes: Illustration from *Illustrated Flora of the Pacific States.*

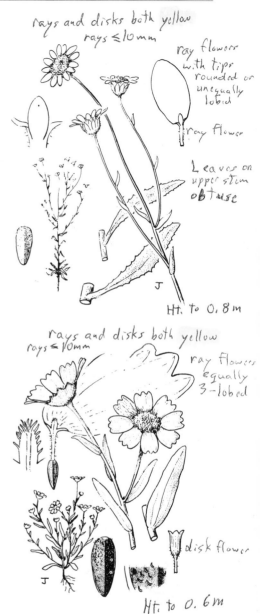

rays and disks both yellow
rays ≤ 10 mm
ray flowers with tips rounded or unequally lobed
ray flower
Leaves on upper stem obtuse
Ht. to 0.8 m

rays and disks both yellow
rays ≤ 10 mm
ray flowers equally 3-lobed
disk flower
Ht. to 0.6 m

rays and disks both yellow

rays ≤ 20 mm

Ht. to 1 m

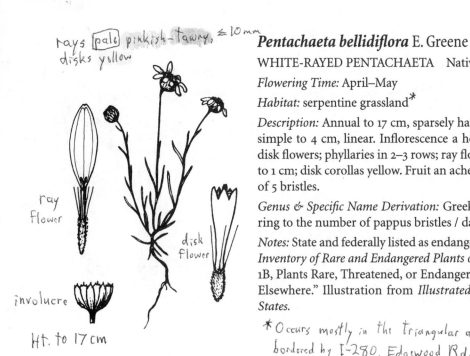

rays [pale] pinkish-tawny, ≤ 10 mm
disks yellow

ray flower

disk flower

involucre

Ht. to 17 cm

/Senecio b.

Packera breweri (Burtt Davy) W. A. Weber & A. Love

BREWER'S BUTTERWEED   Native

Flowering Time: May–June

Habitat: woodland

Description: Biennial or herbaceous perennial to 10 dm. Leaves alternate, simple to 30 cm, deeply lobed to almost appearing compound. Inflorescence open; heads with both ray and disk flowers; phyllaries to 10 mm in 1–2 series; ray flowers to 2 cm, yellow; disk corollas many, yellow. Fruit an achene; pappus of white bristles.

Genus & Specific Name Derivation: Derivation unknown / for W. H. Brewer (1828–1910), geologist and botanist, leader of the California Geological Survey field parties

Notes: Illustration from *Illustrated Flora of the Pacific States.* New name accepted by *Jepson Manual* staff, name in *The Jepson Manual* (1993) *Senecio breweri.*

Pentachaeta bellidiflora E. Greene

WHITE-RAYED PENTACHAETA   Native

Flowering Time: April–May

Habitat: serpentine grassland*

Description: Annual to 17 cm, sparsely hairy. Leaves alternate, simple to 4 cm, linear. Inflorescence a head of both ray and disk flowers; phyllaries in 2–3 rows; ray flowers pinkish-tawny to 1 cm; disk corollas yellow. Fruit an achene to 3 mm; pappus of 5 bristles.

Genus & Specific Name Derivation: Greek: five bristles, referring to the number of pappus bristles / daisy-flower

Notes: State and federally listed as endangered. Listed in *CNPS Inventory of Rare and Endangered Plants of California* on "List 1B, Plants Rare, Threatened, or Endangered in California and Elsewhere." Illustration from *Illustrated Flora of the Pacific States.*

* Occurs mostly in the triangular area bordered by I-280, Edgewood Rd., and Cañada Rd.

✓ *Picris echioides* L.

RC
E
SC

BRISTLY OX-TONGUE   Nonnative / Eurasia and Africa

Flowering Time: April–December

Habitat: grassland, disturbed areas

Description: Annual or biennial to 8 dm, whole plant bristly-hairy. Leaves simple, alternate to 20 cm, lobed and toothed, bristly. Inflorescence an open cyme; heads with ray flowers only; phyllaries in 2–3 overlapping rows; flowers many, yellow. Fruit an achene to 7 mm including beak; pappus of bristles to 7 mm.

Genus & Specific Name Derivation: Greek: bitter / resembling *Echium* which means viper (a name used by Dioscorides)

Notes: One of the invasive nonnative plants Edgewood volunteers are trying to eradicate. Illustration from *Illustrated Flora of the Pacific States.*

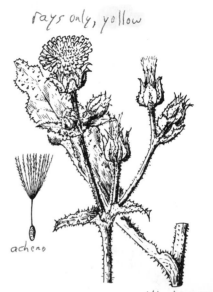

rays only, yellow

achene

Ht. to 0.8 m

✗ *Psilocarphus brevissimus* Nutt. var. *brevissimus*

E

DWARF WOOLLY-HEADS   Native

Flowering Time: April–June

Habitat: serpentine grassland and chaparral

Description: Low-growing, spreading annual, densely hairy. Leaves opposite, simple to 15 mm. Inflorescence solitary or in small groups, flowers hidden by woolly hairs; heads with disk flowers only; phyllaries 0; flowers tubular; chaff scale woolly. Fruit an achene to 2 mm; pappus 0.

Genus & Specific Name Derivation: Greek: slender chaff / short, referring to plant habit

Notes: Illustration from *Illustrated Flora of the Pacific States.*

disks only, hardly visible due to woolly hairs

flower heads <10mm wide

stems prostrate spreading to 10 cm?

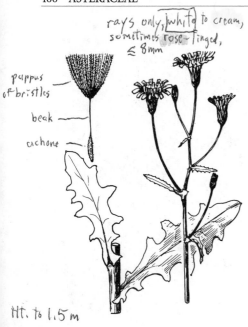

rays only, white to cream, sometimes rose-tinged, ≤ 8mm

pappus of bristles

beak

achene

Ht. to 1.5 m

Rafinesquia californica Nutt.

CALIFORNIA CHICORY   Native

Flowering Time: May–June

Habitat: grassland

Description: Annual to 15 dm. Leaves alternate, simple to 15 cm, lobed. Inflorescence an open panicle-like cluster; heads with ray flowers only; phyllaries in 3–4 series; flowers to 8 mm, white to cream, sometimes rose-tinged. Fruit an achene to 11 mm including beak; pappus bristles to 10 mm, dull white to brown.

Genus & Specific Name Derivation: C. S. Rafinesque, (1783–1840), eccentric U.S. naturalist from Kentucky / from California

Notes: Illustration from *Illustrated Flora of the Pacific States.*

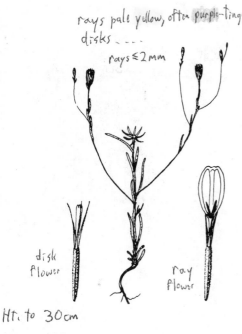

rays pale yellow, often purple-tinged; disks ----

rays ≤ 2 mm

disk flower

ray flower

Ht. to 30cm

Rigiopappus leptocladus A. Gray

RIGIOPAPPUS   Native

Flowering Time: April–June

Habitat: grassland

Description: Annual to 30 cm, hairy. Leaves alternate, simple to 3 cm, linear. Inflorescence terminal; heads with both ray and disk flowers; phyllaries in 2 rows to 8 mm, partly enclosing the outer fruit; ray flowers to 2 mm, pale yellow, often purple-tinged; disk flowers many. Fruit an achene to 4 mm; pappus scales to 5 mm.

Genus & Specific Name Derivation: Greek: stiff pappus / slender-branched

Notes: Illustration from *Illustrated Flora of the Pacific States.*

Senecio aronicoides DC.

CALIFORNIA BUTTERWEED / GROUNDSEL   Native

Flowering Time: April–June

Habitat: chaparral, woodland

Description: Biennial or herbaceous perennial to 9 dm. Leaves alternate, simple to 20 cm, wavy, slightly lobed to toothed. Inflorescence open; heads with disk flowers only; phyllaries in 1–2 series; corollas yellow. Fruit an achene; pappus of white bristles.

Genus & Specific Name Derivation: Latin: old man, referring to the white pappus / may mean resembling *Aronia*

Notes: The genus *Senecio* is one of the world's largest. Illustration from *Illustrated Flora of the Pacific States.*

disks only, yellow

Ht. to 0.9 m

Senecio vulgaris L.

COMMON GROUNDSEL   Nonnative / Eurasia

Flowering Time: all year

Habitat: disturbed areas, trail edges

Description: Annual to 6 dm. Leaves alternate, simple to 10 cm, lobed and toothed. Inflorescence open; heads with disk flowers only; phyllaries in 1–2 series, black tipped; corollas yellow. Fruit an achene; pappus of white bristles.

Genus & Specific Name Derivation: Latin: old man, referring to the white pappus / common

Notes: The genus *Senecio* is one of the world's largest. Illustration from *Illustrated Flora of the Pacific States.*

disks only, yellow

black-tipped

Ht. to 0.6 m

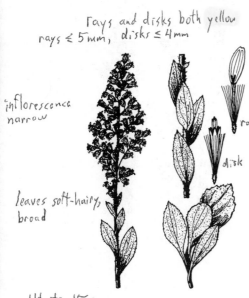

disks only, pink to purple

flower heads ≤ 5 cm wide

Ht. to 3 m

Silybum marianum (L.) Gaertner

SC MILK THISTLE   Nonnative / Mediterranean

Flowering Time: March–August

Habitat: disturbed areas, grassland

Description: Annual to biennial to 30 dm. Leaves alternate, simple, spiny-lobed, blade with white blotches; stem leaves smaller. Inflorescence open terminal heads; heads with disk flowers only; phyllaries in several series, tips spreading, spiny; corollas pink to purple. Fruit an achene to 8 mm; pappus of bristles to 20 mm.

Genus & Specific Name Derivation: Greek: name for thistle-like plant / from the name Mary or from the Sierra Morena

Notes: In the Old World it was thought that the white blotches resulted from drops of milk that fell from the Virgin's breast as she nursed Jesus, thus the name "marianum" meaning "of Mary." Illustration from *Illustrated Flora of the Pacific States.*

Uses Past and Present: The milk thistle was eaten in the same way as other thistles *(Cirsium).*

rays and disks both yellow

rays ≤ 5mm, disks ≤ 4mm

inflorescence narrow

ray

disk

leaves soft-hairy, broad

Ht. to 15 cm

Solidago californica Nutt.

CALIFORNIA GOLDENROD   Native

Flowering Time: July–November

Habitat: chaparral

Description: Herbaceous perennial to 15 cm. Leaves alternate, simple, soft-hairy. Inflorescence panicle-like; heads with both ray and disk flowers; phyllaries in 3–5 overlapping rows; ray flowers to 5 mm, yellow; disk corollas to 4 mm, yellow. Fruit an achene to 1.5 mm; pappus of bristles.

Genus & Specific Name Derivation: Greek: make-well, refer-ring to medicinal uses / from California

Notes: Illustration from *Illustrated Flora of the Pacific States.*

Compare to Euthamia occidentalis

photo in K & B plate 14

Sonchus asper (L.) Hill ssp. *asper*

PRICKLY SOW THISTLE   Nonnative / Europe

Flowering Time: March–July

Habitat: chaparral

Description: Annual to 12 dm. Leaves sessile, clasping, toothed and spiny. Inflorescence a cyme; heads with ray flowers only; phyllaries in 3 rows; flowers yellow. Fruit an achene to 3 mm; pappus of bristles.

Genus & Specific Name Derivation: Ancient Greek name / rough

Notes: The common name is believed to be derived from the fact that pigs like to eat the plant.

Uses Past and Present: Young stems are boiled like asparagus; young leaves are steamed and eaten.

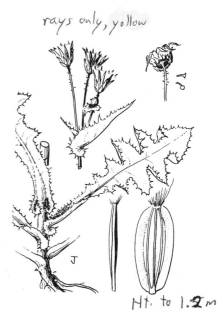

rays only, yellow

Ht. to 1.2 m

Sonchus oleraceus L.

COMMON SOW THISTLE   Nonnative / Europe

Flowering Time: March–September

Habitat: disturbed areas, along trail

Description: Annual to 14 dm. Leaves alternate, simple to 35 cm, sessile, clasping; margin toothed. Inflorescence open; heads with ray flowers only; phyllaries in 3 rows; flowers yellow. Fruit an achene to 4 mm; pappus of bristles.

Genus & Specific Name Derivation: Ancient Greek name / a cultivated vegetable suitable for food

Notes: The common name is believed to be derived from the fact that pigs like to eat this plant.

Uses Past and Present: See *S. asper.*

rays only, yellow

fruit

Ht. to 1.4 m

Stebbinsoseris (key from Jepson manual): heads ray-flowered only; receptacle naked; pappus present; corolla yellow; pappus of scales or awns (not bristles or plumose), pappus scales bristle-tipped; bristle (awn) from notched scale tip; head nodding but not strongly so in bud; outer phyllaries less than 1/3 inner phyllaries in length

rays only, yellow or white often reddish-tinged below

X **Stebbinsoseris heterocarpa** (Nutt.) Chambers

E DERIVED MICROSERIS   Native

Flowering Time: March–May

Habitat: grassland

Description: Annual to 4 dm. Leaves basal, to 3 cm, entire to lobed. Inflorescence scapose; phyllaries to 3 dm; heads with ray flowers only; flowers yellow or white, often reddish-tinged below, withering early. Fruit an achene to 12 mm, light-colored; pappus of scales with an awn in the center of the notched scale.

Genus & Specific Name Derivation: Greek: Stebbins' chicory, for G. L. Stebbins, Jr., American geneticist, evolutionist / diverse fruit

Notes: Illustration from *Illustrated Flora of the Pacific States.*

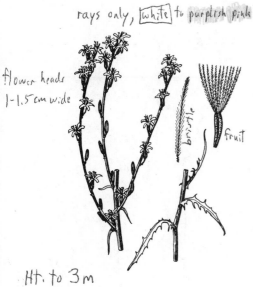

flower heads nodding in bud, but not strongly so

pappus tan
pappus scales notched at tip; awns in notch

leaves basal, with narrow lobes (like Microseris)

involucre

awn

scale

awn

notch at tip of scale

Ht. to 0.4m

ray fruit

J

This species not in Kozloff & Beidleman
Compare to Microseris, Uropappus

rays only, white to purplish pink

Stephanomeria virgata Benth. ssp. **virgata**

VIRGATE STEPHANOMERIA   Native called Tall Stephanomeria in K&B

Flowering Time: June–November

Habitat: chaparral

Description: Annual to 3 m. Leaves alternate, simple; margin lobed. Inflorescence clustered on upper branches; heads with ray flowers only; phyllaries in 2–several rows, outer reflexed; flowers white to purplish pink. Fruit an achene to 4 mm; pappus of bristles.

Genus & Specific Name Derivation: Greek: wreath division / wand-like, referring to the tall, bare stems

Notes: Illustration from *Illustrated Flora of the Pacific States.*

flower heads 1-1.5 cm wide

bristle

fruit

Ht. to 3m

photo in K&B plate 14

√ *Symphyotrichum chilense* (Nees) G. L. Nesom (Aster chilensis) *[handwritten]* rays violet, ≤12mm disks-----

E COMMON CALIFORNIA ASTER   Native

Flowering Time: July–December

Habitat: moist areas in open woodland

Description: Upright herbaceous perennial to 10 dm. Leaves simple, narrow, mostly sessile. Inflorescence a cyme, each head with both ray and disk flowers; phyllaries in 3–5 series; ray flowers to 12 mm, violet. Fruit an achene; pappus of brown bristles.

Genus & Specific Name Derivation: Derivation unknown / from Chile

Notes: Illustration from *Illustrated Flora of the Pacific States.* New name accepted by *Jepson Manual* staff, name in *The Jepson Manual* (1993) *Aster chilensis.*

[handwritten labels] disk flower   Ht. to 1m

√ *Tragopogon porrifolius* L.   *[handwritten]* rays only, purple

Sc SALSIFY / OYSTER PLANT   Nonnative / Europe

Flowering Time: March–October

Habitat: grassland

Description: Biennial to 10 dm. Leaves alternate, simple to 4 cm, linear, clasping the stems. Inflorescence solitary at branch tips; heads with ray flowers only; phyllaries in 1 series to 4 cm; flowers purple. Fruit an achene to 4 cm; pappus of tan bristles.

Genus & Specific Name Derivation: Greek: goat's beard, referring to the bristles / leaves that look like those of leeks

Notes: The flowers open in the early morning and close by midday. Illustration from *Illustrated Flora of the Pacific States.*

Uses Past and Present: The thick, white taproot is cooked as a vegetable and has a flavor similar to oysters.

[handwritten labels] phyllaries & involucre ≤4cm   pappus of bristle   beak   achene   Ht. to 1m

[handwritten] photo in K&B plate 15

———————————

2008 Addendum

√ Taraxacum officinale   DANDELION nonnative

E
Sc   ray flowers only, yellow   in day-camp lawn
plants with solitary flower head at tip of unbranched stem
pappus consisting of straight bristles at end of slender beak on the achene
leaves basal, toothed or lobed

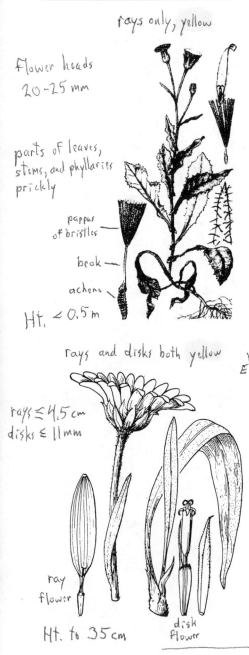

rays only, yellow

Flower heads
20-25 mm

parts of leaves,
stems, and phyllaries
prickly

pappus
of bristles

beak

achene

Ht. < 0.5 m

rays and disks both yellow

rays ≤ 4.5 cm
disks ≤ 11 mm

ray
flower

Ht. to 35 cm

disk
flower

Urospermum picroides (L.) Schmidt

PRICKLY GOLDEDNFLEECE   Nonnative / Eurasia

Flowering Time: September–November

Habitat: disturbed areas

Description: Annual to herbaceous perennial. Leaves basal and stem, alternate to whorled, mostly simple, margin lobed and irregularly toothed, hairy, sessile, bases clasping the stem. Inflorescence a cyme; head with ray flowers only, yellow; phyllaries in 1 row, hairy, deeply lobed. Fruit an achene, beaked; pappus of bristles.

Genus & Specific Name Derivation: Greek: tail-like seed / bitter

Notes: Illustration from *Boletin de la Univ. de Chile.* Number 51. Santiago, September 1964.

Uses Past and Present: This species grows in the wild in Crete, Greece and the leaves are consumed in salads.

✓ *Wyethia angustifolia* (DC.) Nutt.

E   NARROW-LEAVED MULE EARS   Native

Flowering Time: April–May

Habitat: grassland

Description: Herbaceous perennial to 35 cm, hairy. Leaves basal and stem, simple to 50 cm, linear. Inflorescence terminal; head with both ray and disk flowers; phyllaries to 3 cm, linear, soft-hairy; ray flowers to 4.5 cm, yellow; disk corollas to 11 mm, yellow. Fruit an achene to 8 mm; pappus of scales, awn-tipped.

Genus & Specific Name Derivation: Nathaniel J. Wyeth (1802–1856), U.S. explorer / narrow-leaf

Notes: Common name refers to the leaves which look like a mule ear. Illustration from *Illustrated Flora of the Pacific States.*

Photo in K & B plate 15

2008 Addendum

Uropappus lindleyi   SILVER PUFFS
native
plant ht to 0.6m
photo in   pappus white, few flattened scales that
K & B plate 15   end in bristles
both ray flowers only, yellow
some phyllaries 2-3 cm long
flower heads erect even in bud
achene + pappus > 2.5 cm, up to 4 cm
pappus awn from notched
scale tip, as in Stebbinsoseris;   Compare to Microseris, Stebbinsoseris
outer phyllaries shorter than
inner, but not less than 1/4 inner

Wyethia glabra A. Gray

MULE EARS   Native

Flowering Time: March–June

Habitat: grassland

Description: Herbaceous perennial to 4 dm. Leaves to 45 cm, mostly basal. Inflorescence terminal; heads with both ray and disk flowers; phyllaries to 7 cm; ray flowers to 5 cm, yellow; disk corollas to 11 mm, yellow. Fruit an achene to 12 mm; pappus of scales to 5 mm.

Genus & Specific Name Derivation: Nathaniel J. Wyeth (1802–1856), U.S. explorer / smooth, referring to the leaves

Notes: This species forms large colonies, spreading by underground stems. Common name refers to the leaves which look like a mule ear. Illustration from *Illustrated Flora of the Pacific States.*

photo in K & B plate 15

rays and disks both yellow
rays ≤ 5 cm
disks ≤ 11 mm

Ht. to 0.4 m

Boraginaceae — Borage Family

Annuals, biennials or herbaceous perennials. Leaves basal rosettes or cauline, alternate or opposite, simple, entire; stipules absent. Inflorescence buds often arranged on a one-sided coil-like cluster in spikes or panicles. Flowers bisexual, regular; sepals 5, fused to separate; petals 5, fused; stamens 5; pistil 1, ovary superior, 4-lobed, style 1. Fruit of 1–4 nutlets, often roughened, prickly or bristly. Many species may be toxic due to alkaloids or nitrates contained within the plant.

Family Characteristics

inflorescence a
coiled cluster
or scorpioid cyme

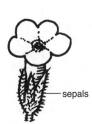

sepals

flower

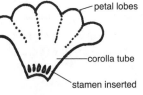

petal lobes

corolla tube

stamen inserted

5 fused petals

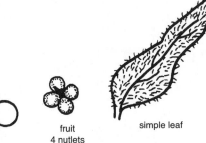

appendages
or scales

fruit
4 nutlets

simple leaf

For key to families *see* Group 3. Herbaceous Flowering Plant Families

1. Corollas mostly blue, sometimes pink
    2. Individual flowers greater than 1 cm wide ....
        .... *Cynoglossum grande* (HOUND'S TONGUE)
    2′ Individual flowers less than 1 cm wide ....
        .... *Myosotis latifolia* (WOOD FORGET-ME-NOT)
1′ Corollas white or yellow to orange
    3. Corollas white
        4. Sepals with white, bristly hairs, fruit a single nutlet ....
            .... *Cryptantha flaccida* (FLACCID CRYPTANTHA)
        4′ Sepals with rusty-brown hairs, fruit mostly with more than 1 nutlet ......
            .... *Plagiobothrys nothofulvus* (POPCORNFLOWER)
    3′ Corollas yellow to orange ....
        .... *Amsinckia menziesii intermedia* (COMMON FIDDLENECK)

Amsinckia menziesii (Lehm.) Nelson & J. F. Macbr. var. *intermedia* (Fisher & C. Meyer) Ganders

COMMON FIDDLENECK   Native

Flowering Time: March-June

Habitat: grassland

Description: Annual to 7 dm, plant bristly. Leaves alternate, simple, clasping the stem, hairy on both surfaces. Inflorescence a coiled cluster. Sepals green; corolla to 11 mm, to 10 mm wide, orange, often with 5 red-orange marks in the corolla tube. Fruit is 4 nutlets to 3 mm long; surface roughened.

Genus & Specific Name Derivation: W. Amsinck, patron of Hamburg Botanic Garden, early nineteenth century / Archibald Menzies (1754–1842), English naturalist on the ship *Discovery*

Notes: Seeds and herbage toxic to livestock (especially cattle) from alkaloids and high nitrate concentrations. Sharp plant hairs irritate human skin. Illustration from *Illustrated Flora of the Pacific States*.

photo in K + B plate 16

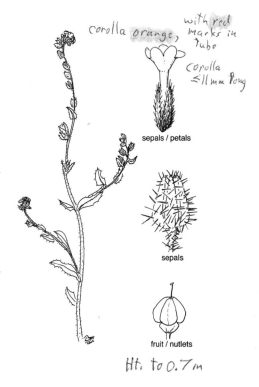

corolla orange, with red marks in tube

corolla ≤ 11 mm long

sepals / petals

sepals

fruit / nutlets

Ht. to 0.7m

width ≤ 4mm

corolla
petals [white]
lobes
≤ 2mm

Sepals with
white bristly hairs

flower

fruit

Ht. to 25 cm

Cryptantha flaccida (Lehm.) E. Greene

FLACCID CRYPTANTHA   Native

Flowering Time: April–June

Habitat: serpentine grassland

Description: Annual to 25 cm with long bristly hairs. Leaves alternate, simple to 1 cm, sessile. Inflorescence a coiled cluster to 7 cm in flower. Flowers sessile to 4 mm wide; sepals green to 4 mm, with white bristly hairs; petals to 2 mm, white with a yellow center. Fruit is a single nutlet.

Genus & Specific Name Derivation: Greek: hidden flowers / soft or limp

Notes: Whole plant with long white bristly hairs. Each flower of this species has only one shiny nutlet enclosed within the sepals. Many others in this genus have 3–4 nutlets.

corolla
~~petals~~ pink to purple
when young
Turning blue

lobes ≤ 9mm

flowers ≤ 1.5 cm wide

Corolla with ring of
white appendages at throat

fruit / nutlets

Ht. to 0.7 m

Cynoglossum grande Lehm.

HOUND'S TONGUE   Native

Flowering Time: February–April

Habitat: woodland

Description: Herbaceous perennial to 7 dm. Leaves simple, alternate, basal leaves to 20 cm, upper shorter, ovate, lower surface hairy; petiole to 30 cm, upper shorter. Inflorescence a branched coiled-cyme, open in flower and fruit. Flowers to 1.5 cm wide. Sepals to 7 cm, fused at the base, blue-green, hairy; petals to 9 mm, fused, pink when young then turning blue. Fruit 4 nutlets, sometimes more than one aborts.

Genus & Specific Name Derivation: Greek: dog tongue, referring to the leaf appearance / grand or large

Notes: There are 4 white, lobed nectar appendages at base of each petal. Each nutlet is covered with short, barbed prickles allowing it to hook onto and be dispersed by animals. The flowers are said to be large, forget-me-not like.

photo in K & B plate 16

Myosotis latifolia Poiret

SC

WOOD FORGET-ME-NOT Nonnative / Northwest Africa

Flowering Time: March–May

Habitat: woodland

Description: Herbaceous perennial to 7 dm. Leaves simple, basal and alternate along upper stem. Inflorescence a coiled cluster, open in full flower and fruit. Sepals to 6 mm; corolla blue to 10 mm wide. Fruit 4 nutlets, black when mature.

Genus & Specific Name Derivation: Greek: mouse ear, from shape of leaves / wide or broad, referring to the leaves

5–8 mm
corolla blue, ≤ 10 mm wide
ring of white appendages at throat
inflorescence
Ht. to 0.7m

Plagiobothrys nothofulvus (A. Gray) A. Gray

E

POPCORNFLOWER Native

Flowering Time: March–July

Habitat: serpentine and nonserpentine grassland

Description: Upright herbaceous perennial to 2 dm. Whole plant bristly-hairy. Leaves simple, in a basal rosette, sometimes dead or dried out when plant is in flower and fruit; stem leaves alternate, sessile, smaller toward the top of plant. Inflorescence a coiled cluster, elongate in fruit. Sepals to 10 mm with rusty hairs, bases fused, lobes fall off and fruit sits in a cup-like structure; corolla to 9 mm wide, fused, white, sometimes with a yellow tube. Fruit 1–3 nutlets to 2 mm.

Genus & Specific Name Derivation: Greek: sideways pit, referring to the position of the nutlet attachment scar / false tawny, reddish-yellow

Notes: The common name refers to the flowers, appearing to look like popcorn. Some species produce a dark purple dye from the leaves and roots.

sepals / fruit
sepals with rusty brown hairs
corolla white
tube (short) may be creamy
calyx with rusty hairs
corolla ≤ 9 mm wide
basal rosette
Ht. to 20cm

Photo in K + B plate 16
2008 Addendum

Pectocarya pusilla LITTLE PECTOCARYA native
E
leaves alternate, corolla white minute calyx lobes with hooked bristles at margin
plant generally < 20cm tall

Brassicaceae — Mustard Family

Annuals, herbaceous perennials, shrubs. Leaves basal and alternate, simple to compound. Inflorescence generally a raceme. Flowers bisexual, regular; sepals and petals 4, separate, petals often in the shape of a cross; stamens 6, 4 long 2 short; pistil 1, ovary superior, style 1, stigma lobes 2. Fruit a silique (long and narrow) or a silicle (short and broad). Some genera cultivated as ornamentals or for food (e.g., broccoli, brussel sprouts, cabbage, cauliflower, mustard, radish, water cress). Many have a pungent juice. Synonym — Cruciferae, meaning cross-like, refers to shape the petals make.

Family Characteristics

flower   sepals   petals   stamens   pistil

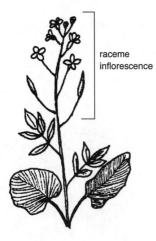

raceme
inflorescence

siliques

silicles

For key to families see Group 3. Herbaceous Flowering Plant Families

1. Fruit a silique, much longer than wide, more or less linear
    2. Leaves simple .... *Guillenia lasiophylla* (CALIFORNIA MUSTARD) *petals cream to pale yellow*
    2′ Leaves compound
        3. Petals all yellow
            4. Fruit (mature) erect, but not appressed to the stem ....
                .... *Barbarea orthoceras* (AMERICAN WINTER CRESS)
            4′ Fruit appressed to the stem, pointing upward
                5. Tip of fruit (beak) swollen at base, beak to 6 mm ....
                    .... *Hirschfeldia incana* (MEDITERRANEAN HOARY-MUSTARD)
                5′ Tip of fruit (beak) short, slender < 2 mm ....
                    .... *Sisymbrium officinale* (HEDGE MUSTARD)
        3′ Petals other than yellow
            6. Plant spreading, rooting at leaf nodes ....
                .... *Nasturtium officinale* (WATER CRESS)
            6′ Plant upright, not rooting at the leaf nodes
                7. Leaves mostly basal ....
                    .... *Cardamine oligosperma* (FEW-SEEDED BITTER-CRESS)
                7′ Leaves mostly distributed on the stem ....
                    8. Petals whitish-pink .... *Cardamine californica* (MILK MAIDS)
                    8′ Petals (ours) brownish pale yellow with darker veins ....
                        .... *Raphanus sativus* (RADISH)
1′ Fruit a silicle, not much longer than wide, various shapes but not linear *petals white (except Lunaria)*
    9. Fruit with a suture line down the center
        10. Fruit oval, roundish; seeds 2 ....
            .... *Lepidium nitidum* (SHINING PEPPERGRASS)
        10′ Fruit more or less heart-shaped to triangular, many-seeded ....
            .... *Capsella bursa-pastoris* (SHEPHERD'S PURSE)
    9′ Fruit roundish, without an obvious suture line down the center
        11. Fruit margin flattened with one seed in the center ....
            .... *Thysanocarpus curvipes* (HAIRY FRINGEPOD)
        11′ Fruit thin with more than 1 seed .... *Lunaria annua* (MOONWORT) *petals magenta-pink-purple*

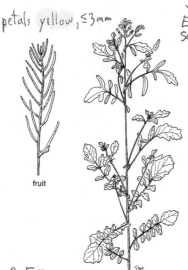

petals yellow, ≤3mm

fruit

Ht. to 0.5m

Barbarea orthoceras Ledeb.

AMERICAN WINTER CRESS   Native

Flowering Time: March–July

Habitat: woodland   stems angled or ridged

Description: Upright herbaceous perennial to 5 dm. Leaves basal and alternate, compound, 1-pinnate; basal leaves to 20 cm, with 3–5 pairs of leaflets; petiole to 3 cm; stem leaves to 10 cm, with 1–2 pairs of leaflets, sessile and clasping the stem. Inflorescence a raceme; peduncle to 2 cm; pedicel to 3 mm; sepals yellow-green to 2 mm; petals yellow to 3 mm; stamens inserted, style 1, stigma slightly 2-lobed. Fruit an upright silique, to 5 cm.

Genus & Specific Name Derivation: Named for Saint Barbara / upright horned, referring to the fruit

petals white ≤1mm

Ht. to 35cm

Capsella bursa-pastoris (L.) Medikus

SHEPHERD'S PURSE   Nonnative / Europe

Flowering Time: March–July

Habitat: woodland

Description: Annual to 35 cm. Leaves simple, basal leaves to 3 cm in a rosette, margin deeply lobed; stem leaves alternate, to 2 cm, margin toothed. Inflorescence a raceme; flowers to 1.5 mm wide; sepals to 0.5 mm, brownish; petals to 1 mm, white. Fruit a silicle, many-seeded, heart-shaped with suture line down middle.

Genus & Specific Name Derivation: Latin: little box / shepherd's purse

Notes: Common name refers to the appearance of the fruit that looks like a purse. The fruits have a peppery taste. Petals fall early and are often overlooked.

Uses Past and Present: Leaves said to be used for greens, flavoring, and a tea brewed for dysentery.

Cardamine californica (Torrey & A. Gray) E. Greene var. *californica*

MILK MAIDS   Native

Flowering Time: December–May

Habitat: woodland

Description: Herbaceous perennial from a rhizome to 4 dm. Leaves alternate, upper stem leaves compound, to 9 cm, margin lobed; lower first leaves simple or compound; petiole < 4 mm. Inflorescence a raceme to 15 cm; peduncle to 4 cm. Flowers to 2.5 cm wide; pedicel to 3 cm; sepals to 3 mm, green; petals to 12 mm, white with pink veins, pink in bud. Fruit a silique to 5 cm.

Genus & Specific Name Derivation: Greek: for a cress with medicinal uses / from California

Notes: New leaves and basal leaves different from stem leaves.

photo in K & B plate 17

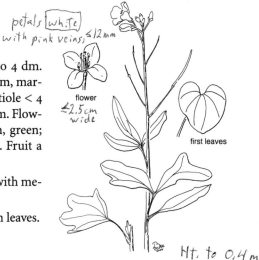

petals white with pink veins, ≤12mm

flower ≤2.5cm wide

first leaves

Ht. to 0.4m

Cardamine oligosperma Torrey & A. Gray

FEW-SEEDED BITTER-CRESS   Native

Flowering Time: February–June

Habitat: woodland

Description: Annual or biennial to 2 dm. Leaves form a basal rosette, compound, 1-pinnate; blade to 3 cm; stem leaves alternate to 2 cm; petiole to 10 mm. Inflorescence a raceme to 15 cm; peduncle to 5 cm. Flowers to 2 mm wide; pedicel to 10 mm. Sepals <1 mm, pale green tinged red; petals to 2 mm, white. Fruit a silique to 3 cm.

Genus & Specific Name Derivation: Greek: for a cress with medicinal uses / small seeds

Notes: Minute flowers are mostly gone when fruiting begins.

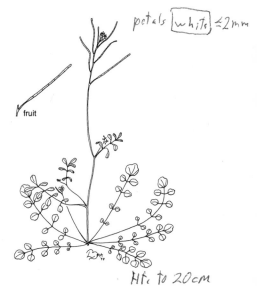

petals white ≤2mm

fruit

Ht. to 20cm

√ *Guillenia lasiophylla* (Hook. & Arn.) E. Greene

CALIFORNIA MUSTARD   Native

E

Flowering Time: February–July

Habitat: serpentine grassland

Description: Upright annual to 4 dm. Leaves simple, alternate to 3 cm, lower leaves lobed, upper simple to slightly lobed; sessile. Inflorescence a raceme. Flowers to 6 mm wide; pedicel to 3 mm; sepals to 5 mm, pale green-yellow; petals to 6 mm, cream to pale yellow. Fruit an upright silique to 4 cm with a 3 mm beak.

Genus & Specific Name Derivation: Father C. Guillen, Jesuit missionary, Mexico, born 1677 / woolly leaves

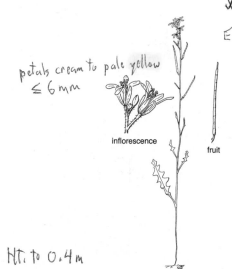

petals cream to pale yellow ≤ 6 mm

inflorescence

fruit

Ht. to 0.4 m

√ *Hirschfeldia incana* (L.) Lagr.-Fossat

SC MEDITERRANEAN HOARY-MUSTARD / SUMMER MUSTARD
E

Nonnative / Mediterranean

Flowering Time: July–November

Habitat: disturbed areas

Description: Herbaceous hairy perennial to 10 dm. Leaves basal rosette, flattened to the ground to 8 cm, margin lobed; stem leaves sessile, simple reduced upward, not clasping the stem. Inflorescence a raceme, elongating in fruit; sepals spreading; petals to 6 mm, pale yellow to white. Fruit erect appressed to the stem to 1.5 cm, glabrous; beak club-like to 6 mm.

Genus & Specific Name Derivation: Named for C. Hirschfeldt (1742–1792), horticulturist / hoary or white referring to the dense hairs on the plant

Notes: Illustration from *Illustrated Flora of the Pacific States.*

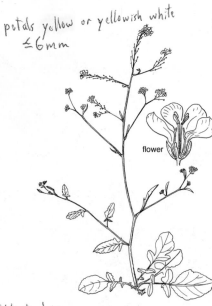

petals yellow or yellowish white ≤ 6 mm

flower

Ht. to 1 m

√*Lepidium nitidum* Torrey & A. Gray var. *nitidum*

E SHINING PEPPERGRASS Native

Flowering Time: February–May

Habitat: serpentine grassland

Description: Annual to 9 cm, often with a reddish cast. Leaves a basal rosette, compound, 1-pinnate, blade to 2 cm; stem leaves alternate, simple to compound, blade to 2 cm. Inflorescence a raceme to 3 cm in fruit; peduncle to 2 cm; pedicel to 3 mm; sepals green < 0.5 mm; petals white to 1 mm. Fruit a silicle to 7 mm, shiny, round with a notch at the top and a suture line down the center.

Genus & Specific Name Derivation: Greek: little scale, referring to the fruit / glossy surface, referring to the fruit.

Notes: Small flowers are often gone when in fruit. The fruits have a peppery taste.

Uses Past and Present: Natives parched the seeds, ground them into a flour, mixed them with other seeds and made a mush. Leaves were used for a hair treatment said to keep the scalp clean and prevent baldness.

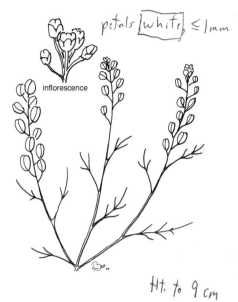

petals [white] ≤ 1mm

inflorescence

Ht. to 9 cm

Lunaria annua L.

MOONWORT Nonnative / Europe / HONESTY

Flowering Time: March–April

Habitat: woodland

Description: Upright annual or biennial to 5 dm in flower, with soft hairs on whole plant. Leaves alternate, simple, to 10 cm, upper shorter, margin shallowly lobed to toothed; lower with a petiole, upper sessile. Inflorescence a raceme to 12 cm. Flowers to 4 cm wide; pedicel 1–2 cm; sepals to 1 cm, pinkish-white, wrinkled; petals to 2 cm, dark magenta-pink-purple with darker veins. Fruit a silicle, to 4 cm, round.

Genus & Specific Name Derivation: Latin: moon, from shiny septum, the wall between the chambers of the ovary / annual

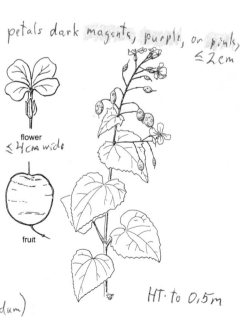

petals dark magenta, purple, or pink, ≤ 2cm

flower ≤ 4 cm wide

fruit

HT. to 0.5m

Addendum (Not in Toni's 2008 addendum)

√ *Lepidium strictum* PROSTRATE CRESS

E Daycamp lawn, other trails

Sepals persistent, often until fruit is mature
~~Petiole~~ Pedicels flattened
Fruit similar to L. nitidum, but more closely spaced

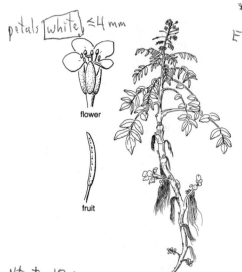

petals [white] ≤4 mm

flower

fruit

Ht. to 10 cm

Nasturtium officinale R. Br. / Rorippa nasturtium-aquaticu

WATER CRESS   Native

E

Flowering Time: March–April

Habitat: riparian woodland

Description: Low-growing herbaceous perennial to 10 cm. Plant rooting at the leaf node. Leaves alternate, compound, 1-pinnate, blade to 8 cm; leaflets to 1.5 cm with 4–8 pairs of leaflets and one leaflet at the tip. Inflorescence a raceme to 3 cm. Flowers to 6 ~~cm~~ mm wide; pedicel to 1 cm; sepals to 3 mm, pale green; petals to 4 mm, white Fruit a silique to 2 cm.

Genus & Specific Name Derivation: Latin: a twisted-nose due to the plant's pungent taste / sold as an herb or used as a medicine

Notes: New name accepted by *Jepson Manual* staff, name in *The Jepson Manual* (1993) *Rorippa nasturtium-aquaticum*.

Uses Past and Present: Cultivated for edible greens.

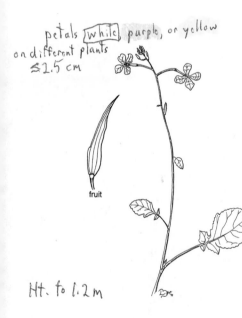

petals [white] purple, or yellow on different plants ≤2.5 cm

fruit

Ht. to 1.2 m

Raphanus sativus L.

SC   RADISH   Nonnative / Europe

RC   *Flowering Time:* February–July

Habitat: woodland

Description: Biennial to 12 dm. Leaves alternate, simple to compound, short-petioled to sessile. Inflorescence a raceme; sepals to 1 cm; petals to 2.5 cm, flower color variable. Fruit a silique to 6 cm.

Genus & Specific Name Derivation: Greek: appearing rapidly, referring to the rapid seed germination / planted or cultivated

Uses Past and Present: In some countries the leaves and pods are a favorite food, rather than the root. In this species the root is too woody to use in the traditional way.

Sisymbrium officinale L.

HEDGE MUSTARD   Nonnative / Europe

Flowering Time: February–August

Habitat: disturbed areas

Description: Annual stem to 6 dm, hairy or glabrous. Leaves simple to 15 cm, deeply lobed, reduced upward, sessile. Inflorescence a raceme. Sepals to 2 mm; petals to 4 mm, yellow. Fruit a silique to 15 mm, appressed upward along the stem, beak short pointed.

Genus & Specific Name Derivation: Greek: for various mustards / sold as an herb or used as a medicine

Notes: Illustration from *Illustrated Flora of the Pacific States.*

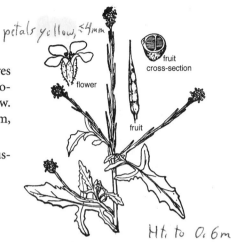

petals yellow, ≤4mm

flower

fruit cross-section

fruit

Ht. to 0.6m

√ *Thysanocarpus curvipes* Hook.

HAIRY FRINGEPOD   Native

Flowering Time: March–May

Habitat: serpentine and nonserpentine grassland

Description: Upright annual to 35 cm; lower stem with fine hairs. Leaves simple, basal and alternate on the stem; basal leaves to 2.5 cm, linear; stem leaves to 2 cm, clasping the stem; leaves hairy. Inflorescence a raceme to 12 cm in fruit. Flowers minute, falling early; petals white; pedicel arching downward in fruit. Fruit a silicle to 7 mm; round; margin thin, center is raised over the seed.

Genus & Specific Name Derivation: Greek: fringe fruit / curved, referring to the arching pedicel

petals white minute

flower

fruit

leaf

Ht. to 35 cm

Photo in K&B plate 17

2008 Addendums

Calycanthaceae / Spicebush family
near footbridge across Cordilleras Creek

. Calycanthus occidentalis SPICEBUSH native (rare in Calif.)

Campanulaceae / Bluebell family

Triodanis biflora SMALL VENUS LOOKING GLASS native
flowers sessile, axillary corolla lobes 5, more than twice as long as wide; and as long as rest of corolla
leaves alternate, widest near base, little longer than wide

Caprifoliaceae — Honeysuckle Family

Shrubs, trees and vines. Leaves opposite, simple or compound. Inflorescence axillary or terminal clusters. Flowers bisexual, regular or irregular. Calyx small, 5-lobed; corolla fused, 5-lobed; stamens 5; pistil 1, ovary inferior, style 1, stigma often head-like. Fruit a berry, drupe or capsule. Some ornamental, e.g., honeysuckle.

For key to woody plants *see* Group 2. Woody Plants

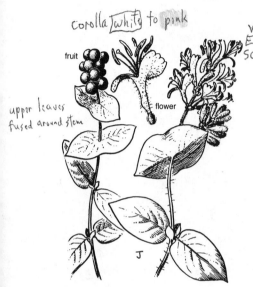

corolla white to pink (handwritten)

fruit

flower

upper leaves fused around stem (handwritten)

J

often semi-evergreen woody vine (handwritten)

Lonicera hispidula Douglas var. *vacillans* A. Gray

HAIRY HONEYSUCKLE   Native

Flowering Time: May–June

Habitat: riparian, woodland

Description: Deciduous vine that can be sprawling and somewhat shrub-like. Vines can be rope-like to 6 m long. Leaves simple, opposite, oblong to ovate, to 8 cm; upper leaves fused in pairs around the stem, lower leaves with short petioles. Inflorescence a spike at the end of the upper branches. Flowers in pairs, sessile; petals white to pink, irregular and two lipped, the upper lip with 4 shallowly lobed petals and the lower with 1 petal; stamens 5, exserted; style 1, stigma rounded. Fruit a berry, red.

Genus & Specific Name Derivation: Adam Lonitzer, German herbalist / bristly, with stiff hairs / variable

Notes: The fruits hang from the ends of the branches in the summer. They look like salmon eggs, but are not edible by humans. Unlike many garden honeysuckles the flowers of this species are not fragrant. Illustration from *Illustrated Flora of the Pacific States.*

Photo in K & B plate 18 (handwritten)

2008 Addendum (handwritten)

Abelia g X grandiflora   GLOSSY ABELIA   nonnative (handwritten)

√ *Sambucus mexicana* C. Presl

E
SC

BLUE ELDERBERRY   Native

Flowering Time: June–July

Habitat: open woodland, riparian

Description: Deciduous, large shrub or small tree to 8 m. Leaves opposite, compound, odd 1-pinnate. Leaflets 3–9, to 20 cm, margin toothed. Inflorescence a flat-topped umbel-like panicle. Flowers regular. Sepals and petals fused, 5 lobed; petals cream-white. Stamens 5, exserted; ovary inferior, style 1, stigma 3-lobed. Fruit a berry-like drupe, round, bluish-black.

Genus & Specific Name Derivation: Greek: the name of a musical instrument made from wood of this genus / from Mexico

Notes: For this species the flowers and fruits are edible, but the red-berried species (*S. racemosa*) is poisonous.

Uses Past and Present: Flowers and leaves dried and used as a diuretic. Flowers brewed into a tea for fevers, upset stomach, colds, and flu. Fruit is a rich source of vitamin C. The stems were used to make arrow shafts, whistles and flutes. A dye from both the twigs and fruit was used in basketry. The flowers were used to make fritters. The fruit is bitter but after drying or cooking it can be made into sauces, jellies, wines, and syrups. Wine is also made from the flowers. Crushed leaves can be used to relieve pain of nettle stings.

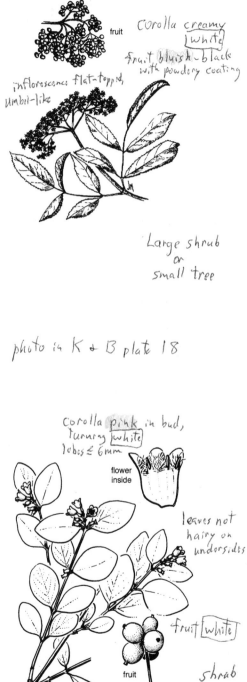

fruit

Corolla creamy [white]

fruit bluish-black with powdery coating

inflorescence flat-topped, umbel-like

Large shrub or small tree

photo in K & B plate 18

√ *Symphoricarpos albus* (L.) S. F. Blake
var. *laevigatus* (Fern.) S. F. Blake

E
SC

SNOWBERRY   Native

Flowering Time: April–June

Habitat: woodland

Description: Deciduous shrub with spreading branches to 1.8 m. Leaves opposite, simple to 6 cm, with wavy, entire to slightly lobed margins. Inflorescence a terminal raceme with 8–16 flowers. Flowers regular, with two fused bracts at the base; early buds pink, flowers later white. Sepals 5, fused; petals 5, to 6 mm, fused, hairy inside. Stamens 5, inserted; ovary inferior, pistil 1, stigma 1, head-shaped. Fruit a round, spongy, white berry, to 12 mm.

Genus & Specific Name Derivation: Greek: to bear fruit together, referring to the berries in clusters / white / polished, smooth, referring to the fruit

Notes: The berries are eaten by birds.Illustration from *Illustrated Flora of the Pacific States.*

Corolla pink in bud, turning [white] lobes ≤ 6mm

flower inside

leaves not hairy on undersides

fruit [white]

shrub

fruit

Photo in K & B plate 18

corolla pink in bud,
turning white
lobes ≤ 4mm

flower   fruit

leaves hairy
on undersides
Fruit [white]

Trailing
shrub
to 0.6m

Symphoricarpos mollis Nutt.

E
SC CREEPING SNOWBERRY   Native

Flowering Time: April–June

Habitat: woodland

Description: Trailing or creeping deciduous low-growing shrub or ground cover to 6 dm. Leaves opposite, simple, to 3 cm, with wavy, entire to slightly lobed margins. Inflorescence a terminal raceme with 2–8 flowers. Flowers regular, with two fused bracts at the base; early buds pink, flowers later white. Sepals 5, fused; petals 5, to 4 mm, fused, hairy inside. Stamens 5, inserted; ovary inferior, pistil 1, stigma 1, head-shaped. Fruit a round, white, spongy berry, to 12 mm.

Genus & Specific Name Derivation: Greek: to bear fruit together, referring to the berries in clusters / softly hairy, referring to the plant

Notes: The berries are eaten by birds. Both species of snowberry grow together in the same habitat.

Photo in K + B plate 18

2008 Addendum

√ Viburnum sp.   VIBURNUM nonnative
woody shrub or small tree,
leaves opposite, simple
inflorescence with numerous flowers
corolla white, with 5 lobes

Caryophyllaceae — Pink Family

Annuals, biennials, or herbaceous perennials. Leaves opposite, simple, often swollen at the leaf nodes. Inflorescence of racemes, cymes, panicles or axillary. Flowers bisexual, regular. Sepals 5, separate or fused; petals 5, separate, sometimes small or absent, some of the petals are deeply lobed and appear to be more than one petal; stamens 5 or 10; pistil 1, ovary superior, styles 2–5 or 1, stigma with 2–3 lobes. Fruit a capsule. Some cultivated as ornamentals, including carnations and baby's-breath.

Family Characteristics

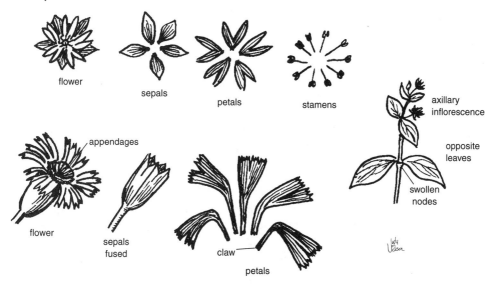

For key to families *see* Group 3. Herbaceous Flowering Plant Families
1. Sepals fused into a cup-like calyx
    2. Petals bright orange-red .... *Silene californica* (CALIFORNIA INDIAN PINK)
    2´ Petals pink to pale pink-white ....
    .... *Silene gallica* (COMMON CATCHFLY/WINDMILL PINK)
1´ Sepals free
    3. Stipules present, scarious .... *Spergularia rubra* (PURPLE SAND-SPURREY)
    3´ Stipules absent
        4. Styles 5-parted .... *Cerastium glomeratum* (MOUSE-EAR CHICKWEED)
        4´ Styles 3-parted
            5. Petals deeply two-lobed .... *Stellaria media* (COMMON CHICKWEED)
            5´ Petals entire to irregularly toothed ....
            .... *Minuartia douglasii* (DOUGLAS' SANDWORT)

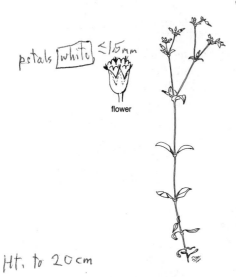

petals [white] ≤ 1.5 mm

flower

Ht. to 20 cm

Cerastium glomeratum Thuill.

MOUSE-EAR CHICKWEED　Nonnative / Europe

Flowering Time: March–June

Habitat: grassland

Description: Upright, hairy, sometimes glandular annual to 20 cm. Leaves opposite, simple to 12 mm, ovate, sessile. Inflorescence axillary. Bracts to 2 mm, green; pedicel to 3 mm. Sepals to 5 mm, glandular-hairy; petals to 1.5 mm or 0, white, lobed; stamens 10; styles and stigma 5-parted. Fruit a capsule to 8 mm.

Genus & Specific Name Derivation: Greek: horn, referring to shape of fruit / collected into heads

Notes: Petals are often missing; when visible they are lobed.

petals [white]
≤ 6 mm
anthers yellow

flower

fruit

Ht. to 30 cm

Minuartia douglasii (Torrey & A. Gray) Mattf.

DOUGLAS' SANDWORT　Native

Flowering Time: March–May

Habitat: serpentine grassland

Description: Annual to 30 cm; stems green to purple, finely glandular-hairy. Leaves opposite, simple to 4 cm, thread-like. Inflorescence a cyme. Sepals to 3.7 mm; petals to 6 mm; styles and stigma 3-parted. Fruit a capsule, teeth 3.

Genus & Specific Name Derivation: J. Minuart a Spanish botanist and pharmacist / for David Douglas (1798–1834), collector in the American northwest for the Royal Horticultural Society

2008 Addendum

✓ Polycarpon tetraphyllum
SC　FOUR-LEAVED ALLSEED nonnative
　　not in K & B
　　plant ≤ 10 cm high, many-branched
　　leaves opposite, appears to be in whorls of four
　　fruit very numerous

Silene californica Durand

CALIFORNIA INDIAN PINK   Native

Flowering Time: May–June

Habitat: woodland

Description: Low-growing, hairy, herbaceous perennial to 15 cm. Leaves opposite, simple to 4.5 cm, sessile. Inflorescence axillary in upper leaves. Bracts small, leaf-like to 5 mm. Flowers to 4 cm wide; sepals to 2 cm, fused, glandular, yellow green; petals to 2 cm, lobed, orange-red; stamens exserted. Fruit a capsule.

Genus & Specific Name Derivation: Greek: probably from mythological Silenus, intoxicated foster-father of Bacchus, who was covered with foam, referring to the sticky secretions of many species / from California

Photo in K & B plate 19

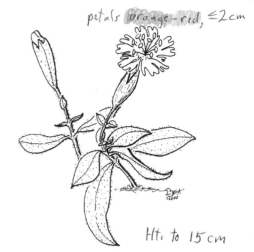

petals orange-red, ≤2cm

Ht. to 15 cm

√ *Silene gallica* L.

SC

E

COMMON CATCHFLY / WINDMILL PINK

Nonnative / Europe

Flowering Time: April–October

Habitat: grassland

Description: Annual to 35 cm; whole plant glandular hairy. Leaves opposite, simple to 3 cm; sessile. Inflorescence a raceme. Pedicel to 2 mm; bracts to 10 mm, green. Flower to 7 mm wide; sepals to 10 mm, fused, green with reddish-purple lines; petals to 4 mm, separate, pinkish-white; stamens included. Fruit a capsule.

Genus & Specific Name Derivation: Greek: Probably from mythological Silenus, intoxicated foster-father of Bacchus, who was covered with foam, referring to the sticky secretions of many species / French

Photo in K & B plate 19

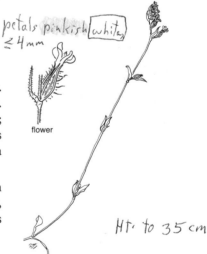

petals pinkish white ≤4mm

flower

Ht. to 35 cm

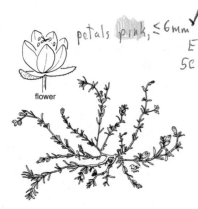

petals pink, ≤6mm

flower

Spergularia rubra (L.) J. S. Presl & C. Presl

or RUBY

PURPLE SAND-SPURREY   Nonnative / Europe

E
SC

Flowering Time: April–June

Habitat: grassland, along trails

Description: Trailing and spreading annual or herbaceous perennial; stems to 15 cm. Leaves opposite, simple to 1 cm, in clusters; stipules obvious, to 5 mm. Inflorescence axillary and in clusters at the end of stems. Flowers to 7 mm wide, opening in full sun; sepals to 4 mm, green, glandular with scarious margin; petals to 6 mm, pink; stamens 6–8. Fruit a capsule.

Genus & Specific Name Derivation: Latin: derivative of *Spergula*, which means scatterer, referring to the scattering of the seeds / red

Notes: This plant grows in the trail, and in disturbed areas that are trampled on.

trailing
to 15cm

Photo in K & B plate 19

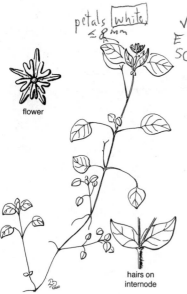

petals white
≤8mm

flower

hairs on
internode

Ht. to 0.5 m

Stellaria media (L.) Villars

E
SC

COMMON CHICKWEED   Nonnative / Europe

Flowering Time: February–October

Habitat: grassland

Description: Annual to 50 cm. Hairs on one side of the stem Leaves opposite, simple to 4 cm. Inflorescence axillary in leafy bracts. Sepals to 6 mm; petals to 8 mm, deeply notched; styles and stigma 3-parted. Fruit a capsule.

Genus & Specific Name Derivation: Latin: star, referring to flower shape / mid-sized

Notes: Stem internodes hairy in a single parallel line.

Chenopodiaceae — Goosefoot Family

Annuals, herbaceous perennials, shrubs and trees, can be monoecious or dioecious. Leaves generally alternate, entire to lobed. Inflorescence a raceme, spike, catkin-like, or clustered. Sepals 1–5 or 0 in pistillate flowers, free or fused, often persistent in fruit; petals 0; stamens 0–5; ovary superior, styles 1–3. Fruit a utricle.

For key to families *see* Group 3. Herbaceous Flowering Plant Families

Chenopodium californicum (S. Watson) S. Watson

CALIFORNIA GOOSEFOOT   Native

Flowering Time: June–July

Habitat: moist areas

Description: Herbaceous perennial to 9 dm. Leaves simple, alternate to 9 cm. Inflorescence axillary, spheric, to 10 mm in diameter; terminal inflorescence to 20 cm. Sepals, usually 5, fused; petals 0; stamens usually 5. Fruit an utricle to 2 mm in diameter.

Genus & Specific Name Derivation: Greek: goose foot, from leaf shape of some / from California

Notes: Some cultivated for food or grain.

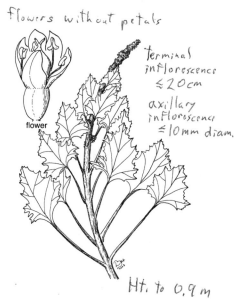

flowers without petals

terminal inflorescence ≤ 20 cm

axillary inflorescence ≤ 10 mm diam.

flower

Ht. to 0.9 m

Cistaceae — Rock-Rose Family

Herbaceous perennials and shrubs. Leaves alternate, opposite, or whorled, simple. Inflorescence axillary, racemes or panicles. Flowers bisexual, regular. Sepals 3–5, separate, often persistent in fruit; petals 5, separate; stamens many; pistil 1, ovary superior, style 1, stigma entire to lobed. Fruit a capsule; seeds many. Some cultivated ornamentals, e.g., *Cistus* and *Helianthemum*.

For key to woody plants *see* Group 2. Woody Plants

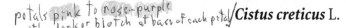

Cistus creticus L.

ROCK-ROSE   Nonnative / Europe

Flowering Time: May–June

Habitat: openings in woodland

Description: Evergrèen shrub to 2 m. Whole plant with soft stellate hairs. Leaves opposite, simple, to 6 cm, often in clusters, margin entire, wavy, gray green, upper and lower surface hairy. Petiole to 15 mm. Inflorescence a panicle-like cyme with 1–7 flowers. Flowers regular. Sepals 5, separate; petals 5, separate, to 3 cm, pink to rose-purple, with a darker blotch at base of each petal. Stamens many, yellow; ovary superior, stigma lobed. Fruit a capsule with 5 valves.

Genus & Specific Name Derivation: Ancient Greek name / from Crete

Notes: Invasive shrub becoming prevalent where it has become established along the Sylvan Trail.

Helianthemum scoparium Nutt.

PEAK RUSH-ROSE   Native

Flowering Time: April–August

Habitat: chaparral

Description: Shrub to 10 dm, broom-like. Leaves simple, alternate, linear to 4 cm. Inflorescence a raceme, sepals 5 to 4.5 mm, petals 5 to 11 mm, yellow. Stamens variable in number from 12–45. Fruit a capsule to 4 mm.

Genus & Specific Name Derivation: Greek: sun flower / broom-like referring to the plant form

Notes: This plant is abundant after a fire. Illustration from *The Jepson Manual.*

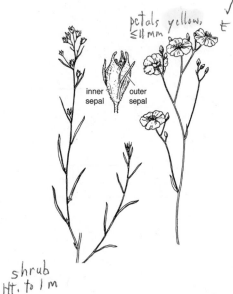

Convolvulaceae — Morning-Glory Family

Annuals, herbaceous perennials, shrubs or vines; stems often twining or trailing. Leaves alternate, simple. Inflorescence solitary or few in clusters, axillary or terminal. Flowers bisexual, regular. Sepals 5, free to fused, often persistent in fruit; petals 5, fused; stamens 5; pistil 1, ovary superior, styles 1–3, stigma entire to lobed. Fruit a capsule; seeds 2–4. Some cultivated as ground covers, e.g., *Dichondra*.

For key to woody plants *see* Group 2. Woody Plants

Key to Herbaceous Plants:

1. Twining, climbing vine, occurring in chaparral, woodland
    2. Plants hairy at least around leaf sinus or top of peduncle ....
    .... *Calystegia occidentalis* (CHAPARRAL MORNING-GLORY)
    2´ Plants not at all hairy ....
    .... *Calystegia purpurata* (SMOOTH WESTERN MORNING-GLORY)
1´ Trailing, herbaceous perennial, occurring in grassland ....
    .... *Calystegia subacaulis* (HILL MORNING-GLORY)

Calystegia occidentalis (A. Gray) Brummitt ssp. *occidentalis*

CHAPARRAL MORNING-GLORY   Native

Flowering Time: April–July

Habitat: chaparral

Description: Perennial vine from a deep, woody root. The vine dies back each year, then in spring it grows very quickly, climbing to the top of the surrounding vegetation. Leaves simple, alternate to 5 cm, arrowhead-shaped, margin sometimes slightly lobed. Petioles to 2 cm, longer at base of plant. Inflorescence axillary, 1-flowered; bracts to 12 mm, linear to round; flowers regular. Sepals to 15 mm, 5 lobed, fused; petals to 40 mm, 5-lobed, fused, white to creamy yellow. Fruit a capsule.

Genus & Specific Name Derivation: Greek: concealing calyx, referring to the bractlets of some / western

Notes: In the spring the vines can grow several feet each month. These vines rarely choke out the existing shrubs they grow on. Illustration from *Illustrated Flora of the Pacific States*.

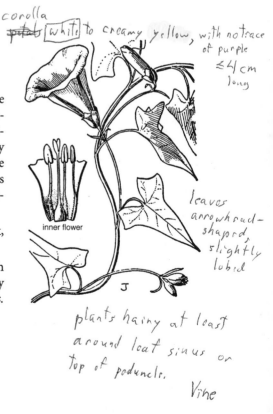

corolla
petals [white] to creamy yellow, with no trace of purple ≤4 cm long

corolla

inner flower

leaves arrowhead-shaped, slightly lobed

plants hairy at least around leaf sinus or top of peduncle.

Vine

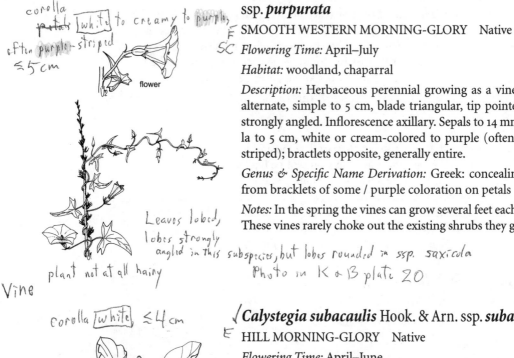

corolla ~~petals~~ [white] to creamy to purple, often purple-striped ≤5cm

flower

Leaves lobed, lobes strongly angled in this subspecies, but lobes rounded in ssp. saxicola

Photo in K & B plate 20

plant not at all hairy

Vine

corolla [white] ≤4cm

Trailing to 8cm

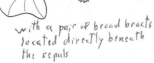

with a pair of broad bracts located directly beneath the sepals

leaf

✓ *Calystegia purpurata* (E. Greene) Brummitt ssp. *purpurata*

SMOOTH WESTERN MORNING-GLORY   Native

Flowering Time: April–July

Habitat: woodland, chaparral

Description: Herbaceous perennial growing as a vine. Leaves alternate, simple to 5 cm, blade triangular, tip pointed, lobes strongly angled. Inflorescence axillary. Sepals to 14 mm; corolla to 5 cm, white or cream-colored to purple (often purple-striped); bractlets opposite, generally entire.

Genus & Specific Name Derivation: Greek: concealing calyx, from bracklets of some / purple coloration on petals

Notes: In the spring the vines can grow several feet each month. These vines rarely choke out the existing shrubs they grow on.

✓ *Calystegia subacaulis* Hook. & Arn. ssp. *subacaulis*

HILL MORNING-GLORY   Native

Flowering Time: April–June

Habitat: serpentine grassland

Description: Trailing herbaceous perennial; stems to 8 cm in flower. Leaves alternate, simple to 3 cm; margin slightly lobed, wavy. Petiole to 3 cm. Inflorescence axillary. Flowers to 4 cm wide; pedicel to 10 mm. Sepals to 15 mm, light yellow-green; petals to 4 cm, white; stigma 2-parted; bractlets 2, to 12 mm, just below the sepals, light green. Fruit a capsule.

Genus & Specific Name Derivation: Greek: concealing calyx, referring to the bractlets of some / lacking an obvious stem

2008 Addendum
Convolvulus arvensis   EUROPEAN BINDWEED
nonnative

herbaceous vine; corolla > 1 cm long; extended well beyond the calyx, not divided into distinct lobes; stigma elongated, divided into 2 lobes; without a pair of broad bracts resembling sepals corolla white or pink
(in all the above traits, this species resembles Calystegia occidentalis and C. purpurata)
It differs from them in having a corolla < 2.5 cm long and in having leaves of a distinct shape.

Cornaceae — Dogwood Family

Shrubs, trees, sometimes dioecious. Leaves generally opposite, simple, generally entire, generally deciduous; stipules 0. Inflorescence a cyme or raceme, umbel or head-like, sometimes subtended by showy, petal-like bracts. Flower white to cream; calyx 4-lobed; petals 0 or 4, sometimes 5; stamens 4 or 5; ovary inferior; style simple, stigma 1–4 lobed. Fruit a drupe or berry; seeds 1 or 2. Some cultivated as ornamentals, some for timber.

For key to woody plants *see* Group 2. Woody Plants

✓*Cornus glabrata* Benth.

"*F.*" BROWN DOGWOOD   Native / SMOOTH DOGWOOD

petals yellowish/white, ≤ 5mm

Large shrub or small tree

Flowering Time: March–June

Habitat: moist woodland   along Edgewood Rd near Canada

Description: Deciduous, large shrub to small tree to 6 m, with brownish twigs. Leaves opposite, simple to 5 cm, gray-green with 3–4 pairs of veins; lower leaf surface sometimes paler and nearly hairless. Petiole to 8 mm. Inflorescence an umbel-like cyme. Flowers regular. Sepals to 1 mm, fused, 4-lobed; petals 4, to 5 mm, separate, yellow-white. Stamens 4; ovary inferior, style 1. Fruit a drupe to 9 mm, white to bluish.

Genus & Specific Name Derivation: Latin: horn, from the hard wood / smooth, without hairs

Uses Past and Present: See *C. sericea.*

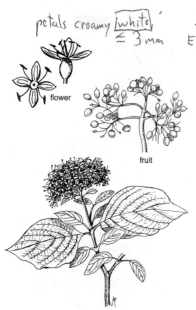

petals creamy white ≤ 3 mm

flower

fruit

Large shrub
or
Small tree

✓*Cornus sericea* L. ssp. *sericea*

E AMERICAN DOGWOOD   Native / WESTERN CREEK DOGWOOD

Flowering Time: May–July

Habitat: moist woodland

Description: Deciduous, large shrub to small tree to 4 m. The stems and twigs are red-brown and stand out in the winter after the leaves have fallen. Leaves opposite, simple to 10 cm. Leaf undersurface paler with dense hairs, veins 4–7 pairs. Inflorescence hairy, arranged in an umbel-like cyme. Flower regular. Sepals 4-lobed, fused, minute; petals 4, to 3 mm, separate, cream-white. Stamens 4, exserted; ovary inferior, style to 2 mm. Fruit a drupe to 9 mm, white to cream-colored, smooth.

Genus & Specific Name Derivation: Latin: horn, from the hard wood / silky-hairy, referring to the hairs on the undersurface of the leaf

Notes: This species can form dense groves in moist areas.

Uses Past and Present: Dried root or bark was boiled and used for fever. Peeled twigs were used as toothbrushes. The bark was also used as an astringent or for smoking. Fruit of some species used for jam and syrup.

photo in K & B plate 21

Crassulaceae — Stonecrop Family

Annuals or herbaceous perennials, succulent. Leaves basal and stem, alternate or opposite, simple. Inflorescence in terminal cymes or solitary and axillary. Flowers bisexual, regular. Sepals 3–5, separate or fused; petals 3–5, separate or fused; stamens 3–10; pistils 3–5, style 1. Fruit a follicle; seeds 1–many. Many cultivated as ornamentals.

For key to families *see* Group 3. Herbaceous Flowering Plant Families

Crassula connata Ruiz Lopez & Pavon

PYGMY-WEED   Native

Flowering Time: February–May

Habitat: serpentine grassland

Description: Low-growing, succulent annual to 6 cm. Leaves opposite, simple to 6 mm, succulent, bases fused. Inflorescence axillary with 1–2 flowers. Flowers minute, appearing reddish. Fruit 3–5 follicles, minute.

Genus & Specific Name Derivation: Latin: diminutive of thick, referring to the leaves / united at the base, referring to leaf bases

Notes: Small plant often overlooked, mostly occurring in the bare serpentine areas. Authority updated from *The Jepson Manual Corrections* — Installment No. 3.

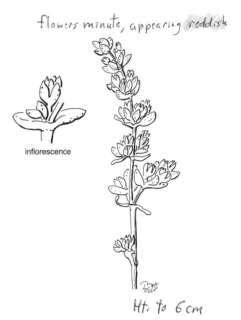

flowers minute, appearing reddish

inflorescence

Ht. to 6 cm

Photo in K & B plate 21

Cucurbitaceae — Gourd Family

Herbaceous perennial vines, usually monoecious, stems vine-like, twining or trailing, usually with tendrils. Leaves alternate, simple. Inflorescence solitary or in racemes or panicles. Flowers regular, unisexual. Calyx 0 or 5-lobed; corolla fused, 5-lobed; stamens 3–5; ovary inferior. Fruit a berry or capsule, generally gourd or melon-like. Some species cultivated for fruit, e.g., melons, squashes, and functional and decorative gourds.

For key to woody plants *see* Group 2. Woody Plants

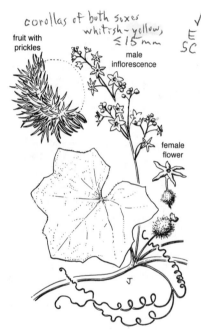

corollas of both sexes
whitish-yellow,
≤ 15 mm

fruit with prickles

male inflorescence

female flower

J

Vine

√ *Marah fabaceus* (Naudin) E. Greene

E
SC

CALIFORNIA MAN-ROOT   Native

Flowering Time: March–April

Habitat: chaparral, woodland

Description: Perennial deciduous vine with a large underground tuber. New growth occurs at a fast rate. The plant has tendrils that attach to and climb over surrounding vegetation. Leaves alternate, simple to 10 cm with 5–7 lobes. Petiole to 6 cm. Flowers unisexual, on the same plant. Male inflorescence a raceme located above the solitary female flowers; both are located in the axils of the leaves. Sepals 0; petals to 15 mm wide, 5-lobed, fused, whitish-yellow. The individual female flower is larger than an individual male flower. Stamens 5, fused, anthers twisted together; ovary inferior, stigma 1, round. Fruit a capsule to 4–5 cm, more or less round, prickles stiff, straight.

Genus & Specific Name Derivation: Latin: bitter, from taste of all parts / bean-like referring to the vine-like habit

Notes: Tuber-like root is large. The common name refers to the tuber being as large as a man's torso. The fruit is poisonous. The ripe fruits can explode and cause injury if touched or shaken. Illustration from *Illustrated Flora of the Pacific States.*

Uses Past and Present: The seeds were crushed by natives to stupefy fish. The seeds were also used in necklaces. It is said that native children used the fruit as marbles.

Cuscutaceae — Dodder Family

Parasitic plants; stems yellow-green to orange, usually twining. Leaves absent or scale-like; stipules absent. Flowers bisexual, regular, in axillary head-like to spike-like clusters. Calyx with 4–5 lobes; corolla with 5 lobes and 5 scales alternating with the lobes; stamens 4–5; pistil 1, ovary superior, styles usually 2. Fruit a capsule with 1–4 seeds.

For key to families *see* Group 3. Herbaceous Flowering Plant Families

Cuscuta californica Hook. & Arn. var. *californica*

DODDER , Native WESTERN

Flowering Time: May–August

Habitat: chaparral

Description: Climbing, parasitic, vine-like annual with orange stems. Leaves reduced, scale-like, triangular; the plant appears leafless. Inflorescence of spike-like clusters; flowers to 4 mm wide, whitish. Fruit a capsule.

Genus & Specific Name Derivation: Arabic: ancient name / from California

Notes: This species has no green chlorophyll and has lost the ability to photosynthesize. The stem anchors into the stem of its host plant, penetrates it and winds around the host plant, getting its nutrients from that plant.

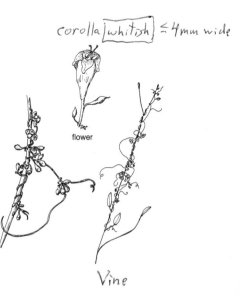

corolla whitish ≤ 4mm wide

flower

Vine

Dipsacaceae — Teasel Family

Annuals to herbaceous perennials, sometimes armed with prickles. Leaves simple, basal and stem leaves opposite, fused at base, or pinnately compound. Inflorescence head-like, subtended by an involucre. Flowers bisexual, regular. Calyx fused, 4–5 lobes; corolla fused, 4–5 lobes; stamens usually 4; ovary inferior, stigma 2-lobed. Fruit an achene. Some cultivated ornamentals, e.g., pincushion flower (*Scabiosa*).

For key to families *see* Group 3. Herbaceous Flowering Plant Families

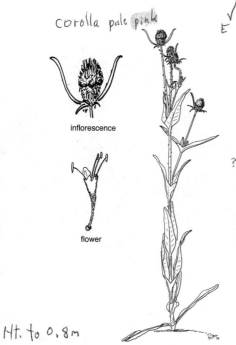

corolla pale pink

inflorescence

flower

Ht. to 0.8m

✓ *Dipsacus sativus* (L.) Honck.

E   FULLER'S TEASEL   Nonnative / Europe

Flowering Time: March–October

Habitat: grassland, seeps, swales

Description: Upright annual to 80 cm. Leaves opposite, simple to 20 cm, sessile, often enclosing the stem. Inflorescence head-like, to 5 cm in flower; peduncle to 20 cm; bracts below inflorescence to 10 cm, curving downward at the tip, bracts below each flower to 6 mm, curving downward at the tip. Flowers to 2 mm wide, sessile; sepals 4-lobed, club-shaped; petals to 7 mm, with 3 upper smaller lobes and 1 lower longer lobe, pale pink; stamens exserted, pollen pink. Fruit an achene to 8 mm.

Genus & Specific Name Derivation: Greek: thirst, referring to the leaf bases that hold water / cultivated

Notes: Stigma and style develop much later than the anthers, so may not be very visible when the pollen is being shed; this insures cross pollination. Water catches in the clasping leaves, attracting insects that may lay their eggs in this reservoir.

Uses Past and Present: Fruit heads used to raise nap on cloth and card wool from sheep.

2008 Addendum
Ebenaceae Persimmon Family
Diospiros sp. PERSIMMON nonnative

Ericaceae — Heath Family

Herbaceous perennials, shrubs or trees. Leaves alternate or opposite, simple, evergreen or deciduous. Inflorescence in racemes, panicles or solitary. Flowers bisexual, regular. Sepals 4–5, mostly separate; petals 4–5, separate or fused; stamens 8–10, anthers opening by pores or slits; pistil 1, ovary superior, style 1, stigma head-like or lobed. Fruit a capsule or berry; seeds few to many. Many cultivated, e.g., *Arctostaphylos*, *Rhododendron*.

For key to woody plants *see* Group 2. Woody Plants

√ *Arbutus menziesii* Pursh

E
5C

PACIFIC MADRONE   Native

Flowering Time: March–May

Habitat: woodland

Description: Evergreen tree to 40 m. Bark red-brown, smooth, shredding. Leaves alternate, simple, to 12 cm, upper bright green, lower whitish, margin finely toothed to entire. Petiole to 3 cm. Inflorescence a panicle. Flowers regular. Sepals fused, 5-lobed; petals to 8 mm, fused, 5-lobed, yellow-white to pink, urn shaped. Stamens 10, inserted; ovary superior, style 1, stigma slightly exserted. Fruit a berry, warty, to 12 mm wide, spherical, orange-red when mature.

Genus & Specific Name Derivation: Latin: name for *A. unedo*, strawberry tree / Archibald Menzies (1754–1842), an English naturalist on the ship *Discovery*

Notes: Flowers are fragrant and attract native bees.

Uses Past and Present: A tea was brewed from the old, scaly bark. Boiled berries are made into a jelly.

Photo in K & B plate 22

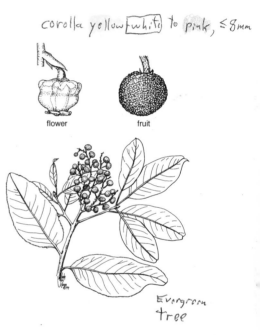

corolla yellow [white] to pink, ≤ 8mm

flower   fruit

Evergreen
tree

corolla white to pale pink, ≤9mm

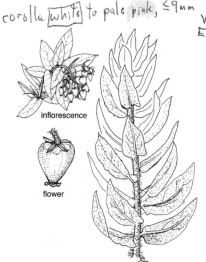

inflorescence

flower

Evergreen
Shrub
Ht. to 6m

√ *Arctostaphylos regismontana* Eastw.
E KINGS MOUNTAIN MANZANITA   Native

Flowering Time: February–April

Habitat: woodland

Description: Evergreen shrub to 6 m with glandular twigs and reddish-brown smooth bark. Leaves alternate, simple, to 6 cm, overlapping and clasping the stem. Margin entire or sharply toothed, base deeply lobed. Leaves glandular, hairy and sticky. Inflorescence a raceme; bracts to 12 mm, leaflike. Flower regular, bell or urn shaped; pedicel to 10 mm, glandular. Sepals 5, separate; petals to 9 mm, 5-lobed, fused, white to pinkish-white. Stamens 10, inserted; ovary superior, glandular, bristly, style 1, stigma head-like. Fruit a berry-like drupe to 8 mm, glandular-hairy, sticky.

Genus & Specific Name Derivation: Greek: bear berries, referring to bears feeding on the fruits / Kings Mountain, referring to the main location for this species. The common name "manzanita" in Spanish means "little apple," referring to the fruit.

Notes: Listed in *CNPS Inventory of Rare and Endangered Plants of California* on "List 1B, Plants Rare, Threatened, or Endangered in California and Elsewhere." The closest population is across Edgewood Road at Pulgas Ridge Open Space Preserve, while the largest populations occur in the Kings Mountain area on Skyline Road. Animals eat the ripened fruit; the seed coat is softened by passing through the gut, readying the seed for germination. Some manzanitas have burls that grow at and just below ground level (however this species does not make burls). If the plant is damaged it is able to resprout.

Uses Past and Present: Natives ate the ripe manzanita berries, which are also used for tea, cider or jelly. See *A. tomentosa* for other uses.

√
E
Arctostaphylos tomentosa (Pursh) Lindley
ssp. *crinita* (McMinn) R. Gankin

HAIRY MANZANITA Native

Flowering Time: February–April

Habitat: woodland

Description: Evergreen shrub to 3 m, with a basal burl. Bark red, smooth, twigs densely hairy with long, white bristles. Leaves alternate, simple, to 5 cm, margin entire or sometimes toothed, leaf base cut straight across or nearly so. Lower leaf surface densely hairy, more so than upper surface. Petiole to 10 mm. Inflorescence a raceme; bracts to 15 mm. Flower regular, bell or urn shaped; pedicel to 5 mm, hairy, sometimes glandular. Sepals 5, separate; petals to 9 mm, 5-lobed, fused, white to pinkish-white. Stamens 10, inserted; ovary hairy, superior, style 1, stigma head-like. Fruit a berry-like drupe to 10 mm, hairy.

Genus & Specific Name Derivation: Greek: bear berries / thickly matted hairs, referring to the hairs on the undersurface of the leaf / with a tuft of long hairs, referring to the long white bristly hairs on the twigs

Notes: This species has a basal burl which allows the plant to resprout after fire or disturbance.

Uses Past and Present: The berries were cooked or ground into meal to be used as a porridge; they may have ranked next to acorns in food value. The leaves were used to make a wash or lotion for poison oak, a drink for headache, or a poultice for sores. The wood was used for utensils and the burls are cherished for their beautiful wood products.

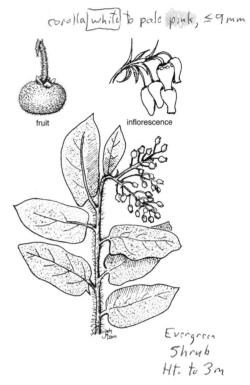

corolla white to pale pink, ≤9mm

fruit

inflorescence

Evergreen
Shrub
Ht. to 3m

Euphorbiaceae — Spurge Family

Annuals, herbaceous perennials, monoecious or dioecious, with milky sap. Leaves simple, alternate or opposite. Inflorescence a panicle, raceme, spike, or axillary. Flowers unisexual, regular. Calyx if present with 3–5 lobes, separate or fused; corolla 0; stamens 1–many; pistil 1, ovary superior, styles and stigmas fused. Fruit a capsule; seeds 3–6. Some species are used for rubber; some for food, e.g., cassava, tapioca; some for oils, e.g., tung oil, and castor oil; many species are highly toxic.

For key to families *see* Group 3. Herbaceous Flowering Plant Families

Key to Herbaceous Plants:

1. Plant gray-green, mat-forming, stellate-hairy ....
    .... *Croton setigerus* (TURKEY MULLEIN / DOVE WEED)
1′ Plant green, may be tinged with red; upright
   2. Leaf margin entire .blade short-ovate... *Euphorbia peplus* (PETTY SPURGE)
   2′ Leaf margin finely toothed ....blade elongate..................................
       .... *Euphorbia spathulata* (RETICULATE-SEEDED SPURGE)

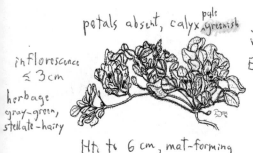

petals absent, calyx pale greenish

inflorescence ≤ 3 cm

herbage gray-green, stellate-hairy

Ht to 6 cm, mat-forming

Eremocarpus

~~*Croton setigerus*~~ Hook.

✗ TURKEY MULLEIN / DOVE WEED   Native

E

Flowering Time: June–November

Habitat: grassland

Description: Gray-green, mat-forming annual to 6 cm; whole plant stellate-hairy. Leaves alternate, simple to 2 cm; petiole to 2 cm. Inflorescence clustered to 3 cm; pedicel 2 mm; staminate flowers above pistillate flowers on same plant (monoecious); sepals greenish-white to 2 mm; petals 0. Fruit a one-seeded capsule.

Genus & Specific Name Derivation: Greek: a tick because of the way the seeds look / bearing bristles, referring to the hairy nature of the plant. Common name refers to use of the seeds for food by turkeys, doves and other birds.

Notes: Long, bristly, stellate hairs on whole plant. Leaves have a pleasant lemony odor. Flower very small; hard to identify parts of the flower. New name accepted by *Jepson Manual* staff, name in *The Jepson Manual* (1993) *Eremocarpus setigerus*.

Uses Past and Present: The stems and leaves contain a poison. Natives threw pieces into streams to stun fish. Plant has been used medicinally for respiratory problems.

~~Not in K+B~~

✓ *Euphorbia peplus* L.

SC
E

PETTY SPURGE   Nonnative / Europe

Flowering Time: all year

Habitat: chaparral

Description: Annual to 11 cm; plants monoecious (the male and female flowers separate but on the same plant). Leaves alternate, simple to 5 mm, green, lower tinged with red; margin entire; sessile. Inflorescence axillary in upper leaves; flowers green; staminate flowers in a small cup-like structure, stamen 1; pistillate flower has a stalked pistil. Fruit a lobed, spheric capsule.

Genus & Specific Name Derivation: Latin: Euphorbus, Physician to the King of Mauritania, 1st century / name for a Mediterranean coastal spurge

Notes: Poinsettia is also in this genus.

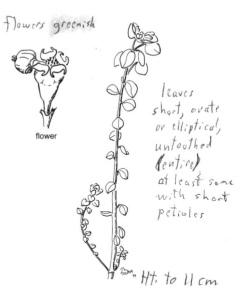

flowers greenish

flower

leaves short, ovate or elliptical, untoothed (entire) at least some with short petioles

Ht. to 11 cm

✓ *Euphorbia spathulata* Lam.

RETICULATE-SEEDED SPURGE   Native / SPATHULATE-LEAVED SPURGE

Flowering Time: April–May

Habitat: grassland

Description: Upright annual to 15 cm; lower stems sometimes pinkish-red; plants monoecious (the male and female flowers separate but on the same plant). Leaves alternate below, whorled at the branching point then opposite upward, simple to 1.5 cm; margin slightly toothed; sessile. Inflorescence axillary; flowers without sepals and petals, pistillate flower on a short stalk with glands at the base; bracts in pairs, opposite, leaf-like. Fruit bright green with bumps on the outer surface, roundish to 3-angled, to 3 mm wide.

Genus & Specific Name Derivation: Latin: Euphorbus, Physician to the King of Mauritania, 1st century / shaped like a spoon, referring to the leaf shape

Notes: See *E. peplus.*

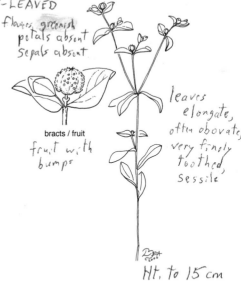

flowers greenish petals absent sepals absent

bracts / fruit

fruit with bumps

leaves elongate, often obovate, very finely toothed, sessile

Ht. to 15 cm

Fabaceae — Legume Family

Annuals, herbaceous perennials, shrubs or trees. Leaves generally alternate, compound. Inflorescence a raceme, spike, umbel, head, or axillary. Flowers bisexual, irregular or regular. Sepals 5, usually fused, often unequal, petals 5, similar in shape or not, some (papilionaceous) with 1 upper banner, 2 side wings, and 2 lower petals fused to form a keel; stamens usually 10, free or filaments united into a tube, sometimes 1 free; pistil 1, ovary superior, style and stigma 1. In papilionaceous flowers the male and female parts are inserted within the keel. Fruit a legume (pod). Roots have nitrogen-fixing nodules. Many species are important foods and sources of protein, e.g., peanuts, soybeans, peas, beans, and alfalfa. Many others are cultivated as ornamentals. Synonym Leguminosae.

Family Characteristics

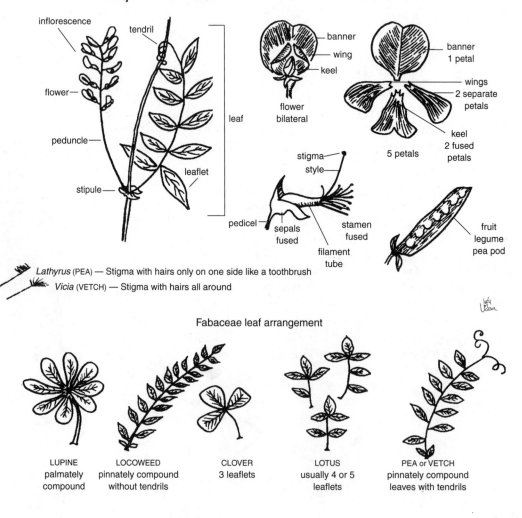

inflorescence
tendril
flower
peduncle
stipule
leaf
leaflet
pedicel

banner
wing
keel
flower
bilateral

banner
1 petal
wings
2 separate
petals
keel
2 fused
petals
5 petals

stigma
style
sepals
fused
stamen
fused
filament
tube

fruit
legume
pea pod

Lathyrus (PEA) — Stigma with hairs only on one side like a toothbrush
Vicia (VETCH) — Stigma with hairs all around

Fabaceae leaf arrangement

| LUPINE | LOCOWEED | CLOVER | LOTUS | PEA or VETCH |
| palmately compound | pinnately compound without tendrils | 3 leaflets | usually 4 or 5 leaflets | pinnately compound leaves with tendrils |

For key to woody plants *see* Group 2. Woody Plants

For key to families *see* Group 3. Herbaceous Flowering Plant Families

Key to Herbaceous Plants:
1. Mature leaves either palmately compound or with 3 leaflets (trifoliate)
   2. Leaves palmately compound, leaflets usually 5 or more
      3. Corolla yellow .... *Lupinus microcarpus* (CHICK LUPINE)
      3´ Corolla blue-white, purple-white to lavender-pink
         4. Inflorescence to 8 cm ....
         .... *Lupinus bicolor* (MINIATURE LUPINE/BICOLOR LUPINE)
         4´ Inflorescence mostly greater than 8 cm
            5. Plant densely hairy .... *Lupinus formosus* (SUMMER LUPINE)
            5´ Plant sparsely hairy to hairless ....
            .... *Lupinus succulentus* (ARROYO LUPINE)
   2´ Leaflets usually 3 (trifoliate)
      6. Inflorescence a raceme; fruit coiled or not
         7. Corolla purple to blue .... *Medicago sativa* (ALFALFA)
         7´ Corolla yellow
            8. Fruit coiled
               9. Corolla less than 3 mm ...... *Medicago lupulina* (BLACK MEDICK)
               9´ Corolla generally greater than 3 mm ....
               .... *Medicago polymorpha* (BURCLOVER)
            8´ Fruit not coiled ... *Melilotus indicus* (INDIAN MELILOT/SOURCLOVER)
      6´ Inflorescence a head-like cluster or axillary
         10. Inflorescence axillary .... *Lotus purshianus*[1] (SPANISH CLOVER)
         10´ Inflorescence a head-like cluster
            11. Inflorescence subtended by an involucre *(brats)*
               12. Corolla becoming inflated
                  13. Sepal lobes without hairs
                     14. Corolla greater than 10 mm, light green-yellow ....
                     .... *Trifolium fucatum* (SOUR CLOVER)
                     14´ Corolla less than 10 mm, pink-purple ....
                     .... *Trifolium depauperatum* var. *truncatum*
                     (PURPLE SACK CLOVER)
                  13´ Sepal lobes hairy .. *Trifolium barbigerum* (BEARDED CLOVER)
               12´ Corolla not inflated in flower
                  15. Involucre cup-shaped (squared off at base) when young
                     16. Involucre hairy ....
                     .... *Trifolium microcephalum* (SMALL-HEADED CLOVER)
                     16´ Involucre not hairy ....
                     ..... *Trifolium microdon* (VALPARAISO CLOVER/CUP CLOVER)
                  15´ Involucre flat or V-shaped at base
                     17. Inflorescence greater than 1 cm high in flower ....
                     .... *Trifolium willdenovii* (TOMCAT CLOVER)

17′ Inflorescence less than 1 cm high in flower ....
.... *Trifolium variegatum* (WHITE-TIPPED CLOVER)
11′ Inflorescence not subtended by an involucre *(bracts absent)*
(may be subtended by uppermost leaves and stipule)
18. Flowers reflexed in age
19. Corolla yellow
20. Heads with more than 20 flowers ....
.... *Trifolium campestre* (HOP CLOVER)

20b Ti subterraneum
3-4 flowers in a head

20′ Heads with less than 20 flowers .*(about 10)*......................
.... *Trifolium dubium* (LITTLE HOP CLOVER)
19′ Corolla pink or purple *or white in T. repens*
21. Peduncle obviously hairy near inflorescence
22. Leaflets longer than broad, deeply notched at tip ......
Trifolium bifidum var. *bifidum* (NOTCH-LEAVED CLOVER)
22′ Leaflets about as long as broad, shallowly
notched at tip ....
... *Trifolium bifidum* var. *decipiens* (DECEPTIVE CLOVER)
21′ Peduncle not obviously hairy but may have a few hairs
23. Calyx lobe edges with bristles ....

23b. Ti repens
corolla white

.... *Trifolium ciliolatum* (TREE CLOVER)
23′ Calyx lobe edges without bristles ....
.... *Trifolium gracilentum* (PINPOINT CLOVER)
18′ Flowers not reflexed in age
24. Inflorescence immediately located above the leaf and
stipule .... *Trifolium hirtum* (ROSE CLOVER)
24′ Inflorescence on a peduncle ....
.... *Trifolium albopurpureum* (COMMON INDIAN CLOVER)
1′ Mature leaves pinnately compound, leaflets usually more than 3
25. Leaves odd-pinnately compound, terminated by a leaflet;
stems erect to prostrate, not conspicuously twining, vine-like or climbing
26. Inflorescence a raceme ....
.... *Astragalus gambelianus* (GAMBELL'S DWARF LOCOWEED)
26′ Inflorescence an umbel or axillary
27. Inflorescence an umbel .... *Lotus corniculatus* (BIRDFOOT TREFOIL)
27′ Inflorescence axillary with 1–3 flowers
28. Corolla yellow
29. Calyx lobes 1–2 times longer than the tube ....
.... *Lotus humistratus* (SHORT-PODDED TREFOIL)
29′ Calyx lobes usually less than 1 time as long as the tube ....
.... *Lotus wrangelianus* (CHILE TREFOIL)
28′ Corolla pink to cream or white
30. Plant hairy; leaflets generally 3 ....
.... *Lotus purshianus*[2] (SPANISH CLOVER)
30′ Plant glabrous or sparsely hairy; leaflets 3–4 ....
.... *Lotus micranthus* (SMALL-FLOWERED TREFOIL)

25′ Leaves even-pinnately compound, terminated by a bristle or tendril; stems often vine-like, twining or climbing

    31. Stigma hairy on one side .... *still present on fruit* .... *Lathyrus vestitus* (COMMON PACIFIC PEA/HILLSIDE PEA)

    31′ Stigma hairy all around tip *still present on fruit*

        32. Inflorescence with usually more than 10 flowers .... *Vicia benghalensis* (PURPLE VETCH)

        32′ Inflorescence usually with less than 10 flowers

           33. Inflorescence on an elongated peduncle *3-10 flowers* .... *Vicia americana* (AMERICAN VETCH)

           33′ Inflorescence sessile, *1-2 flowers (axillary)*

                34. Calyx less than 1 cm; corolla less than 2 cm .... *Vicia sativa.* ssp. *nigra* (NARROW-LEAVED VETCH)

                34′ Calyx longer than 1 cm; corolla longer than 2 cm .... *Vicia sativa* ssp. *sativa* (COMMON VETCH/SPRING VETCH)

[handwritten margin note: wings nearly free from keel; base of each wing with crescent-shaped ridge]

[handwritten margin note: Vicia = wings at least partly joined to keel; wings without ridge at base]

Acacia baileyana F. Muell.

BAILEY ACACIA / COOTAMUNDRA WATTLE

Nonnative / Australia

Flowering Time: March–May

Habitat: grassland, disturbed areas

Description: Evergreen tree to 6 m. Leaves alternate, compound, 2-pinnate to 7 cm, gray-green. Inflorescence an axillary raceme of 8–10 heads. Flowers regular. Sepals and petals inconspicuous; what you see are the many exserted bright yellow stamens. Fruit a pod to 10 cm, brown.

Genus & Specific Name Derivation: Greek: sharp point / for L. H. Bailey 1858–1954, eminent horticulturist and author

Notes: Flowers in this genus are regular unlike most others in the legume (pea) family which typically have irregular sweet-pea-shaped flowers. If you look closely you can find at the base of each flower the lobes of the sepals and petals.

Uses Past and Present: Acacia flowers are a source of high-grade honey.

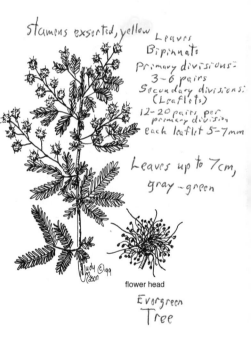

[handwritten labels: Stamens exserted, yellow; Leaves Bipinnate Primary divisions: 3-6 pairs Secondary divisions: (Leaflets) 12-20 pairs per primary division each leaflet 5-7mm; Leaves up to 7cm, gray-green]

flower head

[handwritten: Evergreen Tree]

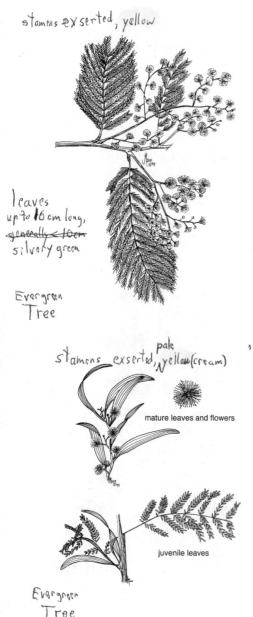

stamens exserted, yellow

leaves
up to 16 cm long,
generally < 10cm
silvery green

Evergreen
Tree

stamens exserted, pak
yellow (cream)

mature leaves and flowers

juvenile leaves

Evergreen
Tree

Acacia dealbata Lin

SILVER WATTLE   Nonnative / Australia

Flowering Time: February–March

Habitat: woodland, disturbed areas

Description: Evergreen tree to 12 m. Leaves alternate, compound, 2-pinnate to 16 cm, silvery-hairy. Inflorescence an axillary raceme or panicle of 25–30 heads. Flowers regular. Sepals and petals inconspicuous; what you see are the many exserted bright yellow stamens. Fruit a pod to 8 cm, light purplish-brown.

Genus & Specific Name Derivation: Greek: sharp point / with a white powdery covering, referring to the stems or leaves

Notes: See *A. baileyana.*

Uses Past and Present: See *A. baileyana.*

Acacia melanoxylon R. Br.

BLACKWOOD ACACIA   Nonnative / Australia

Flowering Time: February–March

Habitat: woodland, disturbed areas

Description: Evergreen tree to 15 m. Leaves of two kinds: juvenile (on seedlings and young branches) compound, 2-pinnate; adult leaves alternate, simple to 15 cm, with 4 prominent parallel veins from base, margin entire. Inflorescence an axillary raceme of 2–8 heads. Flowers regular. Sepals and petals inconspicuous; what you see are the many exserted bright yellow stamens. Fruit a pod to 12 cm, brown, curved or twisted in age.

Genus & Specific Name Derivation: Greek: sharp point / blackwooded, referring to the color of the wood

Notes: See *A. baileyana.*

Uses Past and Present: See *A. baileyana.*

√ *Astragalus gambelianus* E. Sheldon

GAMBELL'S DWARF LOCOWEED   Native

Flowering Time: March–April

Habitat: grassland

Description: Small, hairy annual to 12 cm; sometimes branched at the base. Leaves alternate, compound, 1-pinnate; blade to 4 cm; stipules green with scarious margin; leaflets to 5 mm. Inflorescence a raceme to 5 mm in flower, to 1 cm in fruit; peduncle to 3 cm; flowers minute, pale blue; pedicel minute. Fruit a legume to 4 mm, curving downward, hairy.

Genus & Specific Name Derivation: Greek: anklebone or dice, from the rattling of seeds within fruit / for W. Gambel (1821–1849), an assistant curator at the National Academy of Sciences and an avid collector of western plants

Notes: Some species are known to be toxic to livestock.

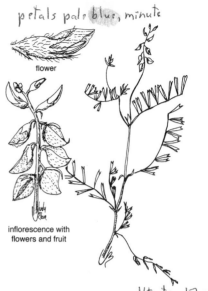

petals pale blue, minute

flower

inflorescence with flowers and fruit

Ht. to 12 cm

√ *Genista monspessulana* (L.) L. Johnson

FRENCH BROOM   Nonnative / Europe

Flowering Time: March–July

Habitat: disturbed woodland

Description: Evergreen shrub to 3 m. Leaves alternate, compound, 1-pinnate, upper surface usually glabrous, lower soft-hairy. Leaflets 3, to 15 mm. Petiole to 5 mm. Inflorescence a raceme. Flowers irregular. Sepals to 5 mm, fused, green, silky-hairy; petals to 15 mm, yellow. Stamens and pistil inserted. Fruit a legume to 20 mm, densely silky-hairy.

Genus & Specific Name Derivation: From *Planta genista,* from which English Plantagenet monarchs took their name / from Montpellier, south France

Notes: This species hybridizes with other *Genista.* Flowers and perhaps all parts toxic. Noxious weed.

Compare to Spartium junceum

petals yellow, ≤15mm

Evergreen Shrub
Ht. to 3m

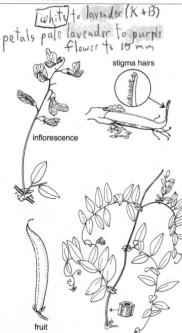

white to lavender (K+B)
petals pale lavender to purple
flower to 15 mm

stigma hairs

inflorescence

fruit

Vine

✓ *Lathyrus vestitus* Nutt. var. *vestitus*

SC
E COMMON PACIFIC PEA / HILLSIDE PEA   Native /

WOODLAND PEA

Flowering Time: March–May

Habitat: woodland

Description: Climbing herbaceous perennial; stems to 70 cm. Leaves alternate, compound, 1-pinnate; blade to 20 cm including tendril, gray-green; leaflets to 2 cm, bristle-tipped; petiole to 5 mm; stipules to 10 cm, in pairs, green. Inflorescence a raceme to 6 cm; peduncle to 7 cm; pedicel to 4 mm; flowers to 15 mm, irregular; sepals green-pink to 4 mm, densely hairy; petals pale lavender to purple, older flowers fade to yellow-brown. Fruit a legume (pod), at first hairy later becoming hairless.

Genus & Specific Name Derivation: Ancient Greek name / a coating of hairs

Notes: Tendrils are modified leaves that enable the plant to climb on surrounding vegetation. Stigma which can be seen at the end of the developing pod has hairs on one side, like a toothbrush.

Compare to Vicia americana
Photo in K&B plate 25

corolla yellow, turning to red
≤ 14 mm

inflorescence
an umbel
on peduncle to 6 cm

inflorescence

Ht. to 0.5 m

✓ *Lotus corniculatus* L.

E   BIRDFOOT TREFOIL   Nonnative / Eurasia

SC   *Flowering Time:* June–July

Habitat: grassland

Description: Herbaceous perennial, spreading to 50 cm. Leaves alternate, compound, 1-pinnate; leaflets 3–5, to 20 mm, sessile; stipules minute, gland-like. Inflorescence an umbel; peduncle to 6 cm; pedicel 1 mm; bracts leaf-like at base of the inflorescence; calyx to 7 mm; corolla to 14 mm, yellow fading red. Fruit a legume (pod) to 2 cm.

Genus & Specific Name Derivation: Greek: derivation unclear, however one reference says "from the Greek and was originally applied to a fruit which was said to make those who tasted it forget their homes" / having horn or spur-like appendages or structures

Uses Past and Present: Plant produces cyanide-releasing compounds that can be toxic.

2008 Addendum
✓ Lathyrus latifolius   PERENNIAL SWEET PEA
E   nonnative
   leaflets two, leaf ending in a tendril; flowers 2-3 cm long;
   inflorescence with several flowers; corolla purplish-pink to white;
                          5-15
   petiole below leaflets winged; stipules large, leaf-like, pronged

✓ *Lotus humistratus* E. Greene

E SHORT-PODDED TREFOIL   Native / COLCHITA

Flowering Time: May–July

Habitat: chaparral, woodland

Description: Low-growing, hairy annual. Leaves alternate, compound, 1-pinnate; leaflets 3–4, to 12 mm; stipules small, gland-like. Inflorescence axillary, usually 1 flowered; sessile; calyx to 6 mm; corolla to 9 mm, yellow. Fruit a legume to 12 mm.

Genus & Specific Name Derivation: Greek: derivation unclear, however one reference says "from the Greek and was originally applied to a fruit which was said to make those who tasted it forget their homes" / on the ground, spreading stem, referring to the growth form

Compare to *L. wrangelianus*
Photo in K & B plate 25

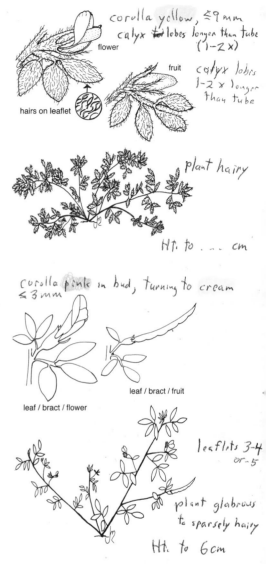

corolla yellow, ≤9 mm
calyx lobes longer than tube
(1–2 x)
flower

fruit   calyx lobes
1–2 x longer
than tube

hairs on leaflet

plant hairy

Ht. to ... cm

✗ *Lotus micranthus* Benth.

SC SMALL-FLOWERED TREFOIL   Native
E

Flowering Time: April–June

Habitat: open grassland, woodland

Description: Low-growing, spreading annual to 6 cm. Leaves alternate, compound, 1-pinnate, leaflets 3–5, to 12 mm; petiole to 1 mm; stipules small, gland-like. Inflorescence axillary, usually 1-flowered; bracts green to 3 mm; pedicel to 2 mm; flowers pink in bud then pale pink to cream; calyx green to 1 mm; corolla to 3 mm. Fruit a legume, wavy-margined.

Genus & Specific Name Derivation: Greek: derivation unclear, however one reference says "from the Greek and was originally applied to a fruit which was said to make those who tasted it forget their homes" / small-flowered

Compare to *L. purshianus*

corolla pink in bud, turning to cream
≤3 mm

leaf / bract / fruit

leaf / bract / flower

leaflets 3–4
or 5

plant glabrous
to sparsely hairy

Ht. to 6 cm

corolla pale pink to cream
≤ 6mm

bract / sepals / flower

bract / sepals / fruit

leaflets generally 3
plant hairy,
dull-colored
but not grayish

Ht: to 25 cm

petals yellow, turning to red
≤ 11 mm

shrub
Ht: to 0.5 m

√
E
SC
Lotus purshianus (Benth.) Clements & E. G. Clements var. *purshianus*

SPANISH CLOVER   Native

Flowering Time: May–June

Habitat: grassland

Description: Upright, hairy annual to 25 cm. Leaves alternate, compound, 1-pinnate to 2 cm; leaflets 3, to 10 mm, gray-green, hairy; petiole to 2 mm; stipules minute, gland-like. Inflorescence axillary, usually 1-flowered; bracts 1, leaflike to 1 cm; calyx to 7 mm, fused, lobes linear, hairy; corolla to 6 mm, pale pink to cream. Fruit a legume to 2.5 cm, without hairs.

Genus & Specific Name Derivation: Greek: derivation unclear, however one reference says "from the Greek and was originally applied to a fruit which was said to make those who tasted it forget their homes" / for F. T. Pursh (1774–1820), from Philadelphia, author of *Flora Americae Septentrionalis*

Compare to L. micranthus
Photo in K & B plate 25

√
E
SC
Lotus scoparius (Nutt.) Ottley var. *scoparius*

CALIFORNIA BROOM / DEERWEED   Native

Flowering Time: May–October

Habitat: chaparral, open woodland

Description: Deciduous shrub to 5 dm, with slender, green, branching stems. Leaves alternate, compound, 1-pinnate. Leaflets 3–6, to 15 mm. Inflorescence a cluster of 2–7 flowers. Flowers irregular. Sepals fused; petals to 11 mm, yellow fading red. Fruit a legume to 2 cm, curved.

Genus & Specific Name Derivation: Greek: derivation unclear, however one reference says "from the Greek and was originally applied to a fruit which was said to make those who tasted it forget their homes" / broom-like

Notes: Stems green, broom-like in spring and summer; plant looks dead in the winter. It survives in hot summer climate by shedding leaves; the green branches carry on photosynthesis. Illustration from *Illustrated Flora of the Pacific States.*

Uses Past and Present: Twigs used for making brushes. Flowers produce nectar that is favored by bees.

photo in K & B plate 25

√ *Lotus wrangelianus* Fischer & C. Meyer

E
SC CHILE TREFOIL   Native / *CALIF. LOTUS*

Flowering Time: April–July

Habitat: grassland

Description: Spreading annual to 15 cm. Leaves alternate, compound, 1-pinnate; leaflets 4–5, to 6 mm; sessile; stipules minute, gland-like, sometimes 0. Inflorescence axillary; calyx to 5 mm, fused, green; corolla to 9 mm, yellow; sessile. Fruit a legume (pod) to 10 mm.

Genus & Specific Name Derivation: Greek: derivation unclear, however one reference says "from the Greek and was originally applied to a fruit which was said to make those who tasted it forget their homes" / derivation unknown

Compare to L. humistratus

Photo in K & B plate 25

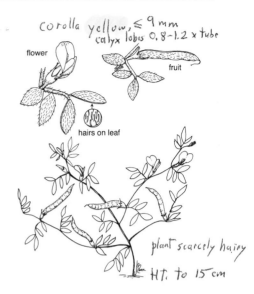

corolla yellow, ≤ 9 mm
calyx lobes 0.8-1.2 x tube
flower
fruit
hairs on leaf
plant scarcely hairy
Ht. to 15 cm

√ *Lupinus albifrons* Benth. var. *albifrons*

E
SC SILVER BUSH LUPINE   Native

Flowering Time: March–May

Habitat: open chaparral, edge of grassland

Description: Deciduous, silver-hairy shrub to 5 m. Leaves alternate, palmately compound, both surfaces hairy. Leaflets 6–10, to 45 mm. Petiole to 5 cm; stipules to 20 mm. Inflorescence a tall spike-like raceme, to 30 cm. Flowers irregular; pedicel to 10 mm; bracts to 15 mm, deciduous. Sepals to 8 mm, fused; corolla to 16 mm, violet to lavender with yellow. Fruit a legume to 5 cm, hairy.

Genus & Specific Name Derivation: Latin: wolf, from mistaken idea that plants rob the soil of nutrients / white leaves, referring to the hairs on the leaves

Notes: Whole plant silver-hairy. Flowers fragrant. This genus has an alkaloid that can be toxic to livestock especially in the seeds, fruits and young herbage. Plants have nitrogen-fixing nodules on their roots that help enrich the soil. Illustration from *Illustrated Flora of the Pacific States*.

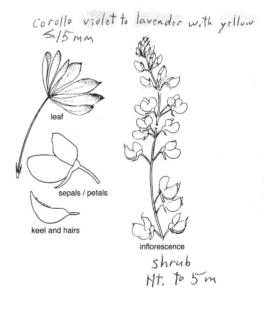

corolla violet to lavender with yellow ≤ 15 mm
leaf
sepals / petals
keel and hairs
inflorescence
shrub Ht. to 5 m

Photo in K & B plate 26

corolla blue and white ≤10mm

Lupinus bicolor Lindley

E
SC
MINIATURE LUPINE / BICOLOR LUPINE   Native

Flowering Time: March–May

Habitat: grassland

Description: Annual to 20 cm. Leaves alternate, palmately compound; petiole to 7 cm; leaflets 5–7, to 3 cm, soft-hairy. Inflorescence to 8 cm, flowers whorled; peduncle to 9 cm; flowers sessile; calyx to 3 mm; corolla to 10 mm, blue and white. Fruit a legume to 3 cm, hairy.

Genus & Specific Name Derivation: Latin: wolf, from mistaken idea that plants rob the soil of nutrients / two colors, referring to the petal colors

Notes: Banner spot white, becoming magenta after pollinated. See *L. albifrons*.

fruit

flower

leaves, flowers, and entire plant small

HT. to 20 cm

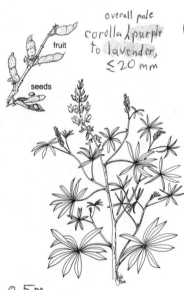

overall pale

corolla purple to lavender, ≤ 20 mm

fruit

seeds

Lupinus formosus E. Greene var. *formosus*

E
SUMMER LUPINE   Native

Flowering Time: May–July

Habitat: grassland

Description: Herbaceous perennial to 5 dm, densely hairy. Leaves alternate, palmately compound; petiole to 5 cm; stipules 1 pair at base of petiole; leaflets to 5 cm. Inflorescence a raceme to 20 cm; flowers mostly whorled; pedicel to 7 mm; bracts to 5 mm, deciduous; calyx to 14 mm, fused, hairy; corolla to 2 cm, purple to lavender. Fruit a legume to 5 cm, hairy.

Genus & Specific Name Derivation: Latin: wolf, from mistaken idea that plants rob the soil of nutrients / beautiful, well formed

Notes: See *L. albifrons*.

HT. to 0.5m

√ *Lupinus microcarpus* Sims
E var. *densiflorus* (Benth.) Jepson
CHICK LUPINE   Native

Flowering Time: April–August

Habitat: grassland

Description: Annual to 8 dm, densely to sparsely hairy. Leaves opposite, palmately compound; petiole to 15 cm; leaflets to 5 cm, lower surface hairy. Inflorescence to 30 cm; flowers whorled; pedicel to 5 mm; calyx to 10 mm, fused; corolla to 18 mm, pale to dark yellow. Fruit a legume to 1.5 cm.

Genus & Specific Name Derivation: Latin: wolf, from mistaken idea that plants rob the soil of nutrients / small fruit / densely flowered

Notes: Fruit migrates to one side of the stem when mature. See *L. albifrons*.

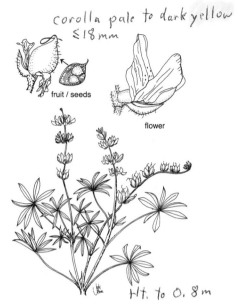

corolla pale to dark yellow ≤18mm

fruit / seeds

flower

Ht. to 0.8m

√ *Lupinus succulentus* Koch
E ARROYO LUPINE   Native
SC
Flowering Time: April–June

Habitat: chaparral, grassland

Description: Annual that can appear to be a herbaceous perennial to 10 dm. Leaves alternate, palmately compound; leaflets to 6 cm; petiole to 15 cm; bracts to 5 mm, deciduous. Inflorescence to 15 cm; flowers whorled; pedicels to 7 mm; stipules 2, linear; calyx to 5 mm, fused; corolla to 18 mm, banner purple, center white to pink with purple dots, wings purple, keel white with purple tip. Fruit a legume to 5 cm.

Genus & Specific Name Derivation: Latin: wolf, from mistaken idea that plants rob the soil of nutrients / fleshy, succulent, referring to the texture of the plant

Notes: See *L. albifrons*.

Photo in K & B plate 26

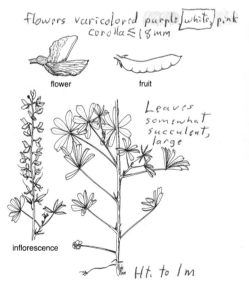

flowers varicolored purple/white/pink
corolla ≤18mm

flower

fruit

Leaves somewhat succulent, large

inflorescence

Ht. to 1m

Genus Medicago= Leaves pinnate with three leaflets but not strictly trifoliate

corolla yellow, usually <3mm

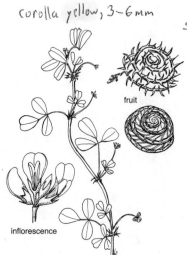

inflorescence

fruit

Ht. to 30cm

Medicago lupulina L.

BLACK MEDICK   Nonnative / Europe

Flowering Time: June–July

Habitat: woodland, disturbed areas

Description: Annual to 30 cm, whole plant hairy, glandular. Leaves alternate, compound, 1-pinnate; leaflets 3, to 2 cm, margin lobed to toothed; stipules to 7 mm. Inflorescence a head-like cluster to 4 cm with 5–20 flowers; corolla to 3 mm, yellow; calyx to 1 mm, fused. Fruit a legume to 2.5 mm, curved to almost coiled at tip, turning black in age.

Genus & Specific Name Derivation: Medea, source of alfalfa, which then bore Greek name Medice / hop-like

corolla yellow, 3~6mm

fruit

inflorescence

Ht. to 25 cm

√ ## *Medicago polymorpha* L.

SC
E BURCLOVER   Nonnative / Mediterranean

Flowering Time: March–July

Habitat: grassland, disturbed areas

Description: Mat-forming annual to 25 cm. Leaves alternate, compound, 1-pinnate; leaflets 3, to 11 mm, heart shaped, notched at the tip, margin toothed; petiole to 20 mm; stipules deeply cut. Inflorescence a head-like cluster of 3–4 flowers; corolla to 6 mm, yellow; calyx to 2 mm, fused. Fruit a legume, coiled with or without prickles.

Genus & Specific Name Derivation: Medea, source of alfalfa, which then bore Greek name Medice / variable

2008 Addendum

√ Medicago arabica   SPOTTED BURCLOVER
E   nonnative
in Day-camp lawn   each leaflets with centrally-located
dark spot

Medicago sativa L.

ALFALFA   Nonnative / Eurasia

Flowering Time: May–June

Habitat: grassland, disturbed areas

Description: Upright to trailing annual to 50 cm. Leaves alternate, compound, 1-pinnate to 3 cm; leaflets 3, to 1.5 cm, margin toothed; petiole to 1 cm; stipules 8 mm, toothed, whitish, tip pointed. Inflorescence a raceme to 3 cm with 8–25 flowers; bracts to 2 mm, linear, whitish-yellow; calyx to 3 mm; corolla to 1 cm, purple, blue, lower whitish. Fruit a legume, short, coiled, hairy.

Genus & Specific Name Derivation: Medea, source of alfalfa, which then bore Greek name Medice / cultivated, not wild

Uses Past and Present: Alfalfa has been cultivated for over 2,000 years as a forage plant. The name alfalfa comes from Arabic meaning "father of all foods" because of its many uses. The leaves are rich in vitamins A, K, and D, and protein. The herb is used as a nutritional tea, helpful in inflammation and recuperation from illness.

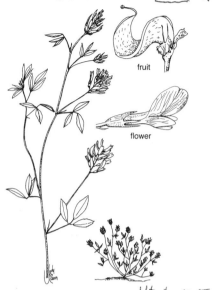

corolla purple or blue, with white ≤ 10 mm

fruit

flower

Ht. to 0.5 m

Genus *Melilotus*: Leaves like those of *Medicago*

✓ *Melilotus indicus* (L.) All.

SC
E

INDIAN MELILOT / SOURCLOVER

Nonnative / Mediterranean

Flowering Time: April–June

Habitat: grassland

Description: Upright annual to 6 dm. Leaves alternate, compound, 1-pinnate; leaflets 3, to 1 cm, margin toothed; petiole to 4 cm; stipules to 4 mm. Inflorescence a raceme to 2 cm in flower; flowers reflexing in age; calyx to 1 mm, fused; corolla to 2 mm, yellow. Fruit a legume to 3 mm, glabrous, with bumps.

Genus & Specific Name Derivation: Greek: honey-lotus / from India or the orient

Notes: Can be toxic when bundled with hay which enhances production of mold toxins that may cause cattle death from hemorrhaging. New name accepted by *Jepson Manual* staff, name in *The Jepson Manual* (1993 *Melilotus indica*.

Uses Past and Present: An important honey plant to beekeepers.

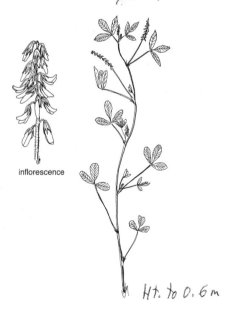

corolla yellow, ≤ 2 mm

inflorescence

Ht. to 0.6 m

Photo in K & B plate 26

petals rose to purple

Evergreen shrub Ht. to 3 m

√ **Pickeringia montana** Nutt. var. *montana*

E CHAPARRAL PEA Native

Flowering Time: May–July

Habitat: chaparral

Description: Evergreen shrub to 3 m, with spiny branch tips. Leaves alternate, compound, 1-pinnate. Leaflets 1–3, to 2 cm. Inflorescence a raceme. Flowers irregular. Sepals to 7 mm, fused, barely lobed; petals to 2 cm, rose to purple. Fruit a legume to 6 cm.

Genus & Specific Name Derivation: Named for C. Pickering (1805–1875), an American naturalist / of the mountains

Notes: Many of our plants at Edgewood are very old. Regeneration of new plants seems to occur after disturbance. This is easily seen along the Clarkia Trail after the brush has been cut back during trail maintenance. The chaparral pea seldom sets viable seeds.

Photo in K & B plate 26

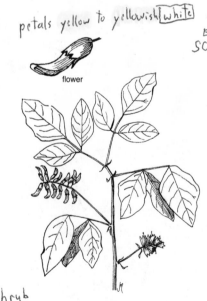

petals yellow to yellowish white

flower

shrub Ht. to 0.5 m

√ **Rupertia physodes** (Hook.) Grimes

E
SC CALIFORNIA TEA Native

Flowering Time: March–July

Habitat: open chaparral and woodland

Description: Deciduous trailing or low-growing shrub to 5 dm. Leaves alternate, compound, 1-pinnate. Leaflets 3, to 7 mm. Petiole to 4 cm; stipules to 10 mm. Inflorescence a raceme; bract to 7 mm, deciduous. Flower irregular. Sepals to 8 mm, fused; petals to 14 mm, yellow to yellowish-white. Fruit a legume to 7 mm, golden-red when mature.

Genus & Specific Name Derivation: Named for botanist Rupert C. Barneby / puffed out, inflated-looking, referring to the fruit

Notes: Leaves when crushed produce a strong resinous scent from the oil glands on the foliage.

Uses Past and Present: The leaves were dried and used as a tea, also an antispasmodic for cramps.

Photo in K & B plate 27

√ *Spartium junceum* L.

SPANISH BROOM Nonnative / Europe

Flowering Time: April–June

Habitat: disturbed areas in woodland

Description: Shrub to 3 m, often with green leafless branches. Leaves alternate to opposite, simple, entire, almost sessile, often falling from the stems so that the stems appear green and leafless. Leaves to 2.5 cm, linear, lower surface hairy. Inflorescence an open raceme. Flowers irregular, fragrant; sepals united, split to base; petals bright yellow. Fruit a pod to 10 cm, hairy.

Genus & Specific Name Derivation: Greek: ancient name meaning broom / rush-like, referring to the naked stems

Notes: Some plants still near the Day Camp.

Uses Past and Present: Brooms were made of one of these species, thus the common name.

Compare to Genista monspessulana Photo in K + B plate 27

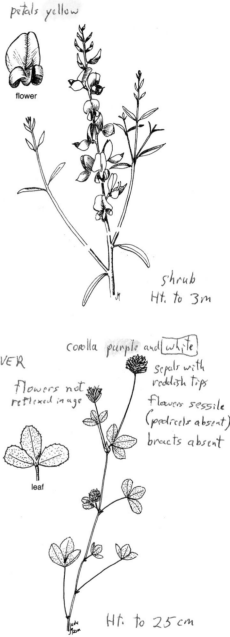

petals yellow

flower

shrub
Ht. to 3m

Trifolium albopurpureum Torrey & A. Gray
var. *albopurpureum*

COMMON INDIAN CLOVER Native / RANCHERIA CLOVER

Flowering Time: April–June

Habitat: grassland, woodland

Description: Hairy annual to 25 cm. Leaves alternate, compound, 1-pinnate; petiole to 5 cm; leaflets 3, soft-hairy, margin toothed. Inflorescence head-like; calyx to 15 mm, lobed, green with reddish tips; corolla to 6 mm, two-colored purple and white. Fruit a short legume-like pod.

Genus & Specific Name Derivation: Latin: 3 leaflets / white purple

Uses Past and Present: Many of the native *Trifoliums* were an important dietary staple to the natives who ate the young leaves and seeds, both raw and cooked. Some tribes celebrated the spring appearance of the clover with special ceremonial dances.

corolla purple and white
sepals with reddish tips
flowers sessile (pedicels absent)
bracts absent

flowers not reflexed in age

leaf

Ht. to 25 cm

Genus Trifolium: Leaves mostly trifoliate, the three leaflets meeting at a point. However, in some species, such as T. campestre and T. dubium, the leaves are pinnate, as in Medicago and Melilotus.

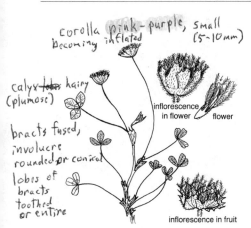

corolla pink-purple, small becoming inflated (5-10 mm)

calyx lobes hairy (plumose)

bracts fused, involucre rounded or conical

lobes of bracts toothed or entire

inflorescence in flower

flower

inflorescence in fruit

Ht. to 20 cm

Trifolium barbigerum Torrey var. *barbigerum*

BEARDED CLOVER   Native

Flowering Time: March–June

Habitat: grassland

Description: Annual to 20 cm. Leaves alternate, compound, 1-pinnate; leaflets 3, to 2.5 cm; stipules conspicuous. Inflorescence head-like, bristly; calyx to 8 mm, plumose; corolla to 10 mm, pink-purple. Fruit a short legume-like pod.

Genus & Specific Name Derivation: Latin: 3 leaflets / bearded, referring to the hairs on the sepal lobes

Uses Past and Present: See *T. albopurpureum.*

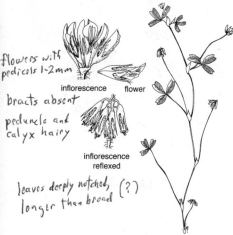

corolla pink-purple, ≤ 9 mm

flowers with pedicels 1-2 mm

inflorescence

flower

bracts absent

peduncle and calyx hairy

inflorescence reflexed

leaves deeply notched, longer than broad (?)

Ht. to 25 cm

Trifolium bifidum A. Gray var. *bifidum*

NOTCH-LEAVED CLOVER   Native / PINOLE CLOVER

Flowering Time: April–May

Habitat: grassland, woodland

Description: Annual to 25 cm. Leaves alternate, compound, 1-pinnate; leaflets 3, to 3 cm, 2–5 times longer than wide. Inflorescence head-like; flowers becoming reflexed; calyx to 5 mm, bristle-tipped; corolla to 9 mm, pink-purple. Fruit a short legume-like pod.

Genus & Specific Name Derivation: Latin: 3 leaflets / deeply two-cleft, referring to the notch in the leaflets

Uses Past and Present: See *T. albopurpureum.*

Compare to T. b. var. decipiens
   also to T. ciliolatum and T. gracilentum

The two subspecies of T. bifidum are not
distinguished in K&B

✗ *Trifolium bifidum* A. Gray var. *decipiens* E. Greene

⅏ DECEPTIVE CLOVER   Native

Flowering Time: April–May

Habitat: grassland, woodland

Description: Annual to 25 cm. Leaves alternate, compound, 1-pinnate; leaflets 3, to 2 cm, 1–5 times longer that wide. Inflorescence head-like; flowers becoming reflexed; calyx to 5 mm, bristle-tipped; corolla to 9 mm, pink-purple. Fruit a short legume-like pod.

Genus & Specific Name Derivation: Latin: 3 leaflets / deeply two-cleft, referring to the notch in the leaflets / deceptive

Uses Past and Present: See *T. albopurpureum.*

Compare to T. b. var. bifidum

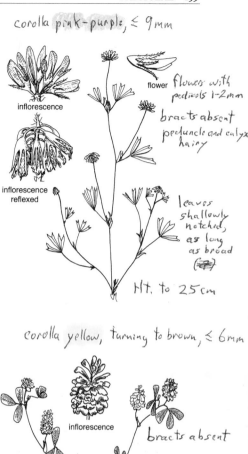

corolla pink-purple, ≤ 9 mm

flower

inflorescence

inflorescence reflexed

flowers with pedicels 1-2mm

bracts absent

peduncle and calyx hairy

leaves shallowly notched, as long as broad

Ht. to 25 cm

✓ *Trifolium campestre* Schreber

⅏ HOP CLOVER   Nonnative / Europe

Flowering Time: May–June

Habitat: grassland

Description: Annual to 15 cm. Leaves alternate, compound, 1-pinnate; leaflets 3, to 1.5 cm. Inflorescence head-like; calyx to 2 mm; corolla to 6 mm, bright yellow, becoming brown. Fruit a short legume-like pod.

Genus & Specific Name Derivation: Latin: 3 leaflets / from the pasture

Uses Past and Present: See *T. albopurpureum.*

Compare to T. dubium

Not in K + B

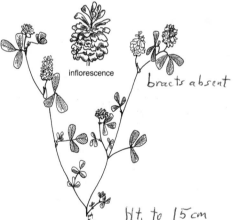

corolla yellow, turning to brown, ≤ 6mm

inflorescence

bracts absent

Ht. to 15 cm

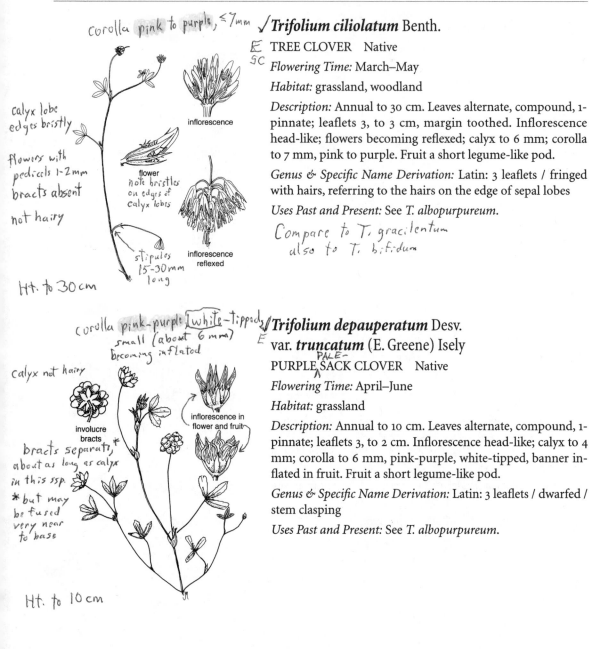

corolla pink to purple, ≤ 7mm

calyx lobe edges bristly

flowers with pedicels 1-2mm

bracts absent

not hairy

inflorescence

flower
note bristles on edges of calyx lobes

stipules 15-30mm long

inflorescence reflexed

Ht. to 30 cm

corolla pink-purple [white-tipped] small (about 6 mm) becoming inflated

calyx not hairy

involucre bracts

bracts separate, about as long as calyx in this ssp.
* but may be fused very near to base

inflorescence in flower and fruit

Ht. to 10 cm

Trifolium ciliolatum Benth.

E
GC
TREE CLOVER   Native

Flowering Time: March–May

Habitat: grassland, woodland

Description: Annual to 30 cm. Leaves alternate, compound, 1-pinnate; leaflets 3, to 3 cm, margin toothed. Inflorescence head-like; flowers becoming reflexed; calyx to 6 mm; corolla to 7 mm, pink to purple. Fruit a short legume-like pod.

Genus & Specific Name Derivation: Latin: 3 leaflets / fringed with hairs, referring to the hairs on the edge of sepal lobes

Uses Past and Present: See *T. albopurpureum.*

Compare to T. gracilentum
also to T. bifidum

Trifolium depauperatum Desv. var. *truncatum* (E. Greene) Isely

E
PURPLE SACK CLOVER   Native
PALE-

Flowering Time: April–June

Habitat: grassland

Description: Annual to 10 cm. Leaves alternate, compound, 1-pinnate; leaflets 3, to 2 cm. Inflorescence head-like; calyx to 4 mm; corolla to 6 mm, pink-purple, white-tipped, banner inflated in fruit. Fruit a short legume-like pod.

Genus & Specific Name Derivation: Latin: 3 leaflets / dwarfed / stem clasping

Uses Past and Present: See *T. albopurpureum.*

✓ *Trifolium dubium* Sibth.

ₑ LITTLE HOP CLOVER Nonnative / Europe /SHAMROCK

Flowering Time: April–May

Habitat: grassland

Description: Annual to 15 cm. Leaves alternate, compound, 1-pinnate; leaflets 3, to 1 cm. Inflorescence head-like; flowers becoming reflexed; calyx to 2 mm; corolla to 4 mm, bright yellow, becoming brown. Fruit a short legume-like pod.

Genus & Specific Name Derivation: Latin: 3 leaflets / uncertain, doubtful

Uses Past and Present: See *T. albopurpureum.*

Compare to T. campestre

✓ *Trifolium fucatum* Lindley

ₑ SOUR CLOVER Native / BULL CLOVER

Flowering Time: March–May

Habitat: grassland

Description: Annual to 30 cm. Leaves alternate, compound, 1-pinnate; leaflets 3, to 2.5 cm. Inflorescence head-like; calyx to 7 mm; corolla to 20 mm, dull white to yellowish, banner inflated in fruit. Fruit a short legume-like pod.

Genus & Specific Name Derivation: Latin: 3 leaflets / painted

Uses Past and Present: See *T. albopurpureum.*

Photo in K & B plate 27

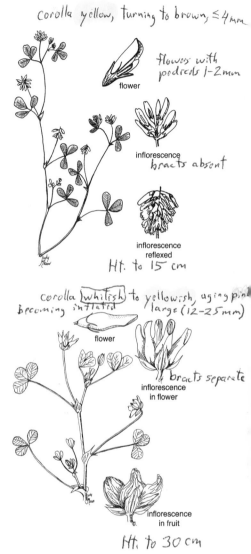

corolla yellow, turning to brown, ≤ 4 mm

flowers with pedicels 1–2 mm

flower

inflorescence
bracts absent

inflorescence
reflexed

Ht. to 15 cm

corolla whitish to yellowish, aging pink becoming inflated / large (12–25 mm)

flower

bracts separate
inflorescence
in flower

inflorescence
in fruit

Ht. to 30 cm

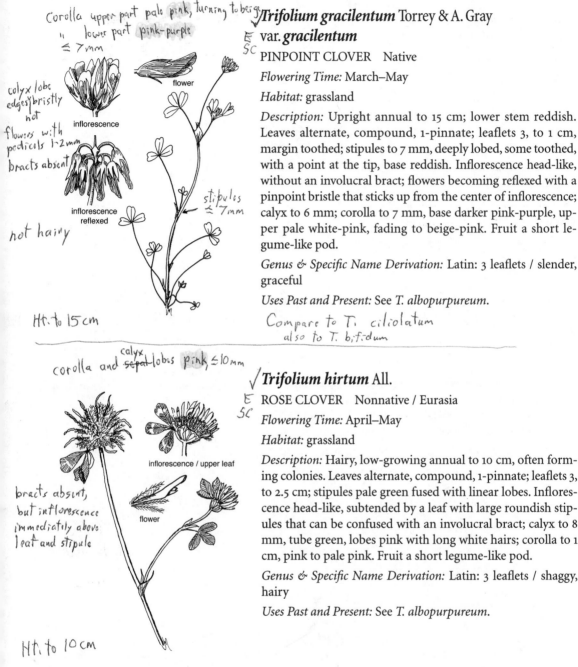

Corolla upper part pale pink, turning to beige
" lower part pink-purple
≤ 7mm

calyx lobe edges bristly not

flowers with pedicels 1-2mm
bracts absent

flower

inflorescence

inflorescence reflexed

not hairy

stipules ≤ 7mm

Ht. to 15cm

Trifolium gracilentum Torrey & A. Gray
var. *gracilentum*

E
SC

PINPOINT CLOVER   Native

Flowering Time: March–May

Habitat: grassland

Description: Upright annual to 15 cm; lower stem reddish. Leaves alternate, compound, 1-pinnate; leaflets 3, to 1 cm, margin toothed; stipules to 7 mm, deeply lobed, some toothed, with a point at the tip, base reddish. Inflorescence head-like, without an involucral bract; flowers becoming reflexed with a pinpoint bristle that sticks up from the center of inflorescence; calyx to 6 mm; corolla to 7 mm, base darker pink-purple, upper pale white-pink, fading to beige-pink. Fruit a short legume-like pod.

Genus & Specific Name Derivation: Latin: 3 leaflets / slender, graceful

Uses Past and Present: See *T. albopurpureum.*

Compare to T. ciliolatum
also to T. bifidum

corolla and calyx ~~sepal~~ lobes pink ≤ 10mm

inflorescence / upper leaf

flower

bracts absent, but inflorescence immediately above leaf and stipule

Ht. to 10 cm

Trifolium hirtum All.

E
SC

ROSE CLOVER   Nonnative / Eurasia

Flowering Time: April–May

Habitat: grassland

Description: Hairy, low-growing annual to 10 cm, often forming colonies. Leaves alternate, compound, 1-pinnate; leaflets 3, to 2.5 cm; stipules pale green fused with linear lobes. Inflorescence head-like, subtended by a leaf with large roundish stipules that can be confused with an involucral bract; calyx to 8 mm, tube green, lobes pink with long white hairs; corolla to 1 cm, pink to pale pink. Fruit a short legume-like pod.

Genus & Specific Name Derivation: Latin: 3 leaflets / shaggy, hairy

Uses Past and Present: See *T. albopurpureum.*

✓ *Trifolium microcephalum* Pursh

SC   SMALL-HEADED CLOVER   Native

Flowering Time: April–June

Habitat: grassland, woodland

Description: Annual to 15 cm. Leaves alternate, compound, 1-pinnate; leaflets 3, to 2 cm. Inflorescence head-like; calyx to 6 mm, bristle-tipped; corolla to 7 mm, pink to lavender. Fruit a short legume-like pod.

Genus & Specific Name Derivation: Latin: 3 leaflets / small flower heads

Uses Past and Present: See *T. albopurpureum.*

Compare to T. microdon

Photo in K & B plate 27

✓ *Trifolium microdon* Hook. & Arn.

E   VALPARAISO CLOVER / CUP CLOVER   Native

Flowering Time: March–July

Habitat: grassland, woodland

Description: Annual to 15 cm. Leaves alternate, compound, 1-pinnate; leaflets 3, to 1.5 cm. Inflorescence head-like; calyx 3 mm; corolla to 6 mm, white to pink. Fruit a short legume-like pod.

Genus & Specific Name Derivation: Latin: 3 leaflets / small-toothed

Uses Past and Present: See *T. albopurpureum.*

Compare to T. microcephalum

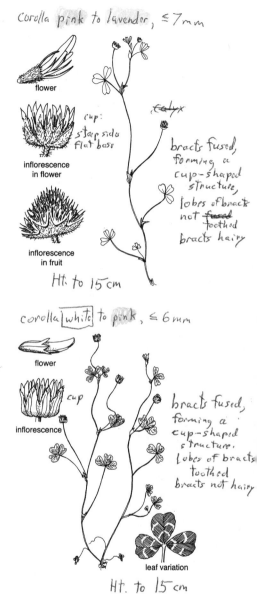

Corolla pink to lavender, ≤7mm

flower

cup:
stop side
flat base

inflorescence
in flower

calyx

bracts fused,
forming a
cup-shaped
structure,
lobes of bracts
not fused
toothed
bracts hairy

inflorescence
in fruit

Ht. to 15 cm

corolla white to pink, ≤6mm

flower

cup

inflorescence

bracts fused,
forming a
cup-shaped
structure,
lobes of bracts
toothed
bracts not hairy

leaf variation

Ht. to 15 cm

2008 Addendums.

✓ Tritolium repens   WHITE CLOVER nonnative
E, SC   in day-camp lawn   flower heads without bracts at base; flowers with pedicels, becoming reflexed; about 5 mm long
peduncle and calyx glabrous; corolla white to pinkish

. Trifolium subterraneum   SUBTERRANEAN CLOVER nonnative
flower heads without bracts at base; pedicels 1-2 mm long;
corolla yellow to white; flowers 8-12 mm long, 3-4 in a head;
petioles 2-10 cm long; sterile flowers without corolla, forming a bur

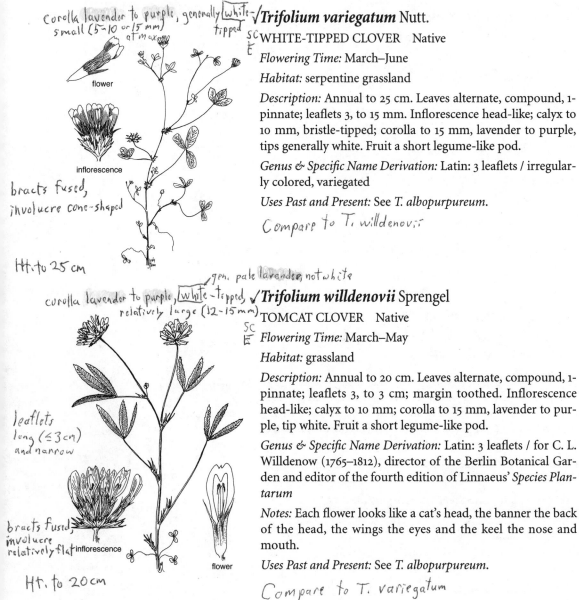

corolla lavender to purple, generally white-tipped
small (5-10 or 15 mm) at max

flower

inflorescence

bracts fused, involucre cone-shaped

Ht. to 25 cm

√*Trifolium variegatum* Nutt.

SC E WHITE-TIPPED CLOVER   Native

Flowering Time: March–June

Habitat: serpentine grassland

Description: Annual to 25 cm. Leaves alternate, compound, 1-pinnate; leaflets 3, to 15 mm. Inflorescence head-like; calyx to 10 mm, bristle-tipped; corolla to 15 mm, lavender to purple, tips generally white. Fruit a short legume-like pod.

Genus & Specific Name Derivation: Latin: 3 leaflets / irregularly colored, variegated

Uses Past and Present: See *T. albopurpureum.*

Compare to T. willdenovii

gen. pale lavender, not white

corolla lavender to purple, white-tipped
relatively large (12-15 mm)

leaflets long (≤3 cm) and narrow

bracts fused, involucre relatively flat

inflorescence

flower

Ht. to 20 cm

√*Trifolium willdenovii* Sprengel

SC E TOMCAT CLOVER   Native

Flowering Time: March–May

Habitat: grassland

Description: Annual to 20 cm. Leaves alternate, compound, 1-pinnate; leaflets 3, to 3 cm; margin toothed. Inflorescence head-like; calyx to 10 mm; corolla to 15 mm, lavender to purple, tip white. Fruit a short legume-like pod.

Genus & Specific Name Derivation: Latin: 3 leaflets / for C. L. Willdenow (1765–1812), director of the Berlin Botanical Garden and editor of the fourth edition of Linnaeus' *Species Plantarum*

Notes: Each flower looks like a cat's head, the banner the back of the head, the wings the eyes and the keel the nose and mouth.

Uses Past and Present: See *T. albopurpureum.*

Compare to T. variegatum

Photo in K & B plate 28

√ *Vicia americana* Willd. var. *americana*

SC
E
AMERICAN VETCH   Native

Flowering Time: April–May

Habitat: woodland

Description: Trailing, vine-like herbaceous perennial, branches to 3 dm; stem four-angled. Leaves alternate, compound, 1-pinnate; blades to 7 cm excluding tendrils; leaflets to 3 cm; stipules to 3 mm, in pairs, lobed and toothed. Inflorescence with 3–10 flowers in an axillary raceme; peduncle to 7 cm; corolla to 2.5 cm, banner purple with darker veins, wings and keel pale purple-white; stigma surrounded by hairs (best seen when petals fall off). Fruit a legume to 3 cm.

Genus & Specific Name Derivation: Latin: vetch / from America

Notes: Tendrils, modified leaves, enable the plant to climb on surrounding vegetation. Stigma, which can be seen at the end of the developing pod, has hairs all around the tip of the style, like a bottle brush.

Compare to Lathyrus vestitus

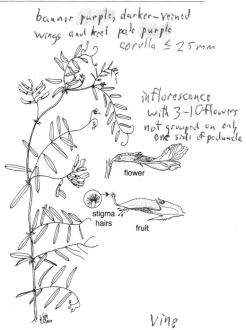

banner purple, darker-veined wings and keel pale purple corolla ≤ 25mm

inflorescence with 3–10 flowers not grouped on only one side of peduncle

flower

stigma hairs

fruit

Vine

√ *Vicia benghalensis* L.

SC PURPLE VETCH   Nonnative / Europe

Flowering Time: April–May

Habitat: grassland

Description: Trailing annual to 40 cm, whole plant soft-hairy. Leaves alternate, compound, 1-pinnate, blade to 4 cm; leaflets to 1.5 cm; stipules to 5 mm, in pairs, linear. Inflorescence with more than 10 flowers in an axillary raceme, to 6 cm including peduncle; pedicels short; calyx to 4 mm; corolla to 1.5 cm, purple-pink, tube lighter pink; stigma surrounded by hairs with hairs. Fruit a legume to 3.5 cm.

Genus & Specific Name Derivation: Latin: vetch / of Bengal, India, of uncertain application

Notes: See *V. americana.*

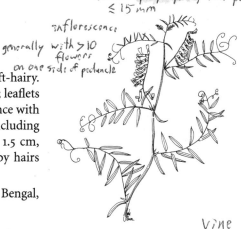

corolla purple pink, tube paler pink ≤ 15mm

inflorescence generally with >10 flowers on one side of peduncle

Vine

Corolla pink-purple to ⌊white⌋ + pink
≤ 20 mm

Vicia sativa L. ssp. *nigra* (L.) Erhart

E
SC

NARROW-LEAVED VETCH   Nonnative / Europe

Flowering Time: March–July

Habitat: grassland

Description: Upright to spreading annual to 3 dm. Leaves alternate, compound, 1-pinnate with tendrils at the tip; leaflets in 3–5 pairs, sessile often with a bristle tip; stipules in pairs. Inflorescence axillary with 1–2 flowers; calyx to 9 mm, fused and lobed; corolla to 2 cm, flower parts pink-purple to white with pink. Fruit a legume to 5 cm, turning black when mature.

Genus & Specific Name Derivation: Latin: vetch / cultivated / black, referring to the color of the mature legume

Notes: See *V. americana.*

Compare to V. s. ssp. sativa

Ht. to 0.3m

corolla pink-purple to ⌊white⌋ + pink
20–30 mm

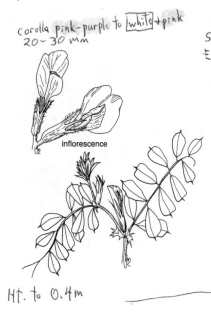

inflorescence

Ht. to 0.4m

Vicia sativa L. ssp. *sativa*

SC
E

COMMON VETCH / SPRING VETCH   Nonnative / Europe

Flowering Time: March–July

Habitat: grassland

Description: Upright to spreading annual to 4 dm. Leaves alternate, compound, 1-pinnate with tendrils at the tip; leaflets in 6–8 pairs, sessile, often with a bristle tip; stipules in pairs, green with a dark red dot in center. Inflorescence axillary with 1–2 flowers; calyx to 15 mm, fused and lobed; corolla to 3 cm, flower parts purple-pink to white with pink; sessile. Fruit a legume to 6 cm, turning dark brown to black when mature.

Genus & Specific Name Derivation: Latin: vetch / cultivated

Notes: See *V. americana.*

Compare to V. s. ssp nigra
Photo in K & B plate 28

2008 Addendum

Vicia lutea   YELLOW VETCH nonnative
not listed in either K & B or Jepson Manual

Fagaceae — Oak Family

Shrubs or trees, monoecious. Leaves alternate, simple, evergreen or deciduous. Flowers unisexual, staminate and pistillate usually in separate inflorescences; staminate flowers in catkins; pistillate flowers solitary or 2–3 per cluster. Calyx minute, with 3–6 lobes; petals absent. Staminate flowers with 4–many stamens; pistillate flowers with inferior ovary, 3–6 styles. Fruit a nut (acorn). One of the most important sources of wood in the northern hemisphere and also used for edible fruits, dyes and cork.

For key to woody plants *see* Group 2. Woody Plants

Family Characteristics

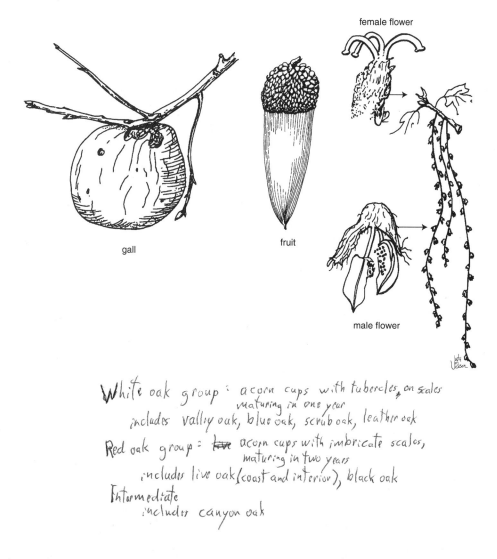

female flower

fruit

male flower

gall

White oak group: acorn cups with tubercles, on scales
          maturing in one year
     includes valley oak, blue oak, scrub oak, leather oak

Red oak group: ~~live~~ acorn cups with imbricate scales,
          maturing in two years
     includes live oak (coast and interior), black oak

Intermediate
     includes canyon oak

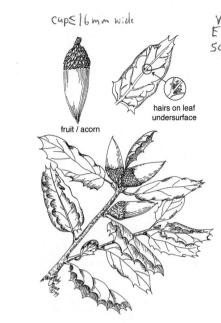

cup ≤ 16 mm wide

fruit / acorn

hairs on leaf undersurface

Evergreen Tree

√ *Quercus agrifolia* Nee var. *agrifolia*

E COAST LIVE OAK / ENCINA   Native

SC *Flowering Time:* February–April

Habitat: woodland

Description: Evergreen tree to 25 m. Leaves alternate, simple to 9 cm; upper surface dark green, lower pale green, hairy at junction of veins; leaf margin spine-tipped, most rolled under; petiole to 15 mm. Flowers unisexual, male and female flowers on the same plant (monoecious). Male inflorescence a catkin; sepals 5–6, minute, stamens 4–10. Female inflorescence axillary among upper leaves, flowers with 3 feathery, red stigmas; sepals 6-lobed. Fruit an acorn produced every year. Cup to 1.6 cm wide, scales thin, flat, brownish; nut to 3.5 cm, slender, tip pointed.

Genus & Specific Name Derivation: Latin: ancient name for oak / farming-leaf

Notes: The male flowers are in showy catkins, the female flowers are small but can be seen at the ends of new branches at the same time as the male flowers. It is the female flowers that will produce the acorn. Hybridizes with *Q. kelloggii, Q. wislizeni.*

Uses Past and Present: The acorns were ground and made into a mush or bread. Acorns of different species of oaks were one of the main substances used by natives as food. There are many sources for information about native preparation methods and uses.

√ *Quercus berberidifolia* Liebm.

SC
E
SCRUB OAK   Native

Flowering Time: March–May

Habitat: woodland, chaparral edge

Description: Evergreen large shrub to small tree to 3 m. Leaves alternate, simple to 3 cm; margin spiny to toothed, upper surface flat to wavy, shiny, green, lower surface hairy, pale green. Flowers unisexual, male and female flowers on the same plant (monoecious). Male inflorescence a long catkin, yellow from the anthers and pollen. Female flowers minute, in the axils of the leaves where the acorns will form. Fruit an acorn produced every year. Cup to 2 cm wide, scales tubercled; nut to 1 cm, ovoid.

Genus & Specific Name Derivation: Latin: ancient name for oak / derivation unknown

Notes: Identification verified by Rod Myatt, a professor at San Jose State University.

Uses Past and Present: See. *Q. agrifolia.*

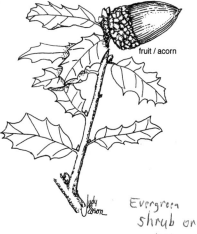

cup ≤ 20 mm wide

fruit / acorn

Evergreen shrub or small Tree Ht. to 3m

√ *Quercus douglasii* Hook. & Arn.

E
SC
BLUE OAK   Native

Flowering Time: March–May

Habitat: woodland

Description: Deciduous tree to 20 m. Leaves alternate, simple, to 8 cm; margin wavy, most slightly lobed; petiole to 9 mm. Flowers unisexual, male and female flowers on the same plant (monoecious). Male inflorescence a catkin; sepals 5–6, minute, stamens 4–10. Female inflorescence axillary among upper leaves, flowers with 3 feathery, red stigmas; sepals 6-lobed. Fruit an acorn produced every year. Cup to 2 cm wide, scales slightly warty; nut 3 cm, slender, tip pointed.

Genus & Specific Name Derivation: Latin: ancient name for oak / for David Douglas (1798–1834), collector in American northwest for the Royal Horticultural Society.

Notes: Hybridizes with *Q. lobata.* Hybrids at Edgewood between *Q. douglasii* and *Q. durata* which is very unusual.

Uses Past and Present: See *Q. agrifolia.*

cup ≤ 20 mm

fruit / acorn

Tree

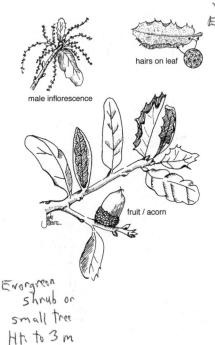

male inflorescence

hairs on leaf

fruit / acorn

Evergreen
shrub or
small tree
Ht to 3 m

√ *Quercus durata* Jepson var. *durata*

E LEATHER OAK   Native

Flowering Time: May–July

Habitat: serpentine chaparral

Description: Evergreen large shrub to small tree to 3 m. Leaves alternate, simple to 3 cm; margin spiny, rolled under; upper and lower surface with golden star-shaped hairs; petiole to 5 mm. Flowers unisexual, male and female flowers on the same plant (monoecious). Male inflorescence a long catkin, yellow from the anthers and pollen. Female flowers minute, in the axils of the leaves where the acorns will form. Fruit an acorn, matures in 1 year.

Genus & Specific Name Derivation: Latin: ancient name for the oak / hard

Notes: This is a serpentine endemic; that is it occurs only on serpentine soil. Many of our plants are very old with lichens covering the branches. They look like small trees along the Clarkia Trail. Hybridizes with *Q. berberidifolia*.

Uses Past and Present: See. *Q. agrifolia*.

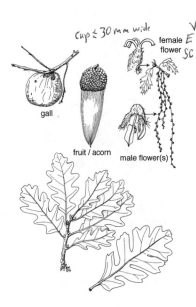

Cup ≤ 30 mm wide

female
flower   E
         SC

gall

fruit / acorn

male flower(s)

Tree

√ *Quercus lobata* Nee

VALLEY OAK / ROBLE   Native

Flowering Time: March–May

Habitat: open grassland, openings in woodland

Description: Deciduous tree to 35 m. Leaves alternate, simple to 12 cm, deeply 6–10 lobed; Petiole to 12 mm. Flowers unisexual, male and female flowers on the same plant (monoecious). Male inflorescence a catkin; sepals 5–6, minute, stamens 4–10. Female inflorescence axillary among upper leaves, flowers with 3 feathery, red stigmas; sepals 6-lobed. Fruit an acorn produced every year. Cup to 3 cm wide, scales warty; nut to 5 cm, tip pointed.

Genus & Specific Name Derivation: Latin: ancient name for oak / with lobes, referring to the leaves.

Notes: Hybridizes with *Q. berberidifolia*, *Q. douglasii*.

Uses Past and Present: See. *Q. agrifolia*.

Garryaceae — Silk Tassel Family

Shrubs or small trees, dioecious. Leaves opposite, simple, evergreen. Flowers unisexual, catkin-like. Staminate flowers in clusters; sepals 4; petals absent; stamens 4. Pistillate flowers in clusters or solitary, sepals and petals absent or sepals 2 and vestigial; ovary inferior, stigma 2-lobed. Fruit a berry; seeds 2. Leaves and bark of some species were used medicinally by natives. Some cultivated as ornamentals.

For key to woody plants *see* Group 2. Woody Plants

Garrya elliptica Lindley

COAST SILK TASSEL   Native

Flowering Time: December–April

Habitat: chaparral, woodland

Description: Evergreen large shrub or small tree to 8 m. Leaves opposite, simple, to 8 cm long, margin wavy, often rolled under, lower surface with soft hairs. Inflorescence a catkin, unisexual: male flowers longer than female flowers; stamens 4; ovary inferior, styles 2. Male and female flowers on different plants (dioecious). Fruit a berry, becoming dark in age.

Genus & Specific Name Derivation: N. Garry, first secretary of Hudson Bay Company, friend of David Douglas / about twice as long as wide, referring to the leaves

Notes: The plants in the chaparral are hard to see because they are well within the chaparral. The plants in the woodland along the Sylvan Trail are more easily seen, but they blend in with the live oaks and can easily be missed.

Uses Past and Present: Natives used leaves as a muscle relaxer and pain reliever, and for stomach cramps and diarrhea.

petals absent

Evergreen large shrub or small tree Ht. to 8 m

Gentianaceae — Gentian Family

Annuals or herbaceous perennials. Leaves opposite or whorled, simple. Inflorescence in racemes, panicles, or solitary. Flowers bisexual, regular. Sepals 4–5, fused, persistent; petals 4–5, fused; stamens 4–5; pistil 1, ovary superior, style and stigma 2-lobed. Fruit a capsule; seeds many. Some cultivated as ornamentals.

For key to families *see* Group 3. Herbaceous Flowering Plant Families

/Zeltnera m.

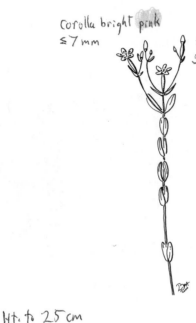

Corolla bright pink
≤ 7 mm

Ht. to 25 cm

Centaurium muehlenbergii (Griseb.) Piper

E JUNE CENTAURY   Native / *MONTEREY CENTAURY*

SC *Flowering Time:* June–August

Habitat: grassland

Description: Upright annual to 25 cm. Leaves opposite, simple to 1.5 cm, sessile. Inflorescence an open, flat-topped panicle-like cyme; calyx lobes 5, keeled; corolla bright pink, to 7 mm wide, lobes to 4 mm; flowers sessile or pedicel < 1 mm above the 2 bracts; bracts leaf-like to 3 mm. Fruit a capsule.

Genus & Specific Name Derivation: Latin: centaur, mythological discoverer of its medicinal properties / for G. H. E. Muhlenberg (1753–1851), a Lutheran minister, botanist in Pennsylvania

Notes: With a hand lens, note the twisted anthers.

Uses Past and Present: This was considered by the early Spanish settlers as a remedy for fevers.

Photo in K & B plate 29

2008 Addendum

Cicendia quadrangularis
OREGON TIMWORT native

Geraniaceae — Geranium Family

Annuals or herbaceous perennials. Leaves basal or cauline, alternate or opposite, simple or compound. Inflorescence a cyme or umbel. Flowers bisexual, regular. Sepals 5, free; petals 5, free; stamens 5 or 10; pistil 1, usually 5-lobed, ovary superior, styles and stigmas 5, fused to central axis or column. Fruit a schizocarp, 5-lobed. Style is persistent and twists at top of seed when dry. Some species are cultivated for perfume oils or as ornamentals.

For key to families *see* Group 3. Herbaceous Flowering Plant Families

Key to Herbaceous Plants:

1. Stamens 5; leaves pinnately lobed
    2. Lower leaves simple .... *Erodium botrys* (LONG-BEAKED STORKSBILL)
    2′ Lower leaves compound ... *Erodium cicutarium* (RED-STEMMED STORKSBILL)
1′ Stamens 10; leaves palmately lobed
    3. Leaves deeply lobed and cut almost to base; sepal lobes awned ....
    .... *Geranium dissectum* (CUT-LEAVED GERANIUM)
    3′ Leaves lobed; sepal lobes acute .... *Geranium molle* (CRANESBILL)

Erodium botrys (Cav.) Bertol.

LONG-BEAKED STORKSBILL   Nonnative / Europe /
Flowering Time: March–July   BROAD-LEAVED FILAREE

Habitat: disturbed areas in all habitats

Description: Prostrate to ascending, hairy annual to 5 dm. Leaves basal, simple; blade to 10 cm, margin deeply lobed and toothed; petiole can be as long as the leaf blade. Inflorescence an umbel of 1–5 flowers; calyx to 10 mm with a short bristle-like hair at the tip; corolla to 12 mm, purple with darker lines; pedicel to 4 mm; stamens 5; beak-like styles elongate in fruit. Fruit when mature to 10 cm including style branch, dividing into 5 one-seeded parts, style coils when fruit matures.

Genus & Specific Name Derivation: Greek: heron, referring to the bill-like fruit / resembling a bunch of grapes

Notes: Filaree is another common name, may refer to the leaves being filigree-like. Another interpretation is that filaree is a corruption of the Spanish word alfilerilla, "needle," referring to the beak. The name clocks comes from the long, pointed styles above the fruit, which separate suddenly into two hands at different angles like those on a clock face.

Uses Past and Present: Most of the nonnative *Erodiums* may have been brought in as fodder plants for cattle.

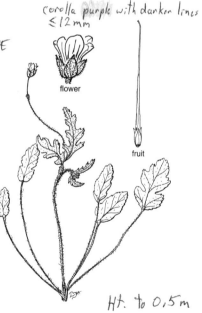

corolla purple with darker lines ≤ 12 mm

flower

fruit

Ht. to 0.5 m

Photo in K & B plate 29

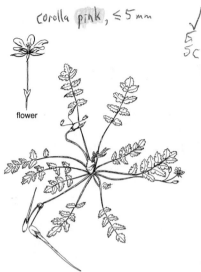

corolla pink, ≤ 5 mm

flower

Ht. to 0.5m

Erodium cicutarium (L.) L'Her.

E
SC

RED-STEMMED STORKSBILL   Nonnative / Eurasia or FILAREE

Flowering Time: February–November

Habitat: grassland

Description: Mat-forming annual spreading to 5 dm: Leaves basal, compound, 1-pinnate; blade to 10 cm, margin deeply toothed; petiole as long as blade. Inflorescence an umbel; calyx to 3 mm with a bristle tip; corolla to 5 mm, pink; stamens 5. Fruit to 7 cm including style branch, dividing into 5 one-seeded parts, style coiling when fruit matures.

Genus & Specific Name Derivation: Greek: heron, referring to the bill-like fruit / the genus *Cicuta*, an ancient Latin name for poison hemlock, having similar leaves

Notes: See *E. botrys.*

Uses Past and Present: See *E. botrys.*

Photo in K & B plate 29

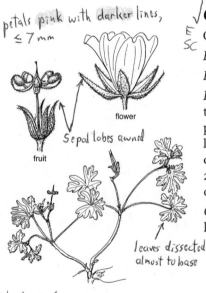

petals pink with darker lines, ≤ 7 mm

flower

Sepal lobes awned

fruit

leaves dissected almost to base

Ht. to 0.6 m

Geranium dissectum L.

E
SC

CUT-LEAVED GERANIUM   Nonnative / Europe

Flowering Time: April–October

Habitat: grassland

Description: Annual, stems to 6 dm. Leaves alternate, simple to 12 cm, margin deeply lobed and each lobe cut, dissected; petiole to 15 cm; stipules pinkish red. Inflorescence umbel-like; calyx to 7 mm, bristle-tipped; petals to 7 mm, pink with darker lines; stamens 10; pedicel to 6 mm; bracts green-red to 2 mm. Fruit to 3 cm including style branch, dividing into 5 one-seeded parts, style coiling when fruit matures.

Genus & Specific Name Derivation: Greek: crane, from beak-like fruit / cut into many deep lobes, referring to the leaves

Photo in K & B plate 29

Geranium molle L.

√

E

SC

CRANESBILL   Nonnative / Europe / *DOVE'S-FOOT GERANIUM*

Flowering Time: April–June

Habitat: grassland

Description: Annual to biennial spreading to 4 dm. Leaves alternate, simple to 12 cm, margin lobed and slightly cut; petiole to 10 cm. Inflorescence umbel-like; calyx to 4 mm; petals to 5 mm, notched, red-purple; pedicel to 20 mm. Fruit to 12 mm including style branch.

Genus & Specific Name Derivation: Greek: crane, from beak-like fruit / soft-hairy, referring to the plant

Notes: Like *G. dissectum* but leaves of *G. molle* are not as dissected, usually just lobed and slightly toothed.

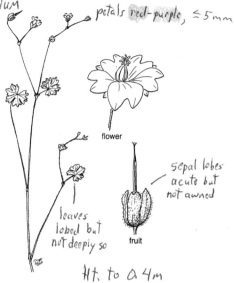

petals red-purple, ≤5mm

flower

sepal lobes acute but not awned

leaves lobed but not deeply so

fruit

Ht. to a 4m

Grossulariaceae — Gooseberry Family

Shrubs; stems spiny or not. Leaves alternate, often clustered, simple. Inflorescence in racemes. Flowers bisexual, regular. Hypanthium present; sepals 5, often petaloid; petals 5; stamens 5; ovary inferior, styles 2, stigma 2-lobed. Fruit a berry, spiny or not. Some species cultivated as ornamentals or for fruit.

For key to woody plants *see* Group 2. Woody Plants

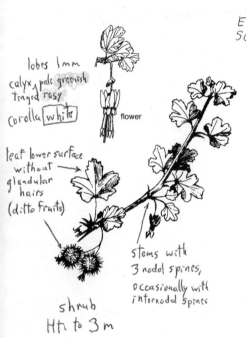

lobes 1mm

calyx, pale greenish tinged rosy

corolla white

flower

leaf lower surface without glandular hairs (ditto fruits)

stems with 3 nodal spines, occasionally with internodal spines

shrub Ht to 3 m

✓*Ribes californicum* Hook. & Arn. var. *californicum*

E
SC   HILLSIDE GOOSEBERRY   Native

Flowering Time: January–April

Habitat: chaparral, woodland

Description: Deciduous shrub to 3 m with 3 nodal spines on the stems, however sometimes the whole stem is covered with spines. Leaves clustered, alternate, simple, to 12 mm, with 3–4 leaves in a cluster, margin lobed and toothed. Inflorescence a pendent raceme of 1–3 flowers; bracts to 1 mm, greenish white. Flowers regular. Sepals 5, to 6 mm, fused, whitish-green tinged rosy-red; petals 5 to 1 mm, fused, white, rolled inward. Stamens 5, exserted; ovary inferior, stigma 2-lobed. Fruit a red berry to 10 mm, round with spines, usually glandular.

Genus & Specific Name Derivation: Name is Arabic, referring to plants of this genus / from California

Notes: Hypanthium is area above ovary; the sepals, petals and stamen are fused to it. The showy part of the flower are the sepals; the flowers and fruit hang down.

Uses Past and Present: Natives used the berries for food.

Photo in K & B plate 30

Ribes malvaceum Sm. var. *malvaceum*

CHAPARRAL CURRANT   Native

Flowering Time: October–April

Habitat: chaparral, woodland

Description: Deciduous shrub to 4 m; without spines. Leaves alternate, simple to 5 cm, sometimes in clusters with stipules, margin lobed and toothed. Leaves densely hairy, glandular, upper surface dull olive-green, lower surface brighter. Petiole to 2 cm. Inflorescence a pendent raceme with up to 20 flowers. Flowers regular. Hypanthium (fused area above ovary) to 8 mm, usually 2 times longer than wide. Sepals 5, to 6 mm, fused, pink-rose, opening outward in full bloom; petals 5, to 3 mm, fused, white to pink, pointing upward, encircling the stigma and stamens. Bracts beige to pink. Stamens 5; ovary inferior, stigma 2-lobed, style base hairy. Fruit a berry to 7 mm, hairs white, glandular, purple when mature.

Genus & Specific Name Derivation: Name is Arabic, referring to plants of this genus / mallow-like, referring to the leaves

Notes: Authority updated from *The Jepson Manual Corrections* — Installment No. 4.

Uses Past and Present: Natives used the berries for food.

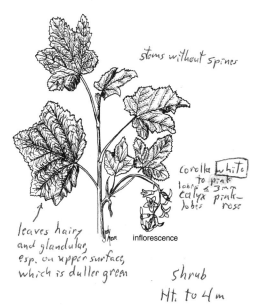

stems without spines

corolla white to pink lobes ≤ 3mm

calyx pink-rose lobes

inflorescence

leaves hairy and glandular, esp. on upper surface, which is duller green

shrub Ht. to 4 m

Ribes menziesii Pursh

CANYON GOOSEBERRY   Native

Flowering Time: March–August

Habitat: woodland

Description: Deciduous shrub to 3 m, stem with 3 nodal spines and internodes dense bristly, some glandular. Leaves alternate, simple to 4 cm, hairy, glandular. Inflorescence 1–3 flowered. Hypanthium (fused area above ovary) to 3 mm. Sepals reflexed to 10 mm, purple; petals to 5 mm, white; anthers exserted; styles exceeding the anthers. Fruit a berry to 10 mm, purple; bristles dense, some glandular.

Genus & Specific Name Derivation: Name is Arabic, referring to plants of this genus / for Archibald Menzies (1754–1842), English naturalist on the ship *Discovery*

Notes: Illustration from *Illustrated Flora of the Pacific States.*

Uses Past and Present: Natives used the berries for food.

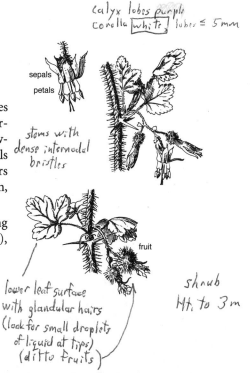

calyx lobes purple corolla white lobes ≤ 5mm

sepals

petals

stems with dense internodal bristles

fruit

lower leaf surface with glandular hairs (look for small droplets of liquid at tips) (ditto fruits)

shrub Ht. to 3 m

photo in K & B plate 30

Hippocastanaceae — Buckeye Family

Large shrub to small tree. Leaves opposite, compound. Inflorescence a panicle or raceme. Flowers regular; some unisexual (staminate). Sepals 5, free or fused; petals 4–5; stamens 5–8; stigma and style 1. Fruit a capsule; seeds 1. Some cultivated as ornamentals.

For key to woody plants *see* Group 2. Woody Plants

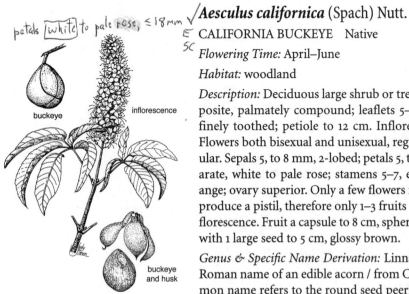

petals [white] to pale rose, ≤ 18mm √

buckeye

inflorescence

buckeye and husk

small tree

Aesculus californica (Spach) Nutt.

E
SC

CALIFORNIA BUCKEYE   Native

Flowering Time: April–June

Habitat: woodland

Description: Deciduous large shrub or tree to 12 m. Leaves opposite, palmately compound; leaflets 5–7, to 17 cm, margin finely toothed; petiole to 12 cm. Inflorescence panicle-like. Flowers both bisexual and unisexual, regular to slightly irregular. Sepals 5, to 8 mm, 2-lobed; petals 5, to 18 mm, nearly separate, white to pale rose; stamens 5–7, exserted, anthers orange; ovary superior. Only a few flowers in each inflorescence produce a pistil, therefore only 1–3 fruits are produced per inflorescence. Fruit a capsule to 8 cm, spherical, leathery outside with 1 large seed to 5 cm, glossy brown.

Genus & Specific Name Derivation: Linnaeus' name from the Roman name of an edible acorn / from Californica. The common name refers to the round seed peering through the covering and looking like a large eye.

Notes: This plant is early deciduous; the leaves start falling by the end of July. Staminate flowers are at the top of the inflorescence; seed-producing flowers are generally at the base. Each inflorescence produces one to several fruits that hang from the ends of the branches in the fall. The nectar and pollen are toxic to honeybees.

Uses Past and Present: Natives used ground seed as a fish poison. During years of poor acorn harvest, the seeds were detoxified by cooking, mashing and leaching to use as a mush like that of the acorn.

Hydrophyllaceae — Waterleaf Family

Annuals, herbaceous perennials, or shrubs. Leaves basal or cauline, alternate or opposite, simple or compound. Inflorescence often arranged in a coiled one-sided cluster, raceme or cyme-like. Flowers bisexual, regular. Sepals 5, mostly fused; petals 5, fused; stamens 5, exserted; ovary superior, styles and stigmas 2. Fruit a capsule.

Family Characteristics

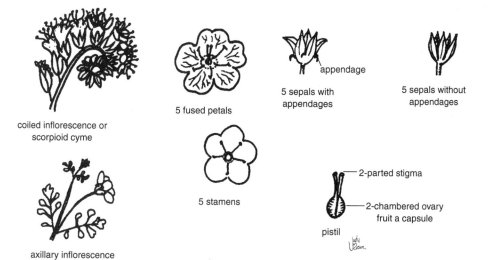

coiled inflorescence or
scorpioid cyme

5 fused petals

5 sepals with
appendages

5 sepals without
appendages

5 stamens

pistil

2-parted stigma

2-chambered ovary
fruit a capsule

axillary inflorescence

For key to woody plants *see* Group 2. Woody Plants

For key to families *see* Group 3. Herbaceous Flowering Plant Families

Key to Herbaceous Plants:

1. Reflexed appendages present between calyx lobes ....
.... *Nemophila heterophylla* (VARIABLE-LEAVED NEMOPHILA)
1´ Without reflexed appendages between calyx lobes
   2. Corolla blue
      3. Leaves entire to slightly lobed ....
      .... *Phacelia divaricata* (DIVARICATE PHACELIA)
      3´ Leaves irregularly toothed to slightly lobed ....
      .... *Phacelia rattanii* (RATTAN'S PHACELIA)
   2´ Corolla white to yellowish
      4. Upper and lower leaves compound ....
      .... *Phacelia distans* (COMMON PHACELIA)
      4´ Lower leaves compound, upper leaves simple

5. Inflorescence tightly coiled in flower; lower compound leaflets usually more than 5; pedicel less than 2 mm .... *Phacelia imbricata* (IMBRICATE PHACELIA)

5′ Inflorescence more open in flower; lower compound leaflets usually less than 5; pedicel longer than 2 mm (be careful! there are stinging hairs all over this plant) .... *Phacelia nemoralis* (STINGING PHACELIA)

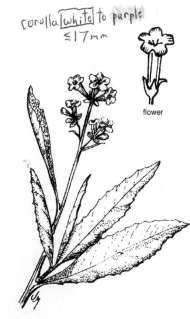

corolla white to purple ≤17mm

flower

Evergreen shrub Ht. to 3 m

√ *Eriodictyon californicum* (Hook. & Arn.) Torrey

YERBA SANTA   Native

Flowering Time: April–July

Habitat: chaparral

Description: Evergreen shrub to 3 m. Leaves alternate, simple, to 15 cm, margin toothed, rolled under; young leaves sticky on upper surface; petiole short. Inflorescence an open panicle-like cyme. Flowers regular. Sepals to 5 mm, 5-lobed, fused; petals to 17 mm, 5-lobed, fused, white to purple. Stamens 5, included; ovary superior, stigmas 2-lobed. Fruit a capsule to 3 mm wide.

Genus & Specific Name Derivation: Greek: woolly net, from undersurface of some leaves / from California

Notes: Leaves slightly aromatic. Once a plant is established the underground roots send up many new shoots to form large colonies. This plant sprouts from the roots or seeds after fire. The leaves and young stems are often infected with a sooty fungus, a member of the genus *Heterosporium*, which turns them black. However, it is not thought to hurt the plant. The common name of this plant means holy or sacred herb from its medicinal uses. Butterflies seek out the flowers for their nectar.

Uses Past and Present: A tea or smoke from the leaves was used as a decongestant for colds and asthma, also for chronic gastritis and urethral irritation. Leaves and flowers were warmed and used as a poultice on aching or sore areas. Mashed leaves were often applied to cuts, wounds, abrasions and fractures to keep swelling down and to aid in mending as well as to relieve pain. It is said that chewing on the leaves helps relieve thirst.

Photo in K & B plate 31

Nemophila heterophylla Fischer & C. Meyer

VARIABLE-LEAVED NEMOPHILA   Native

Flowering Time: January–April

Habitat: woodland

Description: Annual to 12 cm. Leaves opposite, some upper leaves may be alternate, simple to 4 cm; margin deeply lobed, almost appearing compound; petiole to 10 mm. Inflorescence axillary; calyx to 3 mm, almost separate with downward-curving appendage at each lobe; petals to 4 mm, fused, white; stamens with dark anthers. Fruit an ovoid capsule to 7 mm wide.

Genus & Specific Name Derivation: Greek: woodland-loving / diversely-leaved

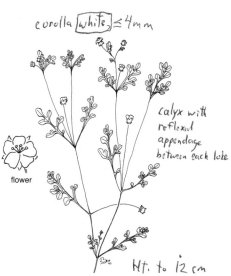

corolla white ≤4mm

flower

calyx with reflexed appendage between each lobe

Ht. to 12 cm

Phacelia distans Benth.

Genus Phacelia: flowers in coiled, one-sided inflorescence, less obvious after flowers open

COMMON PHACELIA   Native / WILD HELIOTROPE

Flowering Time: March–June

Habitat: grassland

Description: Upright, bristly-hairy annual to 30 cm. Leaves alternate, compound, 1-pinnate; blade to 8 cm, margin deeply lobed; petiole to 6 cm. Inflorescence a coiled cluster; flowers to 1 cm wide; calyx to 7 mm; corolla to 8 mm, tan-white with darker veins. Fruit a round capsule to 3 mm.

Genus & Specific Name Derivation: Greek: cluster, referring to the dense inflorescence / widely separated, referring to the deeply split style

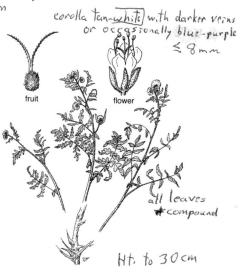

corolla tan-white with darker veins or occasionally blue-purple ≤8mm

fruit   flower

all leaves compound

Ht. to 30 cm

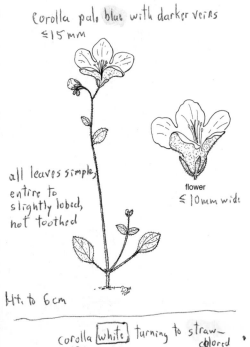

Corolla pale blue with darker veins
≤15mm

all leaves simple,
entire to
slightly lobed,
not toothed

flower
≤ 10mm wide

Ht. to 6 cm

Phacelia divaricata (Benth.) A. Gray

DIVARICATE PHACELIA   Native

Flowering Time: April–May

Habitat: serpentine grassland

Description: Low-growing annual to 6 cm, whole plant hairy. Leaves simple to 1 cm, opposite below, alternate above. Inflorescence a coiled cluster of 5–10 flowers; flowers to 1 cm wide; sepals to 8 mm, almost separate, persistent in fruit; petals to 15 mm, pale blue with darker lines; stamens and stigma exserted. Fruit a round capsule to 8 mm.

Genus & Specific Name Derivation: Greek: cluster, referring to the dense inflorescence / straggling, referring to the character of the plant

corolla [white] turning to straw-colored
≤7mm

flower

upper leaves simple

fruit

inflorescence

lower leaves compound,
leaflets >5 usually

Ht. to 0.45 m

Phacelia imbricata E. Greene ssp. *imbricata*

IMBRICATE PHACELIA   Native   ROCK PHACELIA

Flowering Time: April–June

Habitat: grassland

Description: Hairy, herbaceous perennial to 45 cm. Leaves mostly basal, upper alternate, lower compound, 1-pinnate, upper simple; blade to 15 cm. Inflorescence a tightly coiled cluster of many flowers; calyx to 6 mm, hairy, gray-green, may be longer in fruit; corolla to 7 mm, white fading to straw-colored. Fruit an ovoid capsule to 4 mm, hairy.

Genus & Specific Name Derivation: Greek: cluster, referring to the dense inflorescence / overlapping, referring to the calyx lobes

Notes: Whole plant bristly-hairy.

✗ *Phacelia nemoralis* E. Greene ssp. *nemoralis*

SC STINGING PHACELIA   Native / BRISTLY PHACELIA

Flowering Time: April–May

Habitat: woodland

Description: Annual to 70 cm with stinging hairs. Leaves alternate, lower compound, 3-parted at base, upper simple; lower blade to 15 cm; petiole to 4 cm; upper blade to 9 cm; petiole to 1.5 cm; margins wavy. Inflorescence a coiled cluster; calyx to 4 mm; corolla to 5 mm, cream to tan with darker lines; stamens, style and stigma exserted. Fruit a capsule to 5 mm, ovoid.

Genus & Specific Name Derivation: Greek: cluster, referring to the dense inflorescence / of the woods

Notes: Whole plant covered with stinging hairs.

corolla cream to tan with darker lines, ≤ 5 mm

plant with stinging hairs

upper leaves simple

lower leaves compound, leaflets usually ≤5, mostly only 3

Ht. to 0.7m

Phacelia rattanii A. Gray

RATTAN'S PHACELIA   Native

Flowering Time: May–June

Habitat: chaparral

Description: Low, spreading, branched annual to 30 cm; whole plant hairy. Leaves alternate, simple to 4 cm, lower lobed, upper mostly entire; petiole longer than leaves. Inflorescence a coiled cluster; calyx lobes to 5 mm; corolla to 6 mm, light blue. Fruit a spherical capsule to 3 mm.

Genus & Specific Name Derivation: Greek: cluster, referring to the dense inflorescence / for V. Rattan (1840–1915), teacher of botany in California schools, author of *A Popular California Flora*, which went through 8 editions

Notes: Illustration from *Illustrated Flora of the Pacific States.*

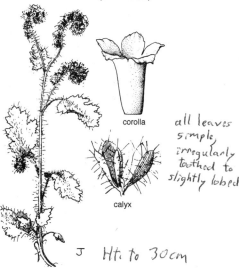

corolla light blue, ≤ 6 mm

corolla

calyx

all leaves simple, irregularly toothed to slightly lobed

J   Ht. to 30cm

Hypericaceae   St. John's Wort family

√ Hypericum sp. (possibly H. calycinum) Rose-of-Sharon
E
SC   low creeping shrub, leaves opposite, flowers yellow, with 5 sepals, 5 petals, numerous stamens

Juglandaceae — Walnut Family

Shrubs or trees, generally monoecious. Leaves alternate, compound, deciduous. Staminate inflorescence in catkins, generally appearing before leaves, generally many-flowered. Sepals 3–6; petals 0; stamens 3–many. Pistillate inflorescence solitary or cluster of 1–3 flowers at tip of new twigs; sepals 3–6; petals 0; ovary inferior, styles 2, plumose. Fruit a drupe-like nut. Cultivated for wood, nuts, hickory and pecan in this family.

For key to woody plants *see* Group 2. Woody Plants

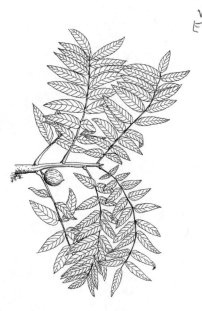

Tree

√ *Juglans californica* S. Watson var. *hindsii* Jepson
ɛ NORTHERN CALIFORNIA BLACK WALNUT

Native / Planted?

Flowering Time: April–May

Habitat: planted at the Day Camp

>10 (usually 15–19) shallowly toothed

Description: Deciduous tree to 25 m. Leaves alternate, compound 1-pinnate; leaflets to 10 cm. Inflorescence a catkin. Flowers unisexual, both male flowers and female flowers on the same tree (monoecious). Male catkin pendent, many-flowered. Female flowers 1–3, at tips of new twigs. Fruit a drupe to 3.5 cm with a round outer husk and the nut enclosed.

Genus & Specific Name Derivation: Latin: walnut / from California.

Notes: Reported as occurring and planted at native campsites. Formerly cultivated as rootstock for *J. regia* with which it hybridizes.

Uses Past and Present: Natives spread the nuts into canyons where they weren't originally found. The fruits are edible, but the shells are so difficult to remove that the black walnut was not considered as a viable commercial crop. The hulls were used to make a dark brown dye.

Juglans regia L.

ENGLISH WALNUT   Nonnative / Europe and Asia

Flowering Time: April–May

Habitat: planted at the Day Camp *up to 11*

Description: Deciduous tree to 30 m. *[up to 11]* Leaves alternate, compound, 1-pinnate; leaflets 7–9, to 12 cm, entire. Inflorescence a catkin. Flowers unisexual, both male flowers and female flowers on the same tree (monoecious). Male catkins pendent, many-flowered. Female flowers 1–3, at tips of new twigs. Fruit a drupe to 5 cm with a round outer husk and the nut enclosed. *longer than wide*

Genus & Specific Name Derivation: Latin: walnut / royal

Uses Past and Present: This tree is widely cultivated for nuts and wood.

Tree

Key

J. Regia: Leaflets generally < 10, drupe to 5 cm

J. calif. = Leaflets generally > 10, drupe to 3.5 cm

Lamiaceae — Mint Family

Annuals, herbaceous perennials, or shrubs, strongly scented. Leaves opposite or whorled, simple to compound. Inflorescence solitary, whorled, axillary or raceme or spike-like clusters. Flowers bisexual, irregular to slightly regular. Calyx regular to irregular, often 5-lobed, persistent in fruit; petals fused, corolla 2-lipped with 2 fused upper petals and 3 fused lower petals; stamens 2 or 4; pistil 1, ovary superior, usually deeply 4-lobed, style 1. Fruit separating into 4 nutlets, some may not develop. Stems 4-angled (square); plant aromatic from gland-tipped hairs. Many cultivated herbs and oils, e.g., lavender, mint, basil, rosemary, thyme; some used in medicine. Synonym Labiatae.

Family Characteristics

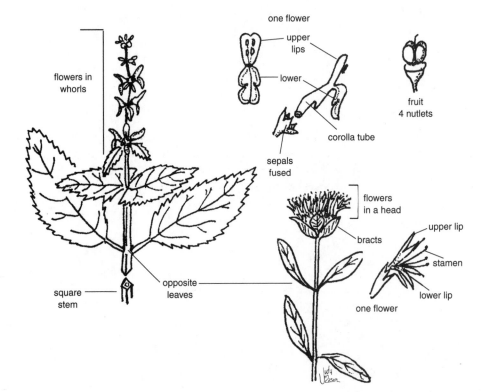

one flower

upper lips

lower

corolla tube

sepals fused

fruit
4 nutlets

flowers in whorls

flowers in a head

bracts

upper lip

stamen

lower lip

one flower

square stem

opposite leaves

For key to woody plants see Group 2. Woody Plants

For key to families *see* Group 3. Herbaceous Flowering Plant Families

Key to Herbaceous Plants:

1. Leaves compound .... *Salvia columbariae* (CHIA)
1´ Leaves simple
    2. Inflorescence axillary with 1–3 flowers
        3. Flowers white .... *Satureja douglasii* (YERBA BUENA)
        3´ Flowers lavender, purple or blue
            4. Leaves aromatic ..... *Pogogyne serpylloides* (THYME-LEAVED POGOGYNE)
            4´ Leaves not aromatic; calyx back with a dome-like ridge ....
                .... *Scutellaria tuberosa* (DANNIE'S SKULLCAP)
    2´ Inflorescence head-like or whorled with more than 3 flowers
        5. Bracts with sharp spines ....
            .... *Acanthomintha duttonii* (SAN MATEO THORNMINT)
        5´ Bracts not spine tipped
            6. Flowers purple to lavender
                7. Terminal inflorescence head-like ....
                    .... *Monardella villosa* (COYOTE-MINT)
                7´ Terminal inflorescence panicle-like ....
                    .... *Mentha pulegium* (PENNYROYAL)
            6´ Flowers pink and white
                8. Inflorescence tightly clustered, whorls barely interrupted ....
                    .... *Stachys pycnantha* (SHORT-SPIKED HEDGE NETTLE)
                8´ Inflorescence elongate, whorls interrupted ....
                    .... *Stachys ajugoides* (RIGID HEDGE NETTLE/WOOD-MINT)

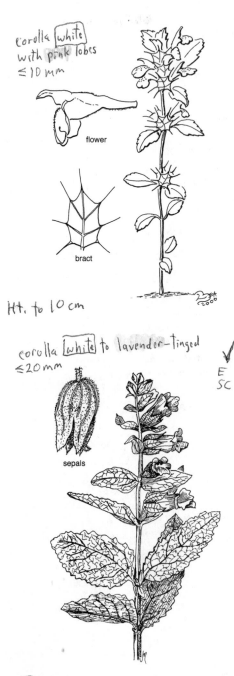

corolla white
with pink lobes
≤10 mm

flower

bract

Ht. to 10 cm

corolla white to lavender-tinged
≤20 mm

sepals

Evergreen
shrub
Ht. to 2m

Acanthomintha duttonii (Abrams) Jokerst

SAN MATEO THORNMINT   Native

Flowering Time: May–June

Habitat: serpentine grassland

Description: Upright annual to 10 cm. Leaves simple, opposite to 1.5 cm; margin toothed; petiole to 5 mm. Inflorescence whorled or head-like at the top of the stem; calyx to 5 mm, fused, green; corolla to 1 cm, white with pink lobes; bracts to 1 cm, roundish with sharp spines to 5 mm; flowers sessile. Fruit 4 small nutlets.

Genus & Specific Name Derivation: Greek: thornmint, referring to the bracts / derivation unknown

Notes: This is one of the rarest plants in our area, ours may be the only extant population in the world. State and federally listed as endangered. Listed in *CNPS Inventory of Rare and Endangered Plants of California* on "List 1B, Plants Rare, Threatened, or Endangered in California and Elsewhere."

✓ *Lepechinia calycina* (Benth.) Epling

E
SC   PITCHER SAGE   Native

Flowering Time: April–July

Habitat: chaparral, open woodland

Description: Evergreen shrub to 2 m. Leaves opposite, simple to 12 cm, upper and lower leaf surface hairy, margin toothed, upper leaf gray-green, paler beneath, sticky, with a strong odor. Some with short petioles. Inflorescence an open raceme. Flowers irregular; sepals 5-lobed, fused, inflated; corolla to 2 cm, fused, white to lavender-tinged, 2-lipped, lower lip longer, upper lip 4-lobed. Stamens 4, inserted; ovary superior, style 2-lobed, inserted. Fruit 4 nutlets, some may abort.

Genus & Specific Name Derivation: I. I. Lepechin (1737–1802), Russian Botanist / with a persistent calyx

Notes: Pitcher-like shape of the sepals, which inflate, gives it its common name. This species recovers quickly after its habitat is disturbed or burned.

Uses Past and Present: Leaves steeped as a tea used for urinary infections.

Photo in K & B plate 32

Mentha pulegium L.

PENNYROYAL   Nonnative / Europe

Flowering Time: June–October

Habitat: seeps, swales

Description: Upright to trailing herbaceous perennial to 6 dm; whole plant short-hairy. Leaves opposite, simple to 3 cm, margins toothed; petiole short. Inflorescence axillary and terminal panicle-like clusters of whorled flowers in leaf-like bracts; calyx to 4 mm; corolla to 8 mm, violet to lavender. Fruit 4 small nutlets.

Genus & Specific Name Derivation: Latin: ancient name for mint / flea-dispeller

Notes: Oil toxic, has been fatal when extract ingested by humans.

Uses Past and Present: Used as insect repellent but can cause rashes in humans and in pets can cause convulsions.

Photo in K & B plate 32

corolla violet to lavender, ≤ 8mm

terminal inflorescence panicle-like

flower

inflorescence

Ht. to 0.6m

√ *Monardella villosa* Benth. ssp. *globosa*
(Jepson) Jokerst

subspecies not in Kozloff and Beidleman

E
SERPENTINE
^ COYOTE-MINT   Native

SC *Flowering Time:* May–June

Habitat: grassland, chaparral, woodland

Description: Upright to trailing, hairy, branched, herbaceous perennial to 5 dm. Leaves opposite, simple to 2 cm, margin toothed; petiole to 5 mm; fragrant when touched. Inflorescence head-like; calyx to 4 mm, hairy, fused, green tinged darker; corolla to 8 mm, lavender, purple, deeply divided; bracts to 1 cm, leaf-like below the flower head, green, with smaller bracts inside. Fruit 4 nutlets.

Genus & Specific Name Derivation: Latin: small *Monarda*, having the appearance of a dwarf plant / with long shaggy hairs

Notes: Nicolas Bautista Monardes (1493–1588), a Spanish physician and botanist whose name was given to a number of plants. He studied American plants and their medicinal uses. His book may have been the first to be published on the flora of the Americas.

Uses Past and Present: Natives made a tea for stomach aches.

Corolla lavender to purple, ≤ 8mm

terminal inflorescence head-like

flower

outer bracts 20-30 mm

leaf blade 20-40 mm wide

Ht. to 0.5m

Jepson says ht. >50 cm

2008 Addendum

Monardella villosa ssp. villosa   COMMON COYOTE-MINT native   outer bracts ≤20mm

differs from ssp. globosa in being < 50 cm in height, leaf blade 10-30mm wide,   not matted

M.v. ssp. globosa + ssp. villosa: leaves narrowly ovate, base tapered to obtuse, stem gen. sparsely to densely hairy, but

not present: M.v. ssp. franciscana: leaves ovate to widely triangular, base gen. truncate, stem gen. densely matted-wooly

corolla lavender, ≤5mm

inflorescence axillary

inflorescence

Ht. to 10cm

Pogogyne serpylloides (Torrey) A. Gray

THYME-LEAVED POGOGYNE   Native

Flowering Time: April–June

Habitat: chaparral, grassland

Description: Small, low-growing annual to 10 cm. Leaves opposite, simple, small, bright green, margins toothed. Inflorescence on lower part of plant in axillary clusters with several flowers and flowers solitary in upper leaf axils; calyx to 4 mm; corolla to 5 mm, lavender. Fruit minute nutlets, hairy.

Genus & Specific Name Derivation: Greek: bearded style / thyme leaves

Notes: This is a belly plant and is often overlooked until the minty odor makes it apparent. A very small mint with a very big odor.

Photo in K & B plate 33

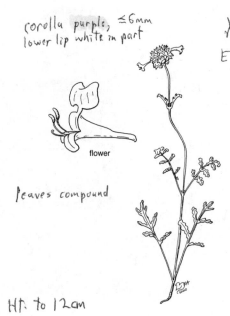

corolla purple, ≤6mm
lower lip white in part

flower

leaves compound

Ht. to 12cm

Salvia columbariae Benth.

CHIA   Native

Flowering Time: March–April

Habitat: chaparral

Description: Upright, soft-hairy annual to 12 cm; whole plant with glandular hairs. Leaves opposite, compound, 1-pinnate to 6 cm; leaflets to 5 mm, margins deeply lobed; petiole to 2 cm. Inflorescence in tiers of whorled heads; flowers 2-lipped; calyx to 3 mm, hairy, awn-tipped; corolla to 6 mm, purple, lower lip with a white patch with purple spots; flowers sessile. Fruit minute nutlets.

Genus & Specific Name Derivation: Latin: to save, referring to medicinal use / species reminded its namer of *Columbaria*, a plant of the Old World genus *Scabiosa*

Uses Past and Present: Tiny seeds are rich in protein and oil and have been reported to sustain a person for up to 24 hours.

Photo in K & B plate 33

√ *Satureja douglasii* (Benth.) Briq.

E YERBA BUENA   Native

Flowering Time: May–August

Habitat: woodland

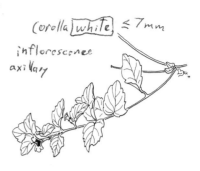

Corolla white ≤7mm
inflorescence axillary

Trailing

Description: Trailing herbaceous perennial. Leaves opposite, simple to 3 cm, margin toothed; petiole to 5 mm. Inflorescence 1–3 flowers in the leaf axils; calyx to 4 mm, fused and lobed; corolla to 7 mm, white; pedicels to 3 mm. Fruit minute nutlets.

Genus & Specific Name Derivation: Latin: savory / David Douglas (1798–1834), collector in American northwest for the Royal Horticultural Society

Notes: Yerba Buena was the original name for San Francisco, and the name still applies to the island in the middle of the bay. Common name is Spanish for "good herb."

Uses Past and Present: Steeped in hot water the leaves make a refreshing mint tea.

Scutellaria tuberosa Benth.

DANNIE'S SKULLCAP   Native / BLUE SKULLCAP

Flowering Time: March–June

Habitat: woodland

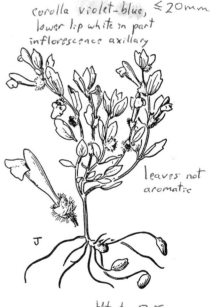

corolla violet-blue, ≤20mm
lower lip white in part
inflorescence axillary

leaves not aromatic

Ht to 25cm

Description: Herbaceous perennial to 25 cm. Leaves opposite, simple to 2 cm, margin lobed or slightly toothed. Inflorescence solitary in the leaf axil; calyx to 5 mm, with a dome-like back; corolla to 20 mm, violet-blue, lower lip white-patched or mottled; pedicel to 4 mm. Fruit small nutlets.

Genus & Specific Name Derivation: Latin: tray, referring to the calyx dome or ridge / tuber, referring to the underground tubers

Notes: The 2 blossoms in the leaf axils twist so that they stand side by side in pairs. The unopened sepals have been compared to the shape of an old-fashioned Quaker bonnet. Quaker bonnets might have been a more appropriate common name than skullcap. Also the sepals look like the old-fashioned skullcaps people used to wear to bed. Although this plant is in the mint family it has unscented leaves. Illustration from *Illustrated Flora of the Pacific States.*

Photo in K & B plate 33

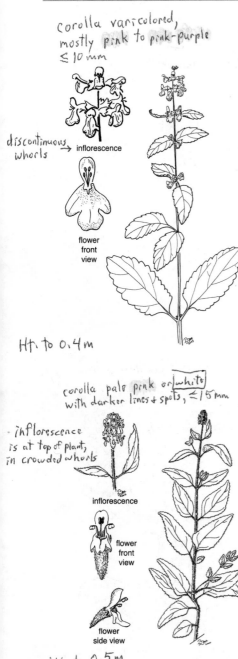

corolla varicolored, mostly pink to pink-purple ≤ 10 mm

discontinuous whorls → inflorescence

flower front view

Ht. to 0.4 m

corolla pale pink or white with darker lines + spots, ≤ 15 mm

- inflorescence is at top of plant, in crowded whorls

inflorescence

flower front view

flower side view

Ht. to 0.5 m

✓ **Stachys ajugoides** Benth. var. ***rigida***
E   Jepson & Hoover
SC RIGID HEDGE NETTLE / WOOD MINT   Native

Flowering Time: April–May

Habitat: grassland, woodland

Description: Upright annual to 4 dm, whole plant hairy, glandular. Leaves opposite, simple to 5 cm, margin toothed. Inflorescence of whorled flowers in the leaf axils; calyx to 6 mm, fused, green, purple tinged; corolla to 1 cm, upper lip rounded, pink, lower lip 3-lobed, largest lobe pale pink-purple with darker dots and lines. Fruit 4 nutlets.

Genus & Specific Name Derivation: Greek: ear of corn, referring to the inflorescence / rigid, referring to the hairs

Notes: An alternate common name for this is wood-mint. The name hedge nettle refers to a superficial resemblance of the leaves to those of stinging nettle.

Uses Past and Present: Tea used for migraine and other headaches, and sore throats.

✓ **Stachys pycnantha** Benth.

E   SHORT-SPIKED HEDGE NETTLE   Native

Flowering Time: July–September

Habitat: seeps, swales

Description: Upright annual to 5 dm, whole plant soft-hairy, glandular. Leaves opposite, simple to 13 cm, margins toothed; petiole to 6 cm. Inflorescence a head of whorled flowers, some whorls may be slightly separated but most are clustered at the top of the plant; calyx to 7 mm, fused, 5-lobed; corolla to 15 mm, pale pink with darker lines and spots. Fruit 4 nutlets.

Genus & Specific Name Derivation: Greek: ear of corn, referring to the inflorescence / densely flowered

Notes: See *S. ajugoides.*

Lauraceae — Laurel Family

Shrubs or trees, generally evergreen, aromatic, rarely dioecious. Leaves alternate, simple, surface with small pits or depressions; stipules 0. Inflorescence a panicle, raceme, umbel, rarely solitary. Flowers bisexual or unisexual, yellow or greenish. Calyx deeply 4–6-lobed, segments in 2 series; petals 0; stamens in 3–4 whorls of 3 each, some sterile, anthers opening by uplifting valves; pistil 1, simple, ovary generally superior, style 1. Fruit a berry or drupe, 1-seeded. Some cultivated, e.g., avocado, cinnamon, camphor.

For key to woody plants *see* Group 2. Woody Plants

√*Umbellularia californica* (Hook. & Arn.) Nutt.

E
SC

CALIFORNIA BAY   Native

Flowering Time: December–April

Habitat: woodland

Description: Evergreen tree to 45 m. Leaves alternate, simple to 10 cm, upper surface shiny, bright green, lower surface dull green; petiole short. Aromatic. Inflorescence an umbel in upper leaf axils. Flowers 6–10, yellow-green; sepals 6, to 8 mm; petals 0; stamens 9, in two rows, with orange glands at base; ovary superior, style 1. Fruit a drupe to 2.5 cm, round-ovoid, green turning dark purple when mature.

Genus & Specific Name Derivation: Latin: small umbrella, referring to the inflorescence / from California

Notes: Bay trees form thickets, sometimes forming a bay forest. There is very little understory vegetation in this forest because the chemicals in the leaves inhibit most understory growth. Flowers are very fragrant. Leaf oils may be toxic to some people. Known as Oregon myrtle in Oregon; used in cooking and by woodworkers.

Uses Past and Present: Natives used bay leaves medicinally to cure headache and as a tea for stomach ailments. Oils from the leaves were rubbed on the body to ease rheumatism. Leaves were also spread on floors to repel fleas; boughs were burned to fumigate lodgings and to fight colds. The nuts were roasted, cracked and eaten. The leaves can be used as a substitute for the Mediterranean bay laurel, but are stronger.

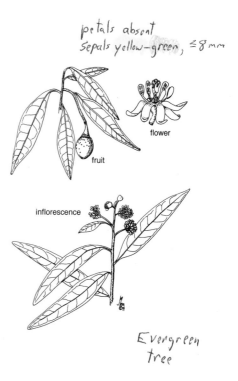

petals absent
Sepals yellow–green, ≤8mm

flower

fruit

inflorescence

Evergreen tree

Photo in K & B plate 34

Linaceae — Flax Family

Annuals, herbaceous perennials, or shrubs. Leaves alternate, opposite or whorled, simple. Inflorescence in racemes, cymes or axillary. Flowers bisexual, regular. Sepals 4–5, free; petals 4–5, free; stamens 4–5; pistil 1, ovary superior, styles 2–5. Fruit a capsule. Some are cultivated ornamentals and some are used for linseed oil.

For key to families *see* Group 3. Herbaceous Flowering Plant Families

Key to Herbaceous plants:

1. Flowers blue .... *Linum bienne* (NARROW-LEAVED FLAX)
1´ Flowers white to pink
    2. Sepal margins glandular; stipule glandular ....
       .... *Hesperolinon congestum* (DWARF FLAX)
    2´ Sepals and stipules not glandular ....
       .... *Hesperolinon micranthum* (SMALL-FLOWERED DWARF FLAX)

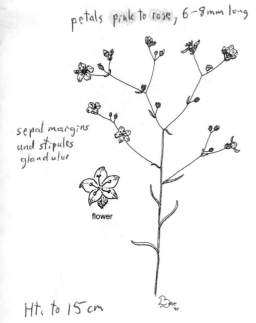

petals pink to rose, 6–8 mm long

sepal margins and stipules glandular

flower

Ht. to 15 cm

Hesperolinon congestum (A. Gray) Small

DWARF FLAX   Native

Flowering Time: May–June

Habitat: serpentine grassland

Description: Annual plant to 15 cm. Leaves alternate, simple to 2 cm, linear. Inflorescence a branched panicle-like cyme, congested to open; pedicels to 8 mm; sepals to 4 mm, hairy, margins glandular; petals to 8 mm, pink to rose; anthers deep pink; styles whitish. Fruit a capsule.

Genus & Specific Name Derivation: Greek: western flax / arranged close together referring to sometimes the flowers are close together

Notes: Rare plant State and Federally listed as Threatened. Listed in *CNPS Inventory of Rare and Endangered Plants of California* on "List 1B, Plants Rare, Threatened, or Endangered in California and Elsewhere." Plant can be seen from the trail on the Serpentine Loop near Sunset Entrance.

Hesperolinon micranthum (A. Gray) Small

SMALL-FLOWERED DWARF FLAX   Native

Flowering Time: May–June

Habitat: grassland, serpentine chaparral

Description: A thread like, branched, annual to 20 cm. Leaves simple, alternate, thread-like to 2 cm. Inflorescence an open panicle-like cyme; sepals to 4 mm; petals to 3.5 mm, white to pale-pink. Fruit a capsule.

Genus & Specific Name Derivation: Greek: western flax / small-flowered

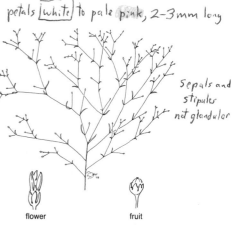

petals [white] to pale pink, 2–3mm long

Sepals and stipules not glandular

flower   fruit

Ht, to 20 cm

✓*Linum bienne* Miller

NARROW-LEAVED FLAX   Nonnative / Mediterranean

Flowering Time: May–August

Habitat: grassland

Description: Biennial, stem to 5 dm. Leaves simple, alternate to 25 mm, linear. Inflorescence a raceme; pedicel to 18 mm; sepals to 6 mm; petals to 10 mm, blue. Fruit a capsule to 10 mm.

Genus & Specific Name Derivation: Latin: flax / biennial, lasting for two years.

Uses Past and Present: Flax is the source of commercial flax fiber from which linen is made. It was planted extensively on the coast during World War II for flax oil used for machinery and other purposes.

Photo in K & B plate 34

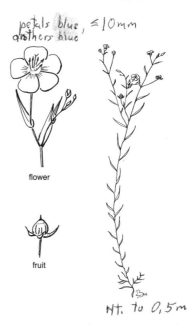

petals blue, ≤10mm
anthers blue

flower

fruit

Ht. to 0,5m

Lythraceae — Loosestrife Family

Annuals or herbaceous perennials. Leaves alternate, opposite, or whorled, simple. Inflorescence axillary, solitary or in racemes, spikes or panicles. Flowers bisexual, regular. Hypanthium present; sepals 4–6, fused, sometimes with appendages; petals 4–6 or absent; stamens 4–6; ovary superior, style slender, stigma head-like. Fruit a capsule; seeds 3–many. Some ornamental or cultivated for medicine, dyes.

For key to families *see* Group 3. Herbaceous Flowering Plant Families

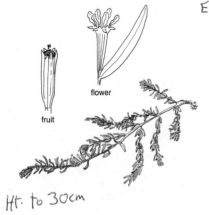

corolla lobes pink to rose, ≤5mm

flower

fruit

Ht. to 30cm

✓ *Lythrum hyssopifolium* L.

E LOOSESTRIFE   Nonnative / Europe / GRASS-POLY

Flowering Time: May–June

Habitat: grassland, seeps

Description: Upright to spreading annual to 30 cm. Leaves alternate, simple to 1.5 cm, sessile, somewhat rolled under. Inflorescence axillary. Flowers small, sepals 6, to 2 mm, appendages to 1 mm; petals to 5 mm, pink to rose, fused into a tube around the ovary; stamens and stigma included; ovary superior. Fruit a many-seeded capsule to 6 mm.

Genus & Specific Name Derivation: Greek: blood, referring to the flower color of some / hyssop-like, referring to the foliage

Malvaceae — Mallow Family

Annuals, herbaceous perennials, shrubs. Leaves alternate, simple, margins lobed or toothed. Inflorescence in racemes, solitary, axillary or terminal. Flowers bisexual, regular. Sepals 5, fused; petals 5, free; stamens many, filaments fused into a column surrounding the style; pistil 1, ovary superior, styles 5 or more, stigmas 5 or more. Fruit a schizocarp with 5 or more parts. Some species cultivated for fiber, e.g., cotton; for food, e.g., okra; others used as ornamentals, e.g., *Hibiscus*.

For key to woody plants see Group 2. Woody Plants

For key to families *see* Group 3. Herbaceous Flowering Plant Families

Key to Herbaceous Plants:

1. Annual; upper leaves deeply lobed, divided almost to base .... *Sidalcea diploscypha* (FRINGED CHECKERBLOOM)
1′ Perennial; upper leaves not so deeply divided .... *Sidalcea malviflora* (CHECKER MALLOW)

√ *Malacothamnus fasciculatus* (Torrey & A. Gray) E. Greene

CHAPARRAL MALLOW   Native

Flowering Time: May–September

Habitat: serpentine chaparral

Description: Erect, spreading evergreen shrub to 5 m. Leaves alternate, simple to 11 cm, gray-green, densely hairy, margin palmately lobed and toothed. Inflorescence a many-flowered spike; bracts to 8 mm. Flowers regular. Sepals 5, to 11 mm, fused, hairy; petals 5, to 2 cm, separate to slightly fused at the base, pale pink. Stamens many, arranged on a column; ovary superior, stigma head-like, when mature sticks up above the stamens. Fruit a capsule with 5 parts (chambers).

Genus & Specific Name Derivation: Greek: soft, tender shrub / clustered in bundles, fascicled, referring to the clustered position of the leaves or flowers

Notes: A synonym is *Malacothamnus arcuatus* listed in *CNPS Inventory of Rare and Endangered Plants of California* on "List 1B, Plants Rare, Threatened, or Endangered in California and Elsewhere." This species was lumped into *Malacothamnus fasciculatus* in *The Jepson Manual*. After a fire in the area where several plants occurred, hundreds of plants germinated, indicating that this species responds to fire or disturbance.

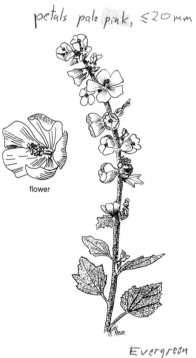

petals pale pink, ≤20mm

flower

Evergreen shrub
Ht. to 5m

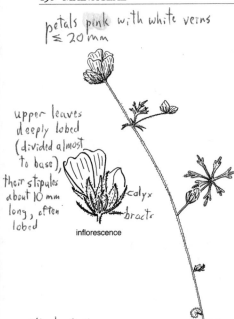

petals pink with white veins
≤ 20mm

upper leaves
deeply lobed
(divided almost
to base),
their stipules
about 10 mm
long, often
lobed

calyx

bracts

inflorescence

Ht. to 0.6m

Sidalcea diploscypha (Torrey & A. Gray) Benth.

FRINGED CHECKERBLOOM   Native

Flowering Time: April–May

Habitat: serpentine grassland

Description: Annual to 6 dm, bristly-hairy. Leaves alternate, simple to 20 mm, deeply divided and lobed; petiole to 20 mm; stipules linear to 10 mm. Inflorescence a spike-like raceme; pedicel to 2 mm; bracts to 1 cm; sepals to 12 mm; petals to 2 cm, pink with white veins; stamen on a column to 10 mm; stigmas linear, thread-like. Fruit a capsule with 5 segments, to 3 mm.

Genus & Specific Name Derivation: Greek: combination of two genera in the Mallow Family, *Sida* and *Alcea* / two cup

Notes: Hollyhock is in this family. Some flowers are unisexual and will have male or female parts only.

Uses Past and Present: Other genera within this family have edible and medicinal uses.

petals pink with white veins
≤ 15mm

upper leaves
moderately
lobed,
their stipules
< 6mm long,
linear

J

Ht. to 0.6m   fruit segment

Sidalcea malviflora (DC.) Benth. ssp. *malviflora*

CHECKER MALLOW   Native / CHECKERBLOOM

Flowering Time: February–June

Habitat: grassland

Description: Perennial from well developed rhizomes, stem to 6 dm, whole plant coarsely to bristly-hairy. Leaves simple, alternate to 3 cm, lower rounded and shallowly lobed, upper more deeply lobed; petiole to 6 cm; stipules linear to 6 mm, on each side of the upper leaves. Inflorescence a spike-like raceme of evenly spaced flowers; pedicel to 6 mm; bracts linear, to 5 mm, sometimes toothed; sepals to 12 mm; petals to 1.5 cm, pink with white veins. Fruit a capsule, segments to 4 mm.

Genus & Specific Name Derivation: Greek: combination of two genera in the Mallow Family, *Sida* and *Alcea* / mallow-flower-like

Notes: See *S. diploscypha*. Illustration from *Illustrated Flora of the Pacific States*. Correct specific epithet and ssp. spelling updated from *The Jepson Manual Corrections* — Installment No. 4.

Uses Past and Present: See *S. diploscypha*.

Photo in R & B plate 35

Myricaceae — Wax Myrtle Family

Large shrubs or small trees, aromatic, evergreen or deciduous, monoecious or dioecious, generally with nitrogen-fixing bacteria in roots. Leaves simple, alternate. Inflorescence a spike, axillary, catkin-like, staminate and pistillate spikes separate. Flowers unisexual. Staminate flowers with 2 bractlets, sepals and petals 0. Pistillate flowers with 2–4 bractlets; ovary superior, styles 2, stigmas 2, short. Fruit a drupe or nut. Fruit of some myrtles are boiled to produce a fragrant wax.

For key to woody plants *see* Group 2. Woody Plants

Morella californica (Cham. & Schltdl.) Wilbur *formerly Myrica*

WAX MYRTLE   Native

Flowering Time: April–June

Habitat: woodland

Description: Evergreen shrub or small tree to 10 m. Leaves alternate, simple to 9 cm, margin toothed, glossy green above, lighter beneath. Petiole to 5 mm, thick, leaf blade tapers into petiole. Flowers unisexual, small, on the same plant (monoecious), located in dense short spikes between leaves near branch tips. Staminate flowers with 7–16 stamens, no sepals or petals but 2 bracts below them. Pistillate flowers with 2–4 bracts; ovary superior, style 1, stigma 2-lobed. Fruit a drupe, covered with dark resin and a whitish wax.

Genus & Specific Name Derivation: Derivation unknown / from California

Notes: Leaf is spicy-scented, especially on warm days. Common name refers to the waxy covering on the fruit. New name accepted by *Jepson Manual* staff, name in *The Jepson Manual* (1993) *Myrica californica*.

Uses Past and Present: The fragrance of bayberry candles comes from the eastern species which have waxier fruits. Leaves and bark used medicinally for inflamed gums, leaves used as a tea for relief of cold, sinus allergies.

petals absent

Evergreen shrub or small tree Ht. to 10m

Myrtaceae — Myrtle Family

Evergreen shrubs or trees, often aromatic. Leaves alternate or opposite, simple. Inflorescence in racemes, umbels, or corymbs. Flowers bisexual, regular. Hypanthium present; perianth parts free or fused into a deciduous cap; sepals 4–5; petals 4–5; stamens many; ovary inferior, style 1. Fruit a berry or capsule. Some cultivated as ornamentals; some species contain toxins.

For key to woody plants *see* Group 2. Woody Plants

fruit

Evergreen
Tree

Eucalyptus globulus Labill.

BLUE GUM   Nonnative / Australia

Flowering Time: April–June

Habitat: disturbed woodland

Description: Evergreen tree to 45 m; bark gray-white, shed in irregular strips. Leaves alternate, simple to 20 cm, aromatic. Inflorescence solitary in leaf axils. Flower regular; hypanthium to 2 cm, warty, bluish-white, waxy; sepals, petals 4–5, separate, minute; stamens many, cream-white; ovary inferior, style 1. Fruit a capsule to 2 cm, 4-ribbed, warty.

Genus & Specific Name Derivation: Greek: well covered, from deciduous flower bud cap / small rounded head

Notes: Most easily recognized because of the solitary flowers and fruits.

Uses Past and Present: Young leaves used for respiratory problems.

Eucalyptus pulverulenta Sims.

SILVER-LEAVED GUM / MONEY TREE

Nonnative / Australia

Flowering Time: February–March

Habitat: disturbed woodland

Description: Evergreen tree, older bark gray-white, shed in thin strips. Leaves of two kinds: juvenile opposite, sessile to 2 cm, gray-green; adult alternate to 10 cm, short-petioled. Inflorescence an umbel, 3-flowered. Flower regular; hypanthium to 6 mm; sepals, petals 4–5, separate, minute; stamens many, white to pale yellow; ovary inferior, style 1. Fruit a cup-shaped capsule to 9 mm.

Genus & Specific Name Derivation: Greek: well covered, from the deciduous flower bud cap / powdery, referring to the white cast to the leaves

Notes: Flower color is from numerous stamens. Introduced into California because of the oval gray leaves that are used in flower arrangements.

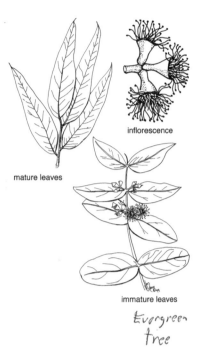

inflorescence

mature leaves

immature leaves

Evergreen tree

Oleaceae — Olive Family

Large shrubs or trees. Leaves alternate or opposite, simple to compound. Inflorescence axillary or terminal in racemes or panicles, sometimes solitary. Flowers bisexual or unisexual, usually regular. Calyx fused with 4 or more lobes; petals 4–6, sometimes absent, fused; stamens 2; pistil 1, ovary superior. Fruit a drupe, achene or samara. Some species cultivated as ornamentals, including jasmine, privet and lilac.

For key to woody plants *see* Group 2. Woody Plants

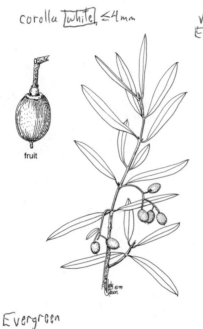

corolla white, ≤4mm

fruit

Evergreen tree

√ *Olea europaea* L.

E OLIVE   Nonnative / Eurasia, Africa

Flowering Time: March–May

Habitat: disturbed open woodland

Description: Evergreen tree to 10 m. Leaves opposite, simple to 3 cm, entire, upper dark green and sparsely hairy, lower white, densely silver-hairy; short-petioled. Sepals and petals 4-lobed, fused; corolla to 4 mm, margins in-rolled, white. Fruit a drupe to 2 cm, oily, green, becoming black.

Genus & Specific Name Derivation: Greek: ancient name / from Europe

Notes: Some trees were probably planted, other have invaded native habitats.

Uses Past and Present: Widely cultivated for food and cooking oil for more than 6,000 years.

Onagraceae — Evening Primrose Family

Annuals, herbaceous perennials. Leaves alternate, opposite, or in a basal rosette. Inflorescence a raceme, solitary or axillary. Flowers bisexual, regular. Calyx 4-lobed; corolla 4-lobed, fused to a hypanthium; stamens 4, 8 or 10, fused to the hypanthium; ovary inferior, style 1, stigma 4-lobed or head-like. Fruit a capsule with 1 to many seeds. Ornamentals include fuchsia.

Family Characteristics

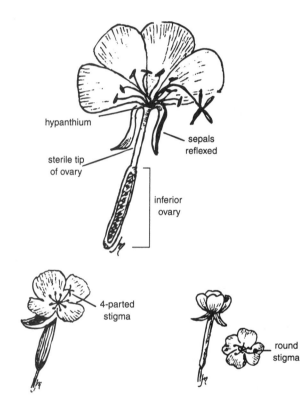

For key to families *see* Group 3. Herbaceous Flowering Plant Families

Key to Herbaceous Plants:

1. Flowers yellow
    2. Leaves linear, narrow ...*Camissonia graciliflora* (SLENDER-FLOWERED PRIMROSE)
    2´ Leaves ovate, margin wavy .... *Camissonia ovata* (SUN CUP)
1´ Flowers white, pink to purple
    3. Petals notched; seeds usually with tufts of silky hairs
        4. Inflorescence spike-like; whole plant glandular-hairy ....
        .... *Epilobium densiflorum* (DENSE-FLOWERED BOISDUVALIA)
        4´ Inflorescence of other types
            5. Annual; stem peeling; leaves narrow, upper often clustered
                6. Plant less than 5 dm, nonglandular ....
                .... *Epilobium minutum* (MINUTE WILLOW HERB)
                6´ Plants greater than 10 dm, glandular ....
                .... *Epilobium brachycarpum* (PANICLED WILLOW HERB)
            5´ Perennial; stem not peeling; leaves not clustered ....
                .... *Epilobium ciliatum* (COMMON WILLOW HERB)
    3´ Petals not notched but may be slightly fringed; seeds without tufts of hairs
        7. Petals less than 1.5 cm, pale pink with an obvious darker spot at tip
            .... *Clarkia purpurea* ssp. *quadrivulnera* (FOUR-SPOT)
        7´ Petals mostly longer than 2 cm, dark pink ....
            .... *Clarkia rubicunda* (FAREWELL-TO-SPRING)

Camissonia graciliflora (Hook. & Arn.) Raven

E   HILL SUN CUP   Native

Flowering Time: March–April

Habitat: serpentine grassland

Description: Low-growing annual to 4 cm. Leaves simple to 4 cm, most at the base of the plant, linear, hairy. Sessile. Inflorescence arising from a cluster of leaves. Sepals to 5 mm, folded back, sometimes paired together; petals 4, to 18 mm, bright yellow; stamens 8, inserted; stigma round; ovary inferior, below the floral tube surrounded by the leaves. Fruit a capsule to 8 mm, 4-angled.

Genus & Specific Name Derivation: L. A. von Chamisso (1781–1838), French-born German botanist, he named the California poppy when he visited California in 1816 / slender or graceful flower

Not in Kozloff and Beidleman
Compari to C. ovata
Jepson manual: annual, fruit winged

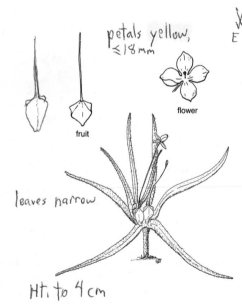

petals yellow, ≤18 mm

flower

fruit

leaves narrow

Ht. to 4 cm

√ *Camissonia ovata* (Torrey & A. Gray) Raven

E SUN CUP   Native

Flowering Time: February–June

Habitat: grassland

Description: Low-growing herbaceous perennial from a fleshy taproot. Leaves basal, simple to 8 cm, margin wavy. Petiole to 1 cm. Inflorescence erect from the base of leaves; flowers to 3 cm wide, bright yellow; sepals separate at base but somewhat fused together at the tip, folded back; petals to 2 cm; stamens 8, exserted, anthers round, pollen yellow, sticky; ovary underground at base of leaves. Fruit a capsule.

Genus & Specific Name Derivation: L.A. von Chamisso (1781–1838), French-born German botanist, he named the California poppy when he visited California in 1816 / egg-shaped, referring to the petal shape

Notes: The pollen must get to the ovary by way of the long floral tube. Seed dispersal from the underground ovary may be by ants or cracking of clay-like soil.

Photo in K & B plate 36

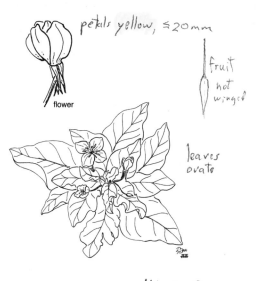

petals yellow, ≤20mm

flower

fruit not winged

leaves ovate

Ht. to 3 cm

√ *Clarkia purpurea* (Curtis) Nelson & J. F. Macbr.

E ssp. *quadrivulnera* (Douglas) Harlan Lewis & M. Lewis

FOUR-SPOT   Native / WINE CUP

Flowering Time: April–July

Habitat: grassland

Description: Upright annual to 30 cm. Leaves simple, alternate to 4 cm, linear, margin entire; sessile. Inflorescence axillary; sessile. Sepals to 1 cm, separate but may fold back in pairs, light green tinged with pink; petals to 15 mm, pink, with a darker spot at the tip and base; stigma slightly 4-lobed. Fruit an elongated capsule to 1.5 cm with 8 ribs.

Genus & Specific Name Derivation: For Captain William Clark, (1770–1838), of the Lewis and Clark Expedition / purple, referring to the color of petals / four purple spots, referring to the spots at petal bases

Compare to C. rubicunda

petals pink with darker spots at tip and base, ≤15mm

Ht. to 30 cm

petals pink, often with darker bases ≤30 mm

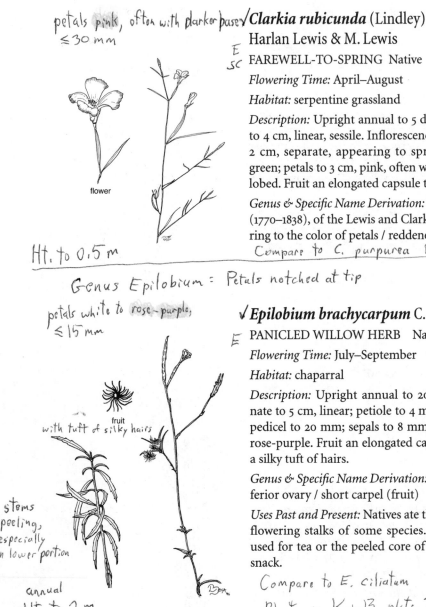

flower

Ht. to 0.5 m

Clarkia rubicunda (Lindley) Harlan Lewis & M. Lewis

E SC

FAREWELL-TO-SPRING Native

Flowering Time: April–August

Habitat: serpentine grassland

Description: Upright annual to 5 dm. Leaves alternate, simple to 4 cm, linear, sessile. Inflorescence axillary; sessile; sepals to 2 cm, separate, appearing to spread to one side, pinkish-green; petals to 3 cm, pink, often with a darker base; stigma 4-lobed. Fruit an elongated capsule to 3 cm.

Genus & Specific Name Derivation: For Captain William Clark, (1770–1838), of the Lewis and Clark Expedition / purple, referring to the color of petals / reddened

Compare to C. purpurea Photo in K & B plate 38

Genus Epilobium = Petals notched at tip

petals white to rose-purple, ≤15 mm

with tuft of silky hairs

fruit

stems peeling, especially in lower portion

annual
Ht. to 2 m

✓ *Epilobium brachycarpum* C. Presl

E

PANICLED WILLOW HERB Native

Flowering Time: July–September

Habitat: chaparral

Description: Upright annual to 20 dm. Leaves simple, alternate to 5 cm, linear; petiole to 4 mm. Inflorescence a raceme; pedicel to 20 mm; sepals to 8 mm; petals to 15 mm, white to rose-purple. Fruit an elongated capsule to 35 mm; seeds with a silky tuft of hairs.

Genus & Specific Name Derivation: Greek: upon pod, from inferior ovary / short carpel (fruit)

Uses Past and Present: Natives ate the young shoots, leaves and flowering stalks of some species. More mature plants were used for tea or the peeled core of the stems was chewed as a snack.

Compare to E. ciliatum
Photo in K & B plate 38

Epilobium ciliatum Raf. ssp. *ciliatum*

COMMON WILLOW HERB   Native

Flowering Time: June–August

Habitat: grassland, seeps

Description: Herbaceous perennial to 20 dm. Leaves opposite, simple to 6 cm; petiole to 8 mm. Inflorescence a raceme; pedicel to 10 mm; sepals to 4 mm; petals to 5 mm, light pink; stigma club-shaped. Fruit a capsule to 10 cm; seeds with a tuft of silky hairs.

Genus & Specific Name Derivation: Greek: upon pod, from inferior ovary / fringed with hairs, referring to the hairs within the inflorescence

Notes: Illustration from *Illustrated Flora of the Pacific States.*

Uses Past and Present: See *E. brachycarpum.*

Compare to E. brachycarpum

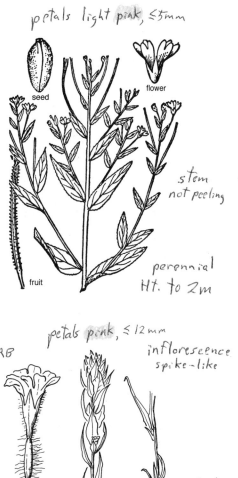

petals light pink, ≤5mm

seed

flower

stem not peeling

perennial
Ht. to 2m

fruit

Epilobium densiflorum (Lindley) P. Hoch & Raven

E   DENSE-FLOWERED BOISDUVALIA   Native/WILLOW HERB

Flowering Time: June–August

Habitat: grassland, seeps

Description: Annual to 5 dm, sometimes branched, whole plant glandular-hairy. Leaves alternate, simple to 3 cm, upper leaves more reduced. Inflorescence a spike, sessile; sepals to 4 mm, fused; petals to 12 mm, fused, deeply lobed, pink; stamens and style inserted. Fruit an elongated capsule to 11 mm.

Genus & Specific Name Derivation: Greek: upon pod, from inferior ovary / densely flowered

Common name Boisduvalia is the former genus name
for several plants now merged into Epilobium

petals pink, ≤12mm

infloresecence
spike-like

flower

plant
glandular-
hairy

Ht. to 0.5m

petals rose-lavender to white,
≤ 4mm

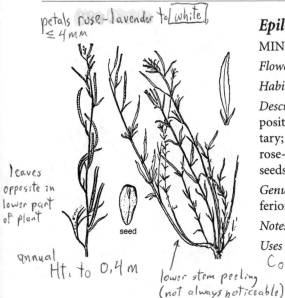

leaves
opposite in
lower part
of plant

seed

annual
Ht. to 0.4 m

lower stem peeling
(not always noticeable)

Epilobium minutum Lehm.

MINUTE WILLOW HERB   Native

Flowering Time: April–May

Habitat: chaparral, grassland, seeps

Description: Annual to 4 dm. Leaves simple, alternate to opposite to 20 mm; petiole to 5 mm. Inflorescence axillary, solitary; pedicels to 10 mm; sepals to 1.5 mm; petals to 4 mm, rose-lavender to white. Fruit an elongate capsule to 2.5 cm; seeds with a silky tuft of hairs.

Genus & Specific Name Derivation: Greek: upon pod, from inferior ovary / small

Notes: Illustration from *Illustrated Flora of the Pacific States.*

Uses Past and Present: See *E. brachycarpum.*

Compare to *E. brachycarpum*

Orobanchaceae — Broom-Rape Family

Plants parasitic, annuals or herbaceous perennials. Leaves reduced, scale-like. Inflorescence spikes or racemes. Flowers bisexual, irregular. Calyx with 4–5 equal to unequal lobes; corolla 2-lipped, with 5 lobes; stamens 4; pistil 1, ovary superior, stigma 2–4-lobed. Fruit a capsule with many seeds.

For key to families *see* Group 3. Herbaceous Flowering Plant Families

Key to Herbaceous Plants:

1. Flowers 1–20; pedicels long, scapose ....
    .... *Orobanche fasciculata* (CLUSTERED BROOM-RAPE)
1´ Flowers usually more than 20; pedicel short, not scapose ....
    .... *Orobanche californica* (JEPSON'S BROOM-RAPE)

Orobanche californica Cham. & Schldl. ssp. *jepsonii* (Munz) Heckard

JEPSON'S BROOM-RAPE   Native

Flowering Time: July–September

Habitat: open chaparral and woodlands

Description: Parasitic herbaceous perennial to 35 cm, stems clustered. No true leaves. Inflorescence dense, clustered; pedicels to 4 mm; calyx to 2 cm, pale pinkish, lobes linear-triangular; corolla to 4 cm, 2-lipped, 5-lobed, whitish or pinkish to pale yellowish brown. Fruit a capsule.

Genus & Specific Name Derivation: Greek: vetch strangler, from parasitic habit / from California / for Willis Linn Jepson (1867–1946)

Notes: Parasitic on roots of host plant usually in the sunflower family. Illustration from *Illustrated Flora of the Pacific States.*

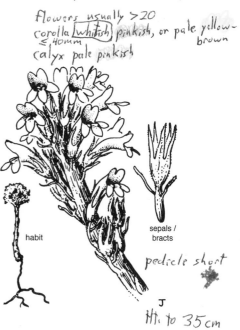

flowers usually >20
corolla whitish pinkish, or pale yellow-brown
≤ 40mm
calyx pale pinkish

habit

sepals / bracts

pedicle short

J

Ht. to 35 cm

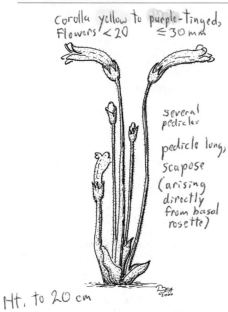

Corolla yellow to purple-tinged,
Flowers < 20   ≤ 30 mm

several
pedicles

pedicle long,
scapose
(arising
directly
from basal
rosette)

Ht. to 20 cm

Photo in K & B plate 39

Orobanche fasciculata Nutt.

CLUSTERED BROOM-RAPE   Native

Flowering Time: April–August

Habitat: chaparral

Description: Parasitic herbaceous perennial to 20 cm, stems clustered. No true leaves. Inflorescence with 1–20 flowers; flowers scapose; pedicels to 15 cm; calyx lobes to 7 mm; corolla to 30 mm, yellow to purple-tinged. Fruit a capsule.

Genus & Specific Name Derivation: Greek: vetch strangler, from parasitic habit / clustered in bunches, referring to the habit

Notes: Parasitic on roots of host plants *Artemisia, Eriodictyon, Eriogonum.*

Oxalidaceae — Wood Sorrel Family

Annuals or herbaceous perennials. Leaves basal or alternate, compound. Inflorescence in racemes or umbels. Flowers bisexual, regular. Sepals 5, separate or fused; petals 5, separate or fused; stamens 10 or 15; pistil 1, ovary superior, styles 3–5. Fruit a capsule; seeds many.

For key to families *see* Group 3. Herbaceous Flowering Plant Families

√ *Oxalis pes-caprae* L.

E
SC

BERMUDA BUTTERCUP   Nonnative / South Africa

Flowering Time: February–June

Habitat: disturbed areas near Day Camp

Description: Herbaceous perennial; roots form bulblets. Leaves compound in a loose rosette; petiole to 12 cm; leaflets 3, to 3.5 cm, often spotted. Inflorescence umbel-like with up to 20 flowers; peduncle to 30 cm; sepals to 7 mm; petals to 3 cm, yellow. No fruit or seeds set in California.

Genus & Specific Name Derivation: Greek: sour / foot of the goat, an allusion to the shape of the leaflet.

Notes: Plants reproduce and spread by bulblets. Many eat the flower stems of this plant, which are sour, but its oxalic acid can cause kidney damage if too much is eaten. Plants toxic to sheep.

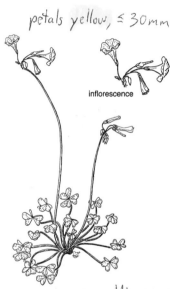

petals yellow, ≤ 30mm

inflorescence

Ht. to 0.5 m

2008 Addendum

Oxalis incarnata

FLESH-COLORED OXALIS nonnative
petals flesh-colored to yellowish, 15-20mm long
height 15-30 cm, leaves not all basal

Papaveraceae — Poppy Family

Annuals, herbaceous perennials, or shrubs. Leaves basal or cauline, usually alternate, simple to deeply dissected. Inflorescence usually solitary. Flowers bisexual, regular. Sepals 2 or 4; petals 4 or 6, free; stamens 4–many; pistil 1, ovary superior, style 1. Fruit a capsule with many seeds. Many are cultivated as ornamentals; the opium poppy is the natural source of morphine.

For key to families *see* Group 3. Herbaceous Flowering Plant Families

1. Petals golden orange, greater than 2 cm ....
    .... *Eschscholzia californica* (CALIFORNIA POPPY)
1′ Petals cream to light yellow, less than 2 cm ....
    .... *Platystemon californicus* (CREAM CUPS)

petals golden-orange,
≤ 6 cm

Ht. to 0.6 m

√ *Eschscholzia californica* Cham.

CALIFORNIA POPPY   Native

Flowering Time: April–June

Habitat: grassland, chaparral, woodland

Description: Upright annual to herbaceous perennial to 6 dm. Leaves, basal and stem to 12 cm, gray-green, compound and deeply lobed. Inflorescence axillary; peduncle to 15 cm; sepals yellow-green, forming a cap on the bud that falls off when the flowers open; petals to 6 cm, bright golden orange; stamens many; ovary elongates as the seeds ripen. Fruit an elongated capsule to 9 cm.

Genus & Specific Name Derivation: Named for J. F. Eschscholtz (1793–1831), Russian surgeon and naturalist who came to the Pacific Coast in 1816 and again in 1824 / from California. Spanish Californians called it dormidera "the drowsy one," because the petals fold at evening

Notes: This is our State flower. The type specimen of this species is in a herbarium in Leningrad, Russia. When the fruit is ripe, it is possible to hear the small black seeds popping out of the capsule. This could be a reason for the common name poppy. The flower size gets smaller as the season progresses, and the base of the petals becomes darker, possibly a signal to the changing pollinators. There are always small black beetles in the open flower. Bumblebees love this plant and can be seen landing in the flower and rolling around in it.

Uses Past and Present: The root was used by natives for numbing toothaches.

Platystemon californicus Benth.

CREAM CUPS   Native

Flowering Time: March–April

Habitat: grassland

Description: Annual to 30 cm, whole plant shaggy-hairy. Leaves basal and opposite along the stem, simple to 4 cm, margin entire, hairy. Flowers solitary, nodding in bud; pedicel to 12 cm; sepals 3, to 1 cm, falling early; petals 6, to 1.5 cm, cream, often with a darker base; stamens many with broad filaments. Fruit a capsule. ＼yellow

Genus & Specific Name Derivation: Greek: wide stamen, referring to the broad filaments / from California

Notes: On cloudy days petals curl together to protect stamens from getting wet, since water can destroy pollen.

petals cream to light yellow, up to 1.5 cm long

Ht. to 30 cm

Photo in K & B plate 40

2008 Addition

Philadelphaceae Mock-orange family

Philadelphus sp.   MOCK ORANGE nonnative

Plantaginaceae — Plantain Family

Annuals or herbaceous perennials. Leaves in basal rosettes, simple. Inflorescence dense, terminal spikes. Flowers bisexual or unisexual, regular or bilateral, each subtended by 1 bract. Calyx with 4 lobes, persistent in fruit; corollas with 4 lobes, scarious, persistent in fruit; stamens 2–4; pistil 1, ovary superior, stigma hairy. Fruit a capsule.

For key to families *see* Group 3. Herbaceous Flowering Plant Families

1.   Leaves linear, thread-like .... *Plantago erecta* (CALIFORNIA PLANTAIN)
1´ Leaves not thread-like
    2.   Leaf margin deeply lobed .... *Plantago coronopus* (CUT-LEAVED PLANTAIN)
    2´ Leaf margin entire to finely toothed ....
    .... *Plantago lanceolata* (ENGLISH PLANTAIN)

√*Plantago coronopus* L.

SC CUT-LEAVED PLANTAIN   Nonnative / Europe

Flowering Time: June–August

Habitat: grassland, woodland

Description: Annual to 30 cm, whole plant hairy. Leaves in a basal rosette, simple to 14 cm, lanceolate, margin lobed. Inflorescence a spike to 20 cm, on a long peduncle; flowers minute; petals papery, stamens exserted, ovary inferior. Fruit a capsule with 2–4 chambers, ovules small, several per chamber.

Genus & Specific Name Derivation: Latin: sole of foot, referring to the plants basal leaves lying on the ground / pupil of the eye

Notes: See *P. lanceolata.*

Uses Past and Present: The history of some species have been traced back to the Egyptians; the seeds have been found in the tombs of pharaohs, and the leaves were used as a potherb in China. The leaves were used for wound dressing, especially bites from reptiles and insects.

flower
minute

compare leaves to Agoseris (Asteraceae)

Ht. to 30 cm

√ *Plantago erecta* E. Morris

E
SC

CALIFORNIA PLANTAIN   Native

Flowering Time: March–May

Habitat: grassland

Description: Upright hairy annual to 14 cm. Leaves basal, linear to 8 cm. Inflorescence a spike to 1.5 cm; peduncle to 12 cm; flowers sessile, with 1 small linear bract at the base each flower. Sepals linear to 3 mm; petals fused, papery, thin, translucent, brown at the base of each lobe. Stamens and pistil inserted. Fruit a capsule with 2–4 chambers, ovules small, several per chamber.

Genus & Specific Name Derivation: Latin: sole of foot / upright, erect

Photo in K & B plate 41

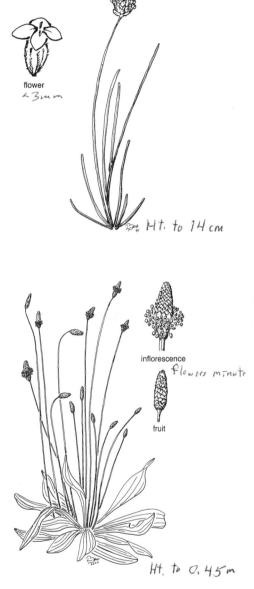

flower
< 3mm

Ht. to 14 cm

√ *Plantago lanceolata* L.

E
SC

ENGLISH PLANTAIN   Nonnative / Europe

Flowering Time: April–May

Habitat: woodland, grassland

Description: Upright, unbranched annual to 45 cm. Leaves in a basal rosette, lanceolate to 20 cm, hairy; margins entire to finely toothed, slightly wavy. Inflorescence a spike to 8 cm, on a long peduncle. Flowers minute; stamens exserted. Fruit a capsule with 2–4 chambers, ovules small, several per chamber.

Genus & Specific Name Derivation: Latin: sole of foot, referring to the basal leaves lying on the ground / narrowed and tapered at both ends, referring to the leaves

Notes: This plant is now distributed worldwide although a native of Europe. It was brought to North America by the early settlers. The natives called it "white man's foot" since it appeared shortly after every new incursion by Europeans.

Uses Past and Present: See *P. coronopus*.

inflorescence

Flowers minute

fruit

Ht. to 0.45m

Addendum (not in Toni's addenda 2008)

√ *Plantago major*   COMMON PLANTAIN Nonnative

E   in day-camp lawn   leaves about 2/3 as wide as long

Platanaceae — Plane Tree or Sycamore Family

Monoecious trees. Leaves alternate, deciduous, simple. Flowers unisexual, regular, subtended by bracts. Flowers in dense, globose heads. Sepals minute, scale-like; petals 3–6 or absent. Staminate flowers with 3–8 stamens. Pistillate flowers with 5–10 pistils, ovary superior, style 1. Fruit an achene. Bark and leaves of native species were used medicinally by natives.

For key to woody plants *see* Group 2. Woody Plants

fruit

Tree

√*Platanus* sp.

E SYCAMORE   Planted

Flowering Time: March–April

Habitat: planted at Day Camp

Description: Deciduous tree to 35 m. Leaves alternate, simple to 25 cm, palmately 3–5 lobed; petiole to 8 cm; stipules to 3 cm. Inflorescence in 3–5 heads in the axils of the leaves, spherical, many-flowered; plant monoecious, flowers unisexual; staminate flowers minute; pistillate flowers minute; ovary superior. Fruit a spherical head of small, hairy achenes.

Genus & Specific Name Derivation: Greek: broad, referring to the leaves / derivation unknown

Notes: Like big-leaf maple except the leaves of sycamore are arranged alternately, whereas the big-leaf maple has opposite leaves. Flowers and fruits are also quite different. Tree is monoecious, male and female flowers on the same plant, but in different locations. Susceptible to sycamore anthracnose.

Polemoniaceae — Phlox Family

Annuals, herbaceous perennials, or shrubs. Leaves basal, cauline, alternate or opposite, simple to compound. Inflorescence in cymes, racemes, or panicles. Flowers bisexual, regular. Calyx 5-lobed; corollas fused, with 5-lobes; stamens 5; pistil 1, ovary superior, style and stigma 3-lobed. Fruit a capsule. Many cultivated.

Family Characteristics

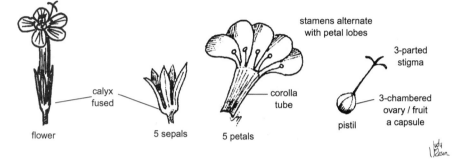

For key to families *see* Group 3. Herbaceous Flowering Plant Families

1. Plant spiny-bristly, mostly low-growing, spreading
   2. Plant densely woolly .... *Eriastrum abramsii* (ABRAMS' ERIASTRUM)
   2′ Plant glandular-hairy, not woolly
      3. Stamens exserted .... *Navarretia heterodoxa* (CALISTOGA NAVARRETIA)
      3′ Stamens included .... *Navarretia squarrosa* (SKUNKWEED)
1′ Plant not spiny-bristly, mostly upright
   4. Leaves opposite or appearing whorled
      5. Inflorescence head-like; corolla tube much longer (>2x) than the lobes
         6. Calyx hairy only on lobe margins; petals pale lavender to pink ....
         .... *Linanthus androsaceus* (COMMON LINANTHUS)
         6′ Calyx hairy throughout; petals cream-colored ....
         .... *Linanthus parviflorus* (SMALL-FLOWERED LINANTHUS)
      5′ Inflorescence not head-like
         7. Leaves opposite, deeply lobed, leaflets mostly thread-like
            8. Petals white with darker veins ....
            .... *Linanthus liniflorus* (FLAX-FLOWERED LINANTHUS)
            8′ Petals blue-purple *or pink* .. *Linanthus ambiguus* (SERPENTINE LINANTHUS)
         7′ Leaves opposite, simple, not deeply lobed ....
         .... *Phlox gracilis* (SLENDER PHLOX)
   4′ Leaves alternate or basal
      9. Petals pink to white ... *Collomia heterophylla* (VARIED-LEAVED COLLOMIA)
      9′ Petals blue .... *Gilia clivorum* (GRASSLAND GILIA)

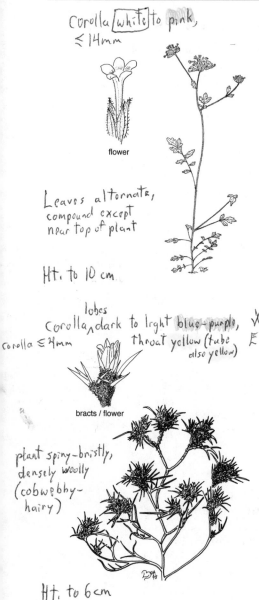

Corolla white to pink,
≤ 14mm

flower

Leaves alternate,
compound except
near top of plant

Ht. to 10 cm

Collomia heterophylla Hook.

VARIED-LEAVED COLLOMIA   Native

Flowering Time: April–July

Habitat: woodland

Description: Small annual to 10 cm, stem usually branched. Leaves alternate, simple, margin deeply lobed. Inflorescence axillary and terminal clusters of up to 25 flowers; calyx to 8 mm; corolla to 14 mm, white to pink. Fruit an ovoid capsule.

Genus & Specific Name Derivation: Greek: glue, from wet seed surface / diverse leaves

Photo in K & B plate 41

lobes
Corolla dark to lrght blue-purple,
throat yellow (tube
also yellow)

corolla ≤ 4mm

bracts / flower

plant spiny-bristly,
densely woolly
(cobwebby-
hairy)

Ht. to 6 cm

Eriastrum abramsii (Elmer) H. Mason

ABRAMS' ERIASTRUM   Native

Flowering Time: June–July

Habitat: chaparral

Description: Low-growing annual to 6 cm, plant with white, cobwebby hairs. Leaves alternate, simple to 2 cm, deeply lobed, thread-like, woolly; sessile. Inflorescence bracted heads, densely woolly; bracts spiny, leaf-like; flowers sessile; calyx fused, lobes to 3 mm; corolla to 4 mm, dark to light blue-purple, throat yellow. Fruit a capsule.

Genus & Specific Name Derivation: Greek: woolly star / for L. Abrams (1874–1956), professor of botany, Stanford University; author of *Flora of Los Angeles and Vicinity* and *Illustrated Flora of the Pacific States*

Compare to Navarretia spp.

Gilia clivorum (Jepson) V. Grant ✓

GRASSLAND GILIA   Native

Flowering Time: March–June

Habitat: grassland

Description: Upright annual to 15 cm. Leaves basal and alternate, blade to 6 cm, simple to compound, 1–2-pinnate; petiole to 7 mm. Inflorescence a cluster of 2–5 flowers; calyx to 5 mm, green with a darker membrane; corolla to 8 mm, fused, blue; anthers with blue pollen. Fruit a capsule with many small seeds.

Genus & Specific Name Derivation: For Felipe Gil (1756–1821), Spanish botanist / of the hills

[handwritten: Corolla blue, ≤ 8mm]

[handwritten: sepals / fruit]

[handwritten: may be whitish on most of lobes except at tips]

[handwritten: leaves alternate compound except near top of plant]

[handwritten: Ht. to 15 cm]

*[handwritten: Genus Linanthus: Leaves opposite or appearing whorled *]*

Linanthus ambiguus (Rattan) E. Greene/ ~~Leptosiphon a.~~ ✓

[handwritten: Retained in Linanthus]

SERPENTINE LINANTHUS   Native

Flowering Time: March–June

Habitat: serpentine grassland

Description: Thread-like annual to 20 cm, branched above. Leaves opposite appearing whorled, palmately compound to simple, deeply lobed, lobes to 5 mm, linear. Inflorescence solitary in leaf axils; peduncle to 5 cm; calyx to 6 mm; corolla to 12 mm, blue-purple-pink to 15 mm wide, throat white to yellow, darker below. Fruit a many-seeded capsule.

Genus & Specific Name Derivation: Greek: flax flower / uncertain relationship, possibly referring to the inflorescence, which is open, compared to other species where the inflorescence is arranged in a compact head

Notes: Listed in *CNPS Inventory of Rare and Endangered Plants of California* on "List 4, Plants of Limited Distribution."

*[handwritten: corolla lobes blue-purple-pink throat white to yellow * corolla ≤ 12mm]*

[handwritten: Corolla tube less than twice as long as calyx]

[handwritten: flower]

*[handwritten: corolla lobes shorter than tube; * the yellowish is at the base of the corolla lobes; deeper in the throat the color is purple]*

[handwritten: Ht. to 20cm]

*[handwritten: * Compare to L. liniflorus]*

*[handwritten: * Genus Linanthus: Leaves mostly opposite, at least on the lower part of the plant, and palmately divided into slender, linear lobes, giving a whorled appearance to the leaves. Calyx lobes of equal length, or nearly so.]*

Inflorescence head-like
corolla pale lavender to purple-pink
Corolla tube much longer than calyx
calyx hairy only on lobe edges

flower
Corolla ≤ 20 mm wide

Ht. to 20 cm

Changed to Leptosiphon

Linanthus androsaceus (Benth.) E. Greene

COMMON LINANTHUS   Native / *PINK-LOBED LINANTHUS*

Flowering Time: March–April

Habitat: grassland

Description: Upright annual to 20 cm. Leaves opposite, appearing whorled, deeply lobed to 1 cm, bristly-hairy. Inflorescence a head of many flowers; flowers pale lavender to purple-pink, to 1.5 cm wide; sepals hidden within the bracted head, margin hairy; corolla to 2 cm wide, petal lobes to 1 cm, floral tube to 3 cm. Fruit a many-seeded capsule.

Genus & Specific Name Derivation: Greek: flax flower / male-shield

Compare to L. parviflorus

corolla white with purple veins
calyx tube no longer than calyx
anthers orange

flower
corolla lobes longer than tube
(≤ 10 mm)   *(≤ 2 mm)*

Ht. to 20 cm

Changed to Leptosiphon

√ Linanthus liniflorus (Benth.) E. Greene

E   FLAX-FLOWERED LINANTHUS   Native

Flowering Time: April–July

Habitat: grassland

Description: Upright annual to 20 cm. Leaves opposite but appearing whorled, palmately compound, deeply lobed, lobes to 3 cm, linear. Inflorescence an open panicle; pedicel to 2 cm; bracts to 2 mm; sepals to 4 mm, green; petals fused, white with purple veins, lobes to 10 mm, tube to 2 mm; anthers orange. Fruit a many-seeded capsule.

Genus & Specific Name Derivation: Greek: flax flower / linear flowers

Compare to Linaceae (flax family)
Compare to L. ambiguus

changed to Leptosiphon

✓*Linanthus parviflorus* (Benth.) E. Greene

E SMALL-FLOWERED LINANTHUS   Native

Flowering Time: April–May

Habitat: grassland

Description: Soft-hairy upright annual to 18 cm, stem often reddish. Leaves opposite, appearing whorled, deeply lobed, lobes to 2 cm. Inflorescence a head of 5–10 flowers; bracts deeply lobed, leaf-like; flowers to 1 cm wide; calyx to 1 cm with glandular hairs on whole surface of sepal lobe; corolla to 1 cm wide, petal lobes to 5 mm, cream-colored (can be pink), often with 2 red dots at the base; corolla tube to 3.5 cm, often pale red-pink. Fruit a many seeded capsule.

Genus & Specific Name Derivation: Greek: flax flower / small flowers

Notes: We have the cream-colored flower type, however there are other populations nearby that have bright pink petals.

Compare to L. androsaceus
Photo in K & B plate 42

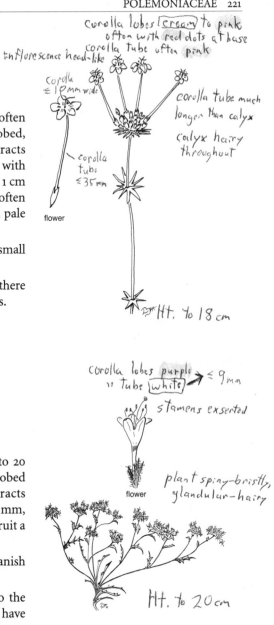

corolla lobes cream to pink often with red dots at base
corolla tube often pink
inflorescence head-like
corolla ≤ 10mm wide
corolla tube ≤ 35 mm
corolla tube much longer than calyx
calyx hairy throughout
flower
Ht. to 18 cm

✗*Navarretia heterodoxa* (E. Greene) E. Greene

E CALISTOGA NAVARRETIA   Native

Flowering Time: June–July

Habitat: woodland

Description: Low-growing branched, glandular annual to 20 cm. Leaves alternate, simple to 2 cm, deeply pinnately lobed and toothed. Inflorescence a head of many flowers; bracts widely ovate with spines and glandular hairs; sepals to 8 mm, green; corolla fused, tube white, lobes to 9 mm, purple. Fruit a many-seeded capsule.
tube ?

Genus & Specific Name Derivation: For F. Navarrete, Spanish physician (1700s) / diverse glory

Notes: Odor skunk-like. This plant adds a showiness to the edge of the chaparral when the grasses and other flowers have mostly gone to seed.
Compare to N. squarrosa

Genus Navarretia: Plant spiny-bristly, glandular-hairy

corolla lobes purple → ≤ 9mm
" tube white
stamens exserted
flower
plant spiny-bristly, glandular-hairy
Ht. to 20 cm

corolla lobes blue-purple, ≤9mm
'' tube white, 10-12mm

stamens not exserted

plant spiny-bristly,
glandular-hairy,
with skunk-
like odor

inflorescence

Ht. to 0.5m

√ *Navarretia squarrosa* (Eschsch.) Hook.& Arn.

E   SKUNKWEED   Native

Flowering Time: May–October

Habitat: grassland and chaparral edges

Description: Low-growing, glandular annual to 50 cm. Leaves alternate, simple to 20 mm, lower 1–2 pinnate, lobes linear, upper shorter, spiny. Inflorescence a head of many flowers; bracts widely ovate with spines and glandular hairs; sepals to 10 mm, green; corolla to 12 mm, petals fused, tube white, lobes to 9 mm, blue-purple. Fruit a many-seeded capsule.

Genus & Specific Name Derivation: For F. Navarrete, Spanish physician (1700s) / rough, spreading in many directions, referring to the forked and spreading spines of the leaves

Notes: Odor skunk-like.

Compare to N. heterodoxa

corolla lobes pink, ≤2mm

leaves opposite, simple, entire

Ht. to 6cm

Phlox gracilis (Hook.) E. Greene

SLENDER PHLOX   Native

Flowering Time: February–April

Habitat: grassland

Description: Upright annual to 6 cm, whole plant hairy. Leaves opposite, simple to 8 mm, margin entire; sessile. Inflorescence one to several terminal flowers; calyx to 6 mm, fused, green, hairy; corolla fused, lobes to 2 mm, pink. Fruit a many-seeded capsule.

Genus & Specific Name Derivation: Greek: flame, ancient name for *Lychnis* of Caryophyllaceae / slender or graceful

Notes: Correct authority updated from *The Jepson Manual Corrections* — Installment No. 5.

Photo in K & B plate 42

Polygonaceae — Buckwheat Family

Annuals, herbaceous perennials, or shrubs, monoecious or dioecious. Leaves basal and cauline, alternate, opposite, or whorled; stipules absent or present and fused into a sheath around the stem. Inflorescence in spikes, panicles, or umbel-like clusters, sometimes subtended by an involucre of bracts. Flowers bisexual to unisexual, regular. <u>Perianth parts 5–6</u>, free or fused, persistent; stamens 3–9, in whorls of 3; pistil 1, ovary superior, styles 2–3. Fruit a 3-angled achene. Some cultivated for food, e.g., rhubarb, sorrel.

For key to woody plants see Group 2. Woody Plants

For key to families *see* Group 3. Herbaceous Flowering Plant Families

Key to Herbaceous Plants:

1. Leaves mostly basal, leaf undersurface white-hairy
    2. Plant a herbaceous perennial greater than 3 dm .... *Eriogonum nudum* (NAKED-STEMMED BUCKWHEAT)
    2′ Plant an annual, usually less than 3 dm .... *Eriogonum luteolum* (WICKER BUCKWHEAT)
1′ Leaves opposite, alternate, not mostly basal
    3. Leaves opposite, simple, margin deeply lobed .... *Pterostegia drymarioides* (PTEROSTEGIA)
    3′ Leaves alternate, some may be basal
        4. Inflorescence axillary with 1–3 flowers, perianth pinkish-white .... *Polygonum arenastrum* (COMMON KNOTWEED)
        4′ Inflorescence open often branched
            5. Plant low-growing, spreading ...... *Rumex salicifolius* (WILLOW DOCK)
            5′ Plant upright
                6. Leaves generally 2-lobed at the base .... *Rumex acetosella* (SHEEP SORREL)
                6′ Leaves without lobes at base
                    7. Inflorescence branched, open
                        8. Inner perianth margin toothed .... *Rumex obtusifolius* (BITTER DOCK)
                        8′ Inner perianth margin entire .... *Rumex conglomeratus* (GREEN DOCK)
                    7′ Inflorescence dense, narrow; inner perianth with a large tubercle .... *Rumex crispus* (CURLY DOCK)

corolla lobes pale pink with darker stripe on back

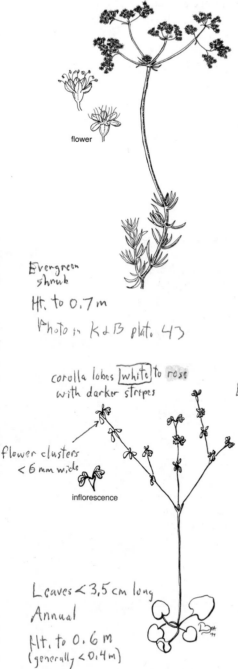

flower

Evergreen shrub

Ht. to 0.7 m

Photo in K & B plat. 43

corolla lobes [white] to rose with darker stripes

flower clusters < 6 mm wide

inflorescence

Leaves < 3.5 cm long

Annual

Ht. to 0.6 m
(generally < 0.4 m)

√ **Eriogonum fasciculatum** Benth.

E var. **foliolosum** (Nutt.) Abrams

CALIFORNIA BUCKWHEAT   Native

Flowering Time: July–September

Habitat: grassland

Description: Evergreen shrub to 7 dm. Leaves alternate, simple, in clusters or fascicles, to 1.5 cm, linear; margin rolled under. Inflorescence of umbel-like heads; bracts at base of umbel sometimes single, sometimes fascicled, to 5 mm, green; flowers in clusters, regular; bract below each cluster fused, to 5 mm; sepals 6; petals to 2 mm, 6 lobed, fused, whitish pink, with darker pink stripe on back; stamens 10, exserted; ovary superior. Fruit an achene to 3 mm.

Genus & Specific Name Derivation: Greek: woolly knees, from hairy nodes of some / fascicled, referring to the leaves being bunched together

Notes: There is only one plant known at Edgewood; it occurs off-trail.

Uses Past and Present: Important honey plant, therefore planted widely. Also used medicinally by natives to soothe and shrink swollen membranes. A tea was used for eyewash and for washing newborn babies. The dried flowers were used as a diuretic.

√ **Eriogonum luteolum** E. Greene. var. **luteolum**

E WICKER BUCKWHEAT   Native / GREENE'S BUCKWHEAT

Flowering Time: July–September

Habitat: serpentine grassland

Description: Upright annual to 60 cm. Leaves mostly basal to 3 cm, round, hairy especially the undersurface. Inflorescence cyme-like, open and unevenly branched; bracts scale-like; perianth segments to 3 mm, white to rose with darker stripes. Fruit an achene to 2 mm.

Genus & Specific Name Derivation: Greek: woolly knees, from hairy nodes of some / yellowish referring to the flower color of some, but not our species

Notes: See *E. nudum.*

Uses Past and Present: See *E. nudum.*

X *Eriogonum nudum* Benth.
E var. *auriculatum* (Benth.) Jepson
S c NAKED-STEMMED BUCKWHEAT   Native / *CURLY-LEAVED*

Flowering Time: June–September

Habitat: serpentine grassland

Description: Herbaceous perennial to 6 dm. Leaves simple to 7 cm, mostly basal, margin wavy, undersurface white-hairy, upper dark green. Petiole to 5 cm. Inflorescence open, branched, flowers in head-like umbels; individual flowers sessile; bracts to 6 mm, vase-like; perianth segments to 2 mm, pinkish-white. Fruit an achene to 3.5 mm.

Genus & Specific Name Derivation: Greek: woolly knees, from hairy nodes of some / naked, referring to the leafless upper stems

Notes: Our species is not the edible buckwheat; that species is *Fagopyrum esculentum* native to Asia.

Uses Past and Present: Natives made a tea for washing newborn babies and for headaches.

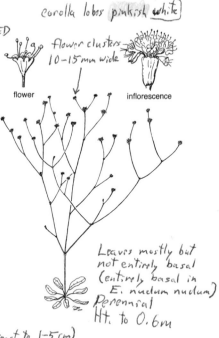

corolla lobes pinkish white

flower clusters 10-15 mm wide

flower   inflorescence

Leaves mostly but not entirely basal (entirely basal in E. nudum nudum) Perennial Ht. to 0.6m

differs from E. nudum nudum in having leaves that are wavy on margins and longer (3-7cm in contrast to 1-5cm)

✓ *Polygonum arenastrum* Boreau
5C COMMON KNOTWEED   Nonnative / Europe

Flowering Time: May–October

Habitat: disturbed areas along trails and roads

Description: Trailing, spreading annual to herbaceous perennial, stems to 30 cm. Leaves alternate, simple to 1.5 cm, sometimes clustered. Stipules to 5 mm, white to tan, pinkish at base; petioles minute. Inflorescence of 1–3 flowers in the leaf axils all along the stem; flowers small to 2 mm, pinkish-white. Fruit an achene; seed hard, black.

Genus & Specific Name Derivation: Greek: many knees, from swollen nodes of some species / resembling *Arenaria*, a sand dweller, referring to its habitat

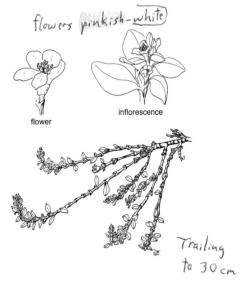

flowers pinkish-white

flower   inflorescence

Trailing to 30 cm

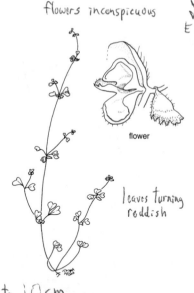

flowers inconspicuous

flower

leaves turning reddish

Ht. to 10 cm

X *Pterostegia drymarioides* Fischer & C. Meyer

E PTEROSTEGIA   Native

Flowering Time: March–April

Habitat: open areas in chaparral, woodland

Description: Low-growing, spreading annual. Leaves opposite, simple to 5 mm, hairy, deeply lobed, turning reddish later; petiole to 5 mm. Inflorescence axillary with 1–2 flowers; flowers inconspicuous, of 2 kinds, staminate and pistillate on same plant, pistillate flowers with an involucre bract. Fruit more obvious than the flowers; fruit to 1.5 mm, brownish when mature.

Genus & Specific Name Derivation: Greek: winged cover, from the involucre / from the forest or woodland, referring to the habitat

Notes: This is the only plant in this genus in California.

perianth reddish

Leaves two-lobed at base

leaf

Ht. to 0.4 m

√ *Rumex acetosella* L.

E SHEEP SORREL   Nonnative / Europe

Flowering Time: March–September

Habitat: nonserpentine grassland

Description: Upright herbaceous perennial to 4 dm, spreading and forming colonies from underground rhizomes. Leaves mostly basal but some alternate, simple to 10 cm, arrowhead-shaped, lobed at the base. Inflorescence open and branched; perianth reddish, lobes 6, margin entire, outer 3 inconspicuous, inner 3 conspicuous in fruit, without tubercles. Fruit an achene, brown, shiny.

Genus & Specific Name Derivation: Latin: sorrel / slightly acid, sour, referring to the sour-tasting leaves of a close relative, French sorrel (*Rumex acetosa*)

Notes: Clonal stands are formed by underground rhizomes.

Photo in K & B plate 44

Rumex conglomeratus Murray

GREEN DOCK   Nonnative / Europe

Flowering Time: April–October

Habitat: wet disturbed areas

Description: Upright herbaceous perennial to 15 dm, branched above in flower. Leaves alternate, simple to 15 cm, upper shorter, margin wavy. Petiole to 5 cm. Inflorescence branched, flowers in whorls; perianth lobes 6, margin entire, outer 3 inconspicuous, inner 3 to 3 mm, conspicuous in fruit; tubercles usually on each lobe. Fruit to 2 mm.

Genus & Specific Name Derivation: Latin: sorrel / clustered, crowded together, referring to crowded flower clusters

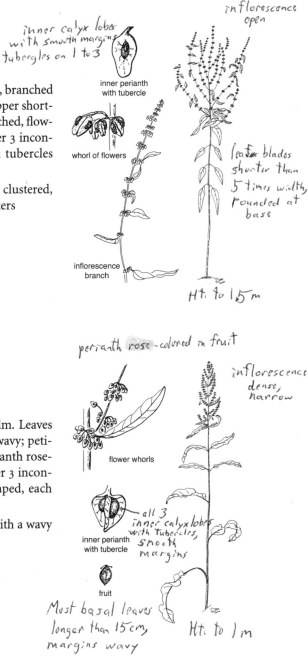

inflorescence open

inner calyx lobes with smooth margins tubercles on 1 to 3

inner perianth with tubercle

whorl of flowers

inflorescence branch

leaf blades shorter than 5 times width, rounded at base

Ht. to 1.5 m

Rumex crispus L.

CURLY DOCK   Nonnative / Eurasia

Flowering Time: April–July

Habitat: disturbed seeps, swales

Description: Upright herbaceous perennial to 10 dm. Leaves alternate, simple to 20 cm, upper shorter, margin wavy; petiole to 5 cm. Inflorescence dense, narrow, leafy; perianth rose-colored when fruiting, lobes 6, margin entire, outer 3 inconspicuous, inner 3 to 5 mm, roundish to heart-shaped, each with a large tubercle. Fruit to 2 mm.

Genus & Specific Name Derivation: Latin: sorrel / with a wavy or curled margin

Notes: This species has a long carrot-like taproot.

Photo in K & B plate 44

perianth rose-colored in fruit

inflorescence dense, narrow

flower whorls

all 3 inner calyx lobes with tubercles, smooth margins

inner perianth with tubercle

fruit

Most basal leaves longer than 15 cm, margins wavy

Ht. to 1 m

margins of lobes
with short teeth

inner perianth
with tubercle

only 1 of the 3
inner calyx lobes
with tubercle

inflorescence
open

Ht. to 1m

✓ *Rumex obtusifolius* L

SC
E

BITTER DOCK   Nonnative / Mediterranean

Flowering Time: May–September

Habitat: woodland

Description: Upright herbaceous perennial to 1 m. Leaves alternate, simple to 12 cm. Inflorescence branched, spreading; perianth lobes 6, outer 3 inconspicuous, inner 3 to 5 mm, with 1 tubercle, margin toothed. Fruit to 3 mm.

Genus & Specific Name Derivation: Latin: sorrel / blunt or rounded

Notes: Hybridizes with *R. crispus*.

Rumex salicifolius J. A. Weinm. var. *salicifolius*

WILLOW DOCK   Native

Flowering Time: May–August

Habitat: grassland

Description: Low-growing, spreading herbaceous perennial. Leaves simple, alternate to 20 cm, blade linear. Inflorescence dense to open; perianth lobes 6, outer 3 inconspicuous, inner 3 to 5 mm, rounded with 1 tubercle, margin entire. Fruit to 3 mm.

Genus & Specific Name Derivation: Latin: sorrel / willow-like, referring to the leaves

Uses Past and Present: Natives pulverized the leaves, moistened them with water, and ate them with salt. The seeds are commonly eaten by ground-feeding birds, and deer browse on the leaves.

inner calyx lobes
with smooth
margins,
with 1 tubercle

outer and
inner perianth
lobes

leaf blades
more than 5 times
longer than wide,
tapering to
petiole

Ht. to 0.8 m

inflorescence

Addendum (not on Toni's 2008 addendum)

✓ *Rumex pulcher*

E FIDDLE DOCK Nonnative

Margins of lobes with many fairly long teeth
all three of inner calyx lobes with tubercles

~~three species~~

Four subspecies of *R. salicifolius*:

R. s. crassus: prostrate to decumbent, inflorescence short (< 15 cm), dense one wide tubercle

not prostrate {

R. s. denticulatus: inner 3 calyx lobes with short teeth no tubercles

R. s. salicifolius: inner 3 calyx lobes not toothed one tubercle, not wide

R. s. transitorius: inner 3 calyx lobes not toothed one wide tubercle

Portulacaceae — Purslane Family

Annuals or herbaceous perennials. Leaves basal and cauline' alternate or opposite. Inflorescence in racemes, panicles or solitary. Flowers bisexual, regular. Sepals usually 2, free or fused; petals 3–many, free or fused at the base; stamens 1–many; ovary superior or partly inferior; style and stigma branches 2–8. Fruit a capsule. Some species are edible or cultivated as ornamentals.

For key to families *see* Group 3. Herbaceous Flowering Plant Families

Key to Herbaceous Plants:

1. Petals usually more than 6 .... *Lewisia rediviva* (BITTER ROOT)
1′ Petals 5
    2. Petals magenta, pollen orange .... *Calandrinia ciliata* (RED MAIDS)
    2′ Petals pink to white
        3. Upper leaves below inflorescence a round disk ....
        .... *Claytonia perfoliata* (MINER'S LETTUCE)
        3′ Upper leaves, narrow, forked ....
        .... *Claytonia exigua* (COMMON MONTIA)

√ *Calandrinia ciliata* (Ruiz Lopez & Pavon) DC.

E   RED MAIDS   Native

Flowering Time: February–June

Habitat: grassland

Description: Spreading annual to 10 cm. Leaves simple, alternate or opposite, to 4 cm, linear, bright green; sessile. Inflorescence axillary; flower 1 cm wide; sepals 2, to 8 mm, green, present when the plant is in fruit; petals 5, to 15 mm, magenta, with darker stripes at base. Stamens 3–10, anthers orange, somewhat exserted. Fruit a many-seeded capsule, seeds shiny, black.

Genus & Specific Name Derivation: For J. L. Calandrini (1703–1758), professor of mathematics and philosophy, from Switzerland / fringed, referring to the slight fringing of the petals

Uses Past and Present: A favorite component of pinole, which is a mixture of seeds gathered seasonally by natives.

Photo in K & B plate 45

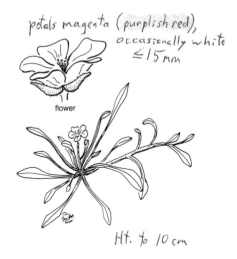

petals magenta (purplish red), occasionally white ≤15 mm

flower

Ht. to 10 cm

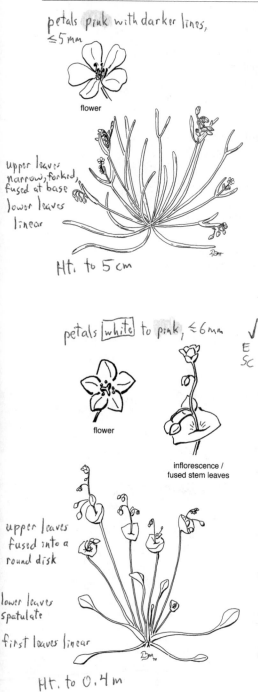

petals pink with darker lines, ≤5mm

flower

upper leaves narrow, forked, fused at base
lower leaves linear

Ht. to 5 cm

petals white to pink, ≤6mm

flower

inflorescence / fused stem leaves

upper leaves fused into a round disk

lower leaves spatulate

first leaves linear

Ht. to 0.4 m

Claytonia exigua Torrey & A. Gray ssp. *exigua*

COMMON MONTIA   Native/COMMON CLAYTONIA

Flowering Time: January–May

Habitat: serpentine grassland

Description: Gray-pink, succulent annual, stem to 5 cm. Basal leaves to 12 cm, linear; stem leaves to 8 cm, crescent-shaped and fused on one side. Inflorescence a terminal raceme with 3–15 flowers. Sepals to 3 mm, separate, pinkish; petals to 5 mm, pink with darker lines; one small bract at the base of the lower flower. Fruit a small capsule to 2 mm.

Genus & Specific Name Derivation: Named for John Clayton (1693–1773), an American botanist and Attorney General for colonial Virginia. He collected for an early flora of Virginia / very small, referring to the size of the whole plant

Uses Past and Present: Probably not used the same way as *C. perfoliata*, since the whole plant is so small.

√ *Claytonia perfoliata* Wild. ssp. *perfoliata*

E
SC
MINER'S LETTUCE   Native

Flowering Time: February–May

Habitat: grassland, woodland

Description: Spreading or upright annual to 40 cm. Leaves of different kinds, first leaves a rosette of linear leaves, followed by spatula-shaped basal leaves to 25 cm, petiole to 3 cm; stem leaves a pair, fused into a disk below the inflorescence. Inflorescence a terminal raceme with 5–40 flowers, with 1 small bract at the base of the lowest flower; sepals 2, to 5 mm, separate, red-brown; petals to 6 mm, white to pink. Fruit a roundish many-seeded capsule; seeds black, shiny.

Genus & Specific Name Derivation: Named for John Clayton (1693–1773), an American botanist and the Attorney General for colonial Virginia. He collected for an early flora of Virginia / the stem appearing to pass through the completely embracing upper leaves

Uses Past and Present: Leaves used raw or boiled, like lettuce. Miners used the leaves as an important source of vitamin C. Natives are reported to have put the leaves near the entrance of red ant holes. After the ants had swarmed on the leaves, they were shaken off, leaving a vinegary taste. This plant has been taken to Europe where it is cultivated under the name winter purslane, used for salads and as a potherb. The seeds are an important source of food for birds.

Lewisia rediviva Pursh

BITTER ROOT   Native

Flowering Time: March–June

Habitat: serpentine grassland

Description: Succulent herbaceous perennial from a deep, carrot-like taproot. Leaves in a basal rosette, to 5 cm, linear, thick. Inflorescence with several stems, flowers scapose. Sepals from 6–8, petal-like; petals from 10–20, to 3 cm, white or pink. Stamens many, stigmas from 6–8. Fruit a capsule; seeds many, dark, shiny.

Genus & Specific Name Derivation: For Captain Meriwether Lewis (1774–1809), of the Lewis and Clark Expedition / coming back to life, reviving, referring to the succulent leaves

Notes: The state flower of Montana. Illustration from *Illustrated Flora of the Pacific States.*

petals [white] to pink, more than 6
≤30mm   (10-20)

Ht. to ----

Photo in K & B plate 45

Primulaceae — Primrose Family

Annuals, herbaceous perennials, or shrubs. Leaves simple, opposite, whorled or basal. Inflorescence in racemes, umbels or axillary. Flowers bisexual, regular. Sepals 5, separate or fused; petals 4–7, separate or fused; stamens 4–5; pistil 1, ovary superior, style 1, stigma head-like. Fruit a capsule. Many species are cultivated as ornamentals.

For key to families *see* Group 3. Herbaceous Flowering Plant Families

Key to Herbaceous Plants:

1. Leaves in a basal rosette, inflorescence an umbel
    2. Anthers sharply pointed .... *Dodecatheon hendersonii* (MOSQUITO BILLS)
    2´ Anthers rounded to blunt ....
       Dodecatheon clevelandii (LOWLAND SHOOTING STAR / PADRE'S SHOOTING STAR)
1´ Leaves in other arrangements
    3. Leaves whorled .... *Trientalis latifolia* (PACIFIC STARFLOWER)
    3´ Leaves opposite .... *Anagallis arvensis* (SCARLET PIMPERNEL)

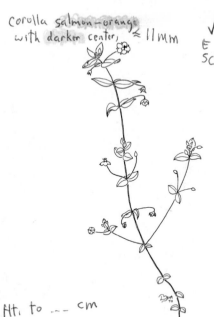

Corolla salmon–orange with darker center, ≤ 11mm

Ht. to --- cm

✓ *Anagallis arvensis* L.

E
SC
SCARLET PIMPERNEL   Nonnative / Europe

Flowering Time: all year

Habitat: grassland, chaparral, woodland

Description: Spreading, low-growing annual. Leaves simple to 20 mm, opposite, sessile. Inflorescence solitary in the leaf axils; pedicel to 3 cm; calyx to 5 mm; corolla to 11 mm, salmon-orange with a darker center. Fruit a capsule.

Genus & Specific Name Derivation: Unpretentious, or from two Greek words meaning "to delight in again," since the flowers open when the sun strikes them / of the field

Notes: Toxic to livestock, humans. Another common name is poor-man's weatherglass.

Photo in K & B plat. 45

Not on most recent addendum =
X Annagalis mollis
E   BLUE PIMPERNEL   Nonnative

Dodecatheon clevelandii E. Greene
ssp. *patulum* (E. Greene) H.J. Thompson
LOWLAND SHOOTING STAR /

PADRE'S SHOOTING STAR   Native

Flowering Time: January–March

Habitat: grassland

Description: Upright herbaceous perennial to 20 cm. Leaves in a basal rosette, simple to 12 cm, narrowed abruptly to the petiole. Inflorescence a scapose umbel of 1–6 flowers; bracts at the base of inflorescence to 7 mm. Sepal and petal lobes reflexed in flower; sepals to 5 mm, fused; petals to 2.5 cm, burgundy at base, yellow and white then pink / lavender at the top; pedicel to 3 cm. Stamens exserted, anthers rounded at tip,* dark purple, filament tube with yellow spot below each anther. Fruit a many-seeded capsule.

*generally rounded

Genus & Specific Name Derivation: Greek: 12 gods (an ancient name) / for Daniel Cleveland (1838–1929), an attorney, founder of the Bank of San Diego and the San Diego Natural History Society, also a botanical collector

Notes: Looks similar to cyclamen, which is in the same family.

(handwritten) Anther color in ssp. sanctarum usually yellow

Range of sanctarum is more coastal

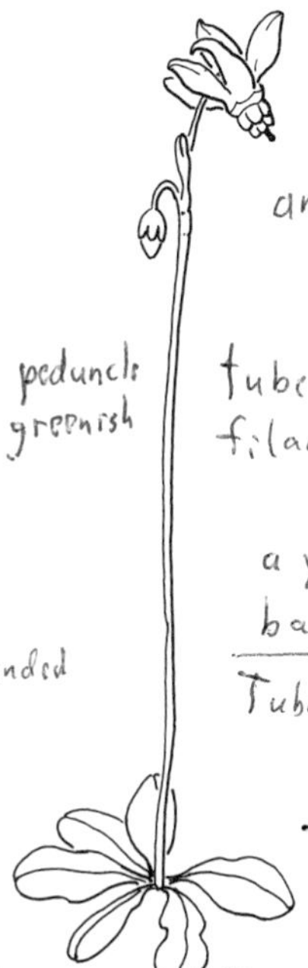

(handwritten annotations beside illustration)
corolla lobes (≤ 25 mm)
tip yellow and/white
turning to pink or lavender
base burgundy

anthers bluntly rounded at tip

peduncle greenish

tube formed by the filaments of the stamens with

a yellow spot near the base of each anther

Tube formed by the filaments 3-4 mm wide

Leaf blade length more than twice the width

Ht. to 20 cm

Dodecatheon hendersonii A. Gray
MOSQUITO BILLS   Native

Flowering Time: February–April

Habitat: grassland, woodland

Description: Upright herbaceous perennial to 40 cm. Leaves in a basal rosette, simple to 16 cm, narrowed abruptly to the petiole. Inflorescence a scapose umbel of 3–17 flowers; bracts at the base of inflorescence to 7 mm. Sepal and petal lobes reflexed in flower; sepals to 4 mm; petals to 2.5 cm, pink to purple; pedicel to 7 cm. Stamens exserted, anthers sharply pointed at tip. Fruit a many-seeded capsule. *(handwritten)* Anther color?

Genus & Specific Name Derivation: Greek: 12 gods (an ancient name) / for L. F. Henderson (1853–1942), professor of botany, Oregon

Notes: See *D. clevelandii.*

(handwritten) Photo in K&B plate 45

(handwritten annotations beside illustration)
corolla lobes pink to purple
≤ 25 mm

anthers sharply pointed at tip

peduncle pinkish-tinged

tube formed by the filaments of the stamens without

a yellow spot at the base of each anther

Tube formed by the filaments less than 3 mm wide

Leaf blade length less than twice the width

Ht. to 0.4 m

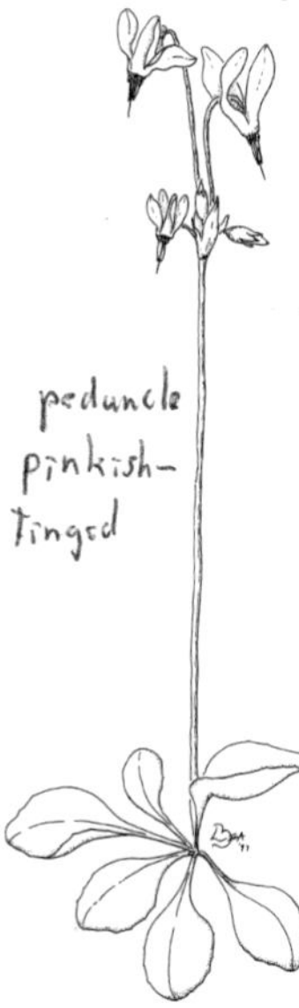

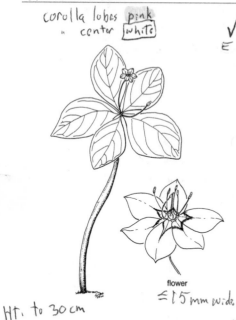

corolla lobes pink
" center white

Ht. to 30 cm

flower

≤ 15 mm wide

√ *Trientalis latifolia* Hook.

€ PACIFIC STARFLOWER   Native

Flowering Time: March–June

Habitat: woodland

Description: Upright herbaceous perennial to 30 cm from a tuber-like root. Leaves in a whorl of 4–5 leaves, simple, to 7 cm, entire, bright green, sessile. Inflorescence originating from the leaf axils, looks as if coming from the center of the whorl of leaves. Flowers from 2–5, to 1.5 cm wide; pedicel to 5 cm. Sepals to 5 mm, separate, green, linear; petals 5–7, petal lobes to 8 mm, pink with white star shaped center. Stamens 6, exserted; ovary partly inferior, stigma and style 1. Fruit a capsule.

Genus & Specific Name Derivation: Latin: one-third of a foot, from height of plant / broad foliage

Notes: Petal number inconsistent, can be from 5–7 lobes.

Photo in K & B plate 45

Ranunculaceae — Buttercup Family

Annuals, herbaceous perennials, or vines. Leaves basal and cauline, alternate or opposite, simple or palmately to pinnately compound. Inflorescence in clusters, racemes, panicles, or solitary. Flowers regular or irregular, bisexual or unisexual. Floral parts free; sepals usually 5, sometimes petaloid; petals 4–many, sometimes absent; stamens 10–many; pistils 1–many, ovary superior, style and stigma 1. Fruit a follicle, achene, or berry. This is a variable family with many different characteristics. What unites it are the variable number of pistils and many stamen. Many are used as ornamentals, including columbine, anemone, larkspur, and a few are sources of medicinal drugs. Some are highly toxic, e.g., larkspur, monkshood, buttercup, baneberry.

For key to woody plants *see* Group 2. Woody Plants

For key to families *see* Group 3. Herbaceous Flowering Plant Families

Key to Herbaceous Plants:

1. Flowers regular
    2. Petals spurred
        3. Plants are densely glandular hairy .... *Aquilegia eximia* (COLUMBINE)
        3´ Plants are slightly hairy, but not glandular hairy ....
            .... *Aquilegia formosa* (CRIMSON COLUMBINE)
    2´ Petals not spurred
        4. Perianth parts in 2 whorls (sepals and petals), petals yellow to white
            5. Petals usually more than 5; plants greater that 2 dm ....
                .... *Ranunculus californicus* (CALIFORNIA BUTTERCUP)
            5´ Petals 5; plants low-growing, less than 2 dm
                6. Fruit prickly *Ranunculus muricatus* (PRICKLE-FRUITED BUTTERCUP)
                6´ Fruit with hooked hairs ....
                    .... *Ranunculus hebecarpus* (PUBESCENT-FRUITED BUTTERCUP)
        4´ Perianth parts in 1 whorl (sepals only) ....
            .... *Thalictrum fendleri* (MEADOW-RUE)
1´ Flowers irregular
    7. Plants usually taller than 10 dm ....
        .... *Delphinium californicum* (COAST OR CALIFORNIA LARKSPUR)
    7´ Plants less than 7 dm
        8. Inflorescence a simple raceme
            9. Leaf lobes usually 3–4; flowers fewer than 20; plants in woodland ....
                .... *Delphinium patens* (SPREADING LARKSPUR)
            9´ Leaf lobes usually 3–10; flowers usually more than 20;
                plants in grassland ....
                .... *Delphinium hesperium* (WESTERN LARKSPUR)
        8´ Inflorescence a branched raceme ....
            .... *Delphinium variegatum* (ROYAL LARKSPUR)

flowers red and yellow
petals spurred; spurs ≤ 40 mm

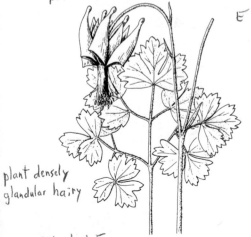

plant densely
glandular hairy

Ht. to 1.5 m

X *Aquilegia eximia* Planchon

COLUMBINE, Native   SERPENTINE

E

Flowering Time: June–August

Habitat: riparian woodland, seeps

Description: Upright herbaceous perennial to 15 dm, plant is densely glandular hairy. Leaves basal and stem, compound, 3-parted, segments to 4 cm, margins lobed and toothed; petioles to 30 cm. Inflorescence an open raceme, flowers nodding, in fruit erect. Sepals to 3 cm, red; petal spurs to 4 cm, tube red, axis red to yellowish. Stamens many, exserted; pistils 5. Fruit 5 elongated follicles.

Genus & Specific Name Derivation: Latin: eagle claws, referring to the spurs / excellent in beauty

Notes: Illustration from *Illustrated Flora of the Pacific States.*

flowers red and yellow, petals spurred,
spurs ≤ 20 mm

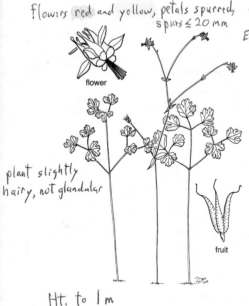

flower

plant slightly
hairy, not glandular

fruit

Ht. to 1 m

Photo in K & B plate 46

✓*Aquilegia formosa* Fischer

E   CRIMSON COLUMBINE   Native

Flowering Time: April–June

Habitat: woodland

Description: Upright herbaceous perennial to 10 dm.

Basal leaves compound, 3-parted, segments to 4 cm, stem leaves generally simple, deeply 3-lobed, margins lobed and toothed; petioles to 30 cm. Inflorescence an open raceme, flowers nodding, in fruit erect. Sepals to 2 cm, red; petal spurs to 2 cm, tube red, blade to 1 cm, yellow. Stamens many, exserted; pistils 5. Fruit 5 elongated follicles.

Genus & Specific Name Derivation: Latin: eagle claws, referring to the spurs / beautiful, well formed

Notes: Spurs hold nectar visited by hummingbirds.

√ *Clematis lasiantha* Nutt.

E

VIRGIN'S BOWER / PIPESTEMS   Native / CHAPARRAL   CLEMATIS

Flowering Time: March–May

Habitat: chaparral

Description: Climbing deciduous, woody vine. Leaves opposite, compound, 1-pinnate with 3–5 leaflets to 5 cm, margins lobed and toothed; petiole twining. Inflorescence axillary with 1 flower. Flowers regular. Sepals to 2 cm, separate, creamy-white; petals 0. Stamens and pistils many. Fruit an achene with a long plume-like style.

Genus & Specific Name Derivation: Greek: twig / shaggy-flowered, referring to the hairy petals

Notes: Plume-like styles at the top of the seed are showy when the plant is going to fruit. The plumes allow the wind to carry the seeds. The leaves superficially resemble leaves of poison oak, but the leaves of *Clematis* are oppositely arranged.

Uses Past and Present: The Spanish used it to cleanse and help heal the wounds of animals.

Photo in K & B plate 46

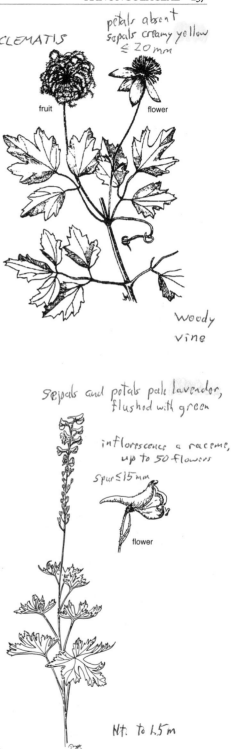

petals absent
sepals creamy yellow
≤ 20 mm

fruit   flower

woody
vine

√ *Delphinium californicum* Torrey & A. Gray ssp. *californicum*

C

COAST or CALIFORNIA LARKSPUR   Native

Flowering Time: April–July

Habitat: woodland

Description: Upright herbaceous perennial to 15 dm, from a fibrous or fleshy root. Leaves basal and stem, simple, blades palmately lobed, margins deeply cut, hairy on lower surface. Inflorescence an elongated raceme with up to 50 flowers. Sepals and petals pale lavender, flushed with green, densely hairy, spur to 1.5 cm; pedicels to 2 cm. Fruit usually 3 follicles to 1.6 cm.

Genus & Specific Name Derivation: Latin: dolphin head, referring to the bud shape looking like a dolphin / from California

Notes: Both sepals and petals are colorful. There are actually 5 sepals, the uppermost spurred; two of the petals also have spurs folded inside the larger sepal spur. This may inhibit would-be nectar robbers from drilling through the spurs to reach nectar.

Uses Past and Present: Some larkspurs are poisonous to sheep and cattle.

sepals and petals pale lavender,
flushed with green

inflorescence a raceme,
up to 50 flowers

spur ≤ 15 mm

flower

Ht. to 1.5 m

Flowers 20-30
Sepals and petals dark blue-purple

spur ≤ 18 mm

inflorescence
a raceme
(unbranched),
slender

flower

leaf lobes 3-10

Ht. to 0.5 m

√*Delphinium hesperium* A. Gray ssp. *hesperium*

E WESTERN LARKSPUR Native

Flowering Time: April–July

Habitat: grassland

Description: Upright herbaceous perennial to 5 dm, from a fibrous or fleshy root. Leaves basal and stem, simple, blades palmately lobed, margins deeply cut, hairy on lower surface. Inflorescence an elongated raceme with up to 30 flowers; sepals and petals dark blue-purple, spur to 1.8 cm; pedicels to 2 cm. Fruit usually 3 follicles to 2 cm.

Genus & Specific Name Derivation: Latin: dolphin head, referring to the bud shape looking like a dolphin / western

Notes: See *D. californicum*. When the flower is hanging down on the stem it looks like a witch hat.

Uses Past and Present: See *D. californicum*.

flowers fewer than 20
sepals and petals dark purple
spur ≤ 15 mm

inflorescence
a raceme
(unbranched)

leaves hairy
only on lower surface
lobes usually 3-4
              5

Ht. to 0.6 m

X *Delphinium patens* Benth. ssp. *patens*

SC SPREADING LARKSPUR Native
E

Flowering Time: March–May

Habitat: woodland

Description: Upright herbaceous perennial to 6 dm, from a fibrous or fleshy root. Leaves basal and stem, simple, blades palmately lobed, margins deeply cut, hairy on lower surface. Inflorescence an elongated raceme with up to 20 flowers. Sepals and petals dark purple; spur to 1.5 cm; pedicel to 7 cm. Fruit usually 3 follicles to 2.3 cm.

Genus & Specific Name Derivation: Latin: dolphin head, referring to the bud shape looking like a dolphin / spreading out from the stem, referring to the flowers along the stem

Notes: See *D. californicum*.

Uses Past and Present: See *D. californicum*.

Delphinium variegatum Torrey & A. Gray
ssp. *variegatum*

ROYAL LARKSPUR   Native

Flowering Time: February–May

Habitat: grassland

Description: Upright herbaceous perennial to 5 dm, from a fibrous or fleshy root. Leaves basal and stem, simple, blades palmately lobed, margins deeply cut, hairy on lower surface. Inflorescence a branched raceme with up to 25 flowers. Sepals dark blue, spur to 2 cm; petals whitish; pedicels to 5 cm. Fruit usually 3 follicles to 2 cm.

Genus & Specific Name Derivation: Latin: dolphin head, referring to the bud shape looking like a dolphin / irregularly colored or variegated, referring to the petals

Notes: See *D. californicum.*

Uses Past and Present: See *D. californicum.*

Photo in K & B plate 46

Ranunculus californicus Benth.

CALIFORNIA BUTTERCUP   Native

Flowering Time: February–April

Habitat: grassland

Description: Herbaceous perennial to 7 dm. Leaves simple to compound, basal and alternate, blades to 8 cm, margin toothed to deeply cut; petioles to 15 cm. Inflorescence an open cyme. Sepals 5, greenish-yellow to 7 mm, folded back; petals to 13 mm, variable in number, bright yellow, shiny. Fruit a cluster of achenes, each to 13 mm, roundish with a curved beak, the beak is actually the style and stigma.

Genus & Specific Name Derivation: Latin: little frog, referring to this genus occurring in moist areas / from California

Notes: Shiny petals fade to white in age. This species has a variable number of petals.

Uses Past and Present: Natives parched the seeds by tossing them in flat baskets with hot embers and pebbles. The seeds were then ground into a meal. The taste is reported to resemble that of parched corn.

Photo in K & B plate 46

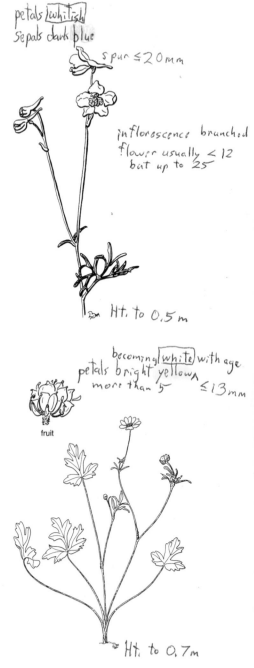

petals whitish
sepals dark blue

spur ≤ 20 mm

inflorescence branched
flower usually < 12
but up to 25

Ht. to 0.5 m

becoming white with age
petals bright yellow
more than 5   ≤ 13 mm

fruit

Ht. to 0.7 m

numbering 5 at first
petals pale yellow, ≤ 1 mm,
soon deciduous.

fruit with hooked hairs,
slenderer than in R. muricatus

fruit

Ht. to 6 cm

√ *Ranunculus hebecarpus* Hook.& Arn.

PUBESCENT-FRUITED BUTTERCUP   Native/ DOWNY BUT.

Flowering Time: March–May

Habitat: woodland

Description: Herbaceous perennial to 6 cm. Leaves basal and stem, stem leaves to 1 cm, alternate, margin lobed; petiole to 4 cm. Inflorescence solitary in leaf axils of upper leaves. Petals 5, to 1 mm, pale yellow, often not seen, as they fall off the plant early; sepals to 1 mm. Fruit a cluster of achenes, body to 2 mm, with hooked hairs.

Genus & Specific Name Derivation: Latin: little frog, referring to this genus occurring in moist areas / pubescent-fruited

Notes: This plant is so small, and without showy petals that it is easily overlooked.

Uses Past and Present: See *R. californicus.*

petals yellow, numbering 5,
5-8 mm long

fruit prickly

fruit

flower

Ht. to 15 cm

• *Ranunculus muricatus* L.

PRICKLE-FRUITED BUTTERCUP   Nonnative / Europe

Flowering Time: February–June

Habitat: woodland

Description: Low spreading annual or biennial to 15 cm. Leaves basal and stem, simple, toothed and deeply 3-lobed, blades to 5 cm; petioles to 10 cm. Inflorescence on open cyme. Sepals to 7 mm; petals to 8 mm, yellow. Fruit a cluster of achenes, body to 7 mm, prickly.

Genus & Specific Name Derivation: Latin: little frog, referring to this genus occurring in moist areas / rough with short tubercles, referring to the prickles on the fruit

Notes: Low-growing and often overlooked in flower, but fruit with obvious prickles more noticeable. Illustration from *Illustrated Flora of the Pacific States.*

Photo in K & B plat. 46

√ *Thalictrum fendleri* A. Gray var. *polycarpum* Torrey

E
SC

MEADOW-RUE   Native

Flowering Time: March–May

Habitat: woodland

Description: Upright, branching herbaceous perennial to 20 dm. Plants dioecious. Leaves alternate, compound, new leaves bright green, blade to 40 cm; leaflet to 2 cm; stipule lobes to 2 mm, whitish. Inflorescence a panicle. Bracts to 2 mm, linear, green. Sepals 5, to 3 mm, separate, green; petals 0. Male and female flowers on separate plants (dioecious). Female flowers with purple stigmas, curling in fruit; male flowers with showy yellow anthers. Fruit an achene to 5 mm, stigmas remaining.

Genus & Specific Name Derivation: Name given by Dioscorides, Greek physician-botanist meaning to flourish / derivation unknown / many carpels (fruits)

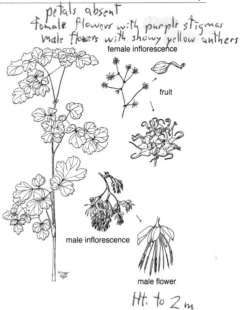

petals absent
Female flowers with purple stigmas
Male flowers with showy yellow anthers

female inflorescence

fruit

male inflorescence

male flower

Ht. to 2 m

Rhamnaceae — Buckthorn Family

Shrubs, trees, or vines. Leaves alternate or opposite, evergreen or deciduous. Inflorescence solitary, in panicles, or umbel-like clusters. Flowers bisexual or unisexual. Sepals 4–5, partly fused; petals 4–5, often with distinct claws; stamens 4–5; pistil 1, ovary superior or partly inferior, styles and stigmas 1–3-lobed. Fruit a capsule or drupe; seeds 1–10.

For key to woody plants *see* Group 2. Woody Plants

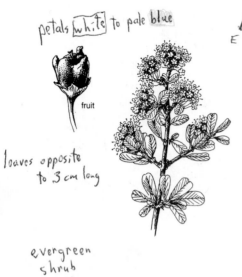

petals white to pale blue

fruit

leaves opposite to 3 cm long

evergreen shrub Ht. to 3m

✓ *Ceanothus cuneatus* (Hook.) Nutt. var. *cuneatus*

E   BUCK BRUSH   Native

Flowering Time: February–August

Habitat: chaparral

Description: Erect evergreen shrub to 3 m; with branches that angle out in all directions. Leaves opposite, simple, thick, leathery to 3 cm, margin entire or toothed; petiole to 3 mm. Inflorescence a raceme-like umbel. Flowers regular; sepals 5, separate, white to pale blue; petals 5, separate, white to pale blue, hooded. Stamens 5, exserted; ovary superior, 3-lobed, with a fleshy nectar gland at the base; style and stigma 3-lobed. Fruit a 3-parted capsule, to 6 mm, spherical, sometimes with horns near top.

Genus & Specific Name Derivation: Greek: thorny plant, referring to the thorn-like branch ends / wedge-shaped, referring to the leaf shape

Notes: Flowers have a musty odor that attracts bees; look for the raised nectar glands where petals and sepals are attached. Important to the ecology of the chaparral, the roots have tiny nodules where nitrogen-producing bacteria live; when the roots die, these nutrients are released to enrich the surrounding soils. The plants will regenerate after a fire or disturbance from seeds that lie dormant in the soil. Illustration from *Illustrated Flora of the Pacific States.*

Uses Past and Present: Roots and bark were ground up, mixed with water and gargled as a mouthwash for sore throat or sores in the mouth. Flowers and fruits were mashed to produce a soap. Stems of some species were used in basketry; seeds of some species were eaten.

Photo in R & B plate 47

✓ *Rhamnus californica* Eschsch. ssp. *californica*

E CALIFORNIA COFFEEBERRY Native

Flowering Time: May–July

Habitat: chaparral, open woodland

Description: Evergreen shrub to 6 m. New branches red. Leaves alternate, simple to 8 cm, margin toothed or entire, sometimes rolled under; upper surface dark green, lower brighter green; petiole to 10 mm. Inflorescence umbel-like. Flowers regular. Sepals 5-lobed, fused; petals 5, yellow-green. Stamens 5, inserted; ovary partly inferior. Fruit a drupe to 15 mm, black when mature.

Genus & Specific Name Derivation: Greek: name for plants of this genus / from California

Notes: Illustration from *Illustrated Flora of the Pacific States.* Leaf undersurface illustration by Judy Mason.

Uses Past and Present: Bark of limbs and small trunks was ground and added to water for use as a laxative. This plant has no relationship to coffee other than that the ripe berries may look like coffee beans. Birds and other animals eat the fruit. Leaves and bark can be toxic if ingested by humans.

Photo in K & B plate 47

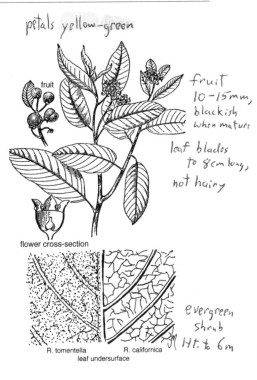

petals yellow-green

fruit
10-15mm,
blackish
when mature

leaf blades
to 8cm long,
not hairy

flower cross-section

R. tomentella   R. californica
leaf undersurface

evergreen
shrub
Ht. to 6m

✓ *Rhamnus crocea* Nutt.

E SPINY REDBERRY Native

Flowering Time: February–May

Habitat: chaparral, woodland

Description: Evergreen shrub to 2 m; with spreading, stiff branches, some spine-tipped. Leaves alternate, simple to 2 cm sometimes clustered, margin sharply toothed or entire; petiole to 4 mm. Inflorescence 1–6 flowers in leaf axils. Flower unisexual, regular. Sepals 4, yellow-green, petals 0. Stamens 4; ovary inferior. Fruit a berry to 6 mm, red when mature.

Genus & Specific Name Derivation: Greek: name for plants of this genus / saffron-colored, yellow, referring to the flower color

Notes: Illustration from *Illustrated Flora of the Pacific States.*

Uses Past and Present: See *R. californica.*

Photo in K & B plate 47

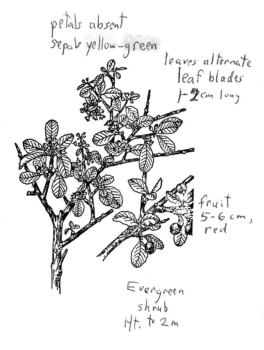

petals absent
sepals yellow-green

leaves alternate
leaf blades
1-2cm long

fruit
5-6cm,
red

Evergreen
shrub
Ht. to 2m

petals yellow-green

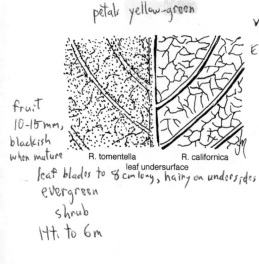

fruit
10-15mm,
blackish
when mature

R. tomentella   R. californica
leaf undersurface

leaf blades to 8 cm long, hairy on undersides

evergreen

shrub

Ht. to 6m

√*Rhamnus tomentella* Benth. ssp. *tomentella*

HOARY COFFEEBERRY   Native

Flowering Time: May–July

Habitat: chaparral, open woodland

Description: Evergreen shrub to 6 m. New branches red. Leaves alternate, simple to 8 cm, margin toothed or entire, sometimes rolled under; upper surface dark green, lower surface white, hairy; petiole to 10 mm. Inflorescence umbel-like. Flower regular. Sepals 5-lobed, fused; petals 5, yellow-green. Stamens 5, inserted; ovary partly inferior. Fruit a drupe to 15 mm, black when mature.

Genus & Specific Name Derivation: Greek: name for plants of this genus / matted hairs referring to the underside of the leaves

Notes: This species was recently found at Edgewood and may have been overlooked because it is so much like *R. californica* except for the undersides of the leaves which are hairy in *R. tomentella.*

Uses Past and Present: See *R. californica.*

Rosaceae — Rose Family

Annuals, herbaceous perennials, shrubs. Leaves alternate or opposite, simple to compound. Inflorescence in racemes, panicles, umbels, or axillary. Flowers mostly bisexual, regular. <u>Hypanthium present</u>; sepals mostly 5; petals mostly 5, free from each other, attached to top of the hypanthium; <u>stamens 5–many</u>; pistils 1 to many, ovary inferior or superior, styles 1–5. Fruit an achene, follicle, drupe, or pome. Many cultivated for their flowers and for their fruit, e.g., cotoneaster, strawberry, apple, plum, cherry, rose, blackberry.

For key to woody plants *see* Group 2. Woody Plants

For key to families *see* Group 3. Herbaceous Flowering Plant Families

Key to Herbaceous Plants:

1. Inflorescence head-like; flowers purplish-red ....
    .... *Sanguisorba minor* (GARDEN BURNET)
1´ Inflorescence in other arrangements
    2. Plant low-growing; flowers axillary, minute ....
        .... *Aphanes occidentalis* (DEW CUP / LADY'S MANTLE)
    2´ Plant upright; inflorescence open ....
        .... *Potentilla glandulosa* (STICKY CINQUEFOIL)

√*Adenostoma fasciculatum* Hook. & Arn.

E
SC

CHAMISE   Native

Flowering Time: May–July

Habitat: chaparral

Description: Much-branched evergreen shrub to 4 m. Leaves alternate, simple, to 10 mm, needle-like, clustered or fascicled, bright green; stipules small. Inflorescence a panicle of terminal clusters. Flowers regular. Sepals 5, lobes to 1.5 mm; petals 5, to 1.5 mm, fused, cream to white. Stamens more than 10 in clusters; ovary superior. Fruit an achene, rust-colored.

Genus & Specific Name Derivation: Greek: glandular mouth, refers to the 5 glands at the mouth of the sepals / fascicled, referring to the leaves, which appear in bundles

Notes: Plants have a basal burl that allows them to sprout after fire or disturbance. Widespread and drought-tolerant, often found in pure stands, especially along Ridgeview Trail. The dry branches are very flammable. Illustration from *Illustrated Flora of the Pacific States.*

Photos in K & B plate 48

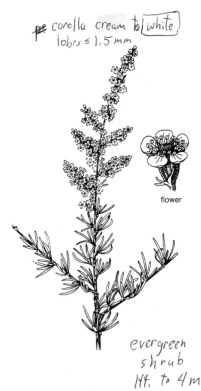

corolla cream to white lobes ≤ 1.5 mm

flower

evergreen shrub Ht. to 4 m

flowers inconspicuous, ≤ 2 mm
red when mature

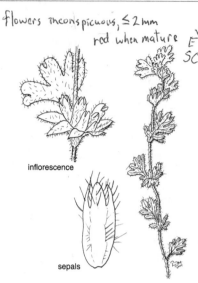

inflorescence

sepals

Ht. to 10 cm

✓*Aphanes occidentalis* (Nutt.) Rydb.

DEW CUP / LADY'S MANTEL   Native

Flowering Time: February–May

Habitat: grassland

Description: Inconspicuous annual to 10 cm. Leaves simple to 5 mm; margin lobed and toothed. Inflorescence of several flowers in leaf axils. Flowers inconspicuous, less than 2 mm, reddish when mature. Fruit an achene to 1 mm.

Genus & Specific Name Derivation: Greek: unseen, from hidden flowers / western

Notes: This is the only species of this genus in California.

Photo in K & B plate 48

corolla white

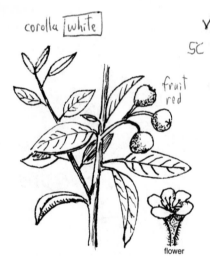

fruit red

flower

evergreen shrub
Ht. to 3.5m

✓*Cotoneaster pannosa* Franchet

COTONEASTER, Nonnative / China *SILVER-LEAVED*

Flowering Time: April–June

Habitat: disturbed areas in grassland and woodland

Description: Evergreen shrub to 3.5 m. Leaves alternate, simple to 4 cm, dull green above with fine hairs, white-hairy below. On some new branches the leaves look clustered. Inflorescence a cyme. Flowers regular. Sepals 5-lobed; petals 5, fused, white. Stamens more than 10; ovary inferior, styles 2–5. Fruit a drupe-like, round pome to 6 mm, red when mature.

Genus & Specific Name Derivation: Latin: quince-like, from leaf shape / woolly, referring to the leaf

2008 Addendum
Chaenomeles japonica FLOWERING QUINCE
nonnative

√*Crataegus monogyna* Jacq.

SC

ENGLISH HAWTHORN   Nonnative / Europe and Asia

Flowering Time: N/A

Habitat: planted at the Day Camp

Description: Deciduous large shrub or small tree to 15 m; with spines at the base of leaf clusters. Leaves alternate, clustered, simple, to 6 cm, margin lobed and toothed; petiole to 4 cm. Inflorescence a raceme. Flower regular. Sepals 5, to 1 mm, separate but fused at the top of the hypanthium, becoming reddish; petals 5, to 6 mm, separate but fused to the top of the hypanthium, white. Stamens 10, exserted; ovary inferior. Fruit a drupe-like pome, red turning black-purple.

Genus & Specific Name Derivation: Greek: flower thorn, or strength, from strong wood or thorns / one seed

Notes: There are several of these in the Day Camp area.

Uses Past and Present: New leaves and unripened (red) berries are used for a heart medicine. The chemical constituents are flavonoids that occur in the leaves and fruit.

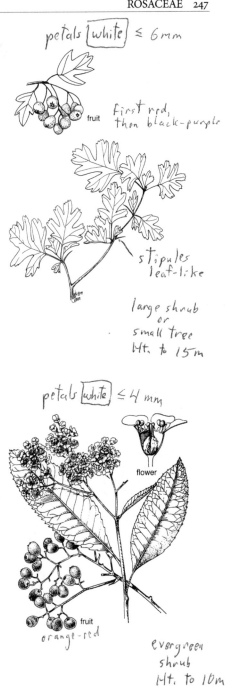

petals white ≤ 6mm

fruit

first red, then black-purple

stipules leaf-like

large shrub or small tree Ht. to 15m

√*Heteromeles arbutifolia* (Lindley) Roemer

E
SC

CHRISTMAS BERRY / TOYON   Native

Flowering Time: June–July

Habitat: chaparral, woodland

Description: Evergreen shrub to 10 m. Leaves alternate, simple to 11 cm, margin coarsely toothed; petiole to 2 cm, often pale pink to red. Inflorescence a loose, compound panicle. Flowers regular. Sepals 5, to 2 mm, fused; petals 5, to 4 mm, fused, white. Stamens 10, exserted; ovary inferior, styles 2–3-lobed. Fruit a round, berry-like pome to 10 mm, orange-red when mature.

Genus & Specific Name Derivation: Greek: different apple / likeness of the leaves to those of madrone

Notes: Berries are sweet and spicy. Illustration from *Illustrated Flora of the Pacific States.*

Uses Past and Present: Natives and Spanish toasted or boiled the fruit. leaves slightly fragrant when crushed

petals white ≤ 4 mm

flower

fruit orange-red

evergreen shrub Ht. to 10m

Photo in K & B plate 48

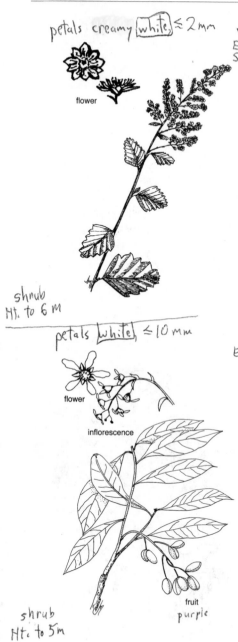

petals creamy white ≤ 2mm

flower

shrub
Ht. to 6 m

petals white ≤ 10 mm

flower

inflorescence

shrub
Ht. to 5m

fruit
purple

√ *Holodiscus discolor* (Pursh) Maxim.

E
SC
OCEANSPRAY   Native

Flowering Time: April–July

Habitat: woodland

Description: Deciduous shrub to 6 m. Leaves alternate, simple to 12 cm, veins strongly raised, margin coarsely toothed. Inflorescence a terminal panicle. Flowers regular. Sepals 5, to 2 mm, fused; petals 5, to 2 mm, separate, creamy white. Stamens more than 10; ovary superior, pistils 5, stigma 2-lobed. Fruit an achene to 1.5 mm.

Genus & Specific Name Derivation: Greek: whole disk / of different colors

Notes: Leaf has a fruity aroma when rubbed. Flowers turn rusty brown and hang from the shrub into winter. The common name oceanspray refers to the frothy clusters of flowers.

Photo in K & B plate 48

√ *Oemleria cerasiformis* (Hook. & Arn.) J. W. Landon

E
OSO BERRY   Native

Flowering Time: February–April

Habitat: openings in woodland, chaparral

Description: Deciduous shrub to 5 m; mostly dioecious. Leaves alternate, simple to 13 cm, often in clusters, margin entire, may be slightly rolled under, upper surface bright green, lower paler; petiole to 15 mm. Inflorescence a raceme. Flowers fragrant, mostly unisexual some bisexual. Sepals 5-lobed to 5 mm; petals 5-lobed to 10 mm, white. Stamens more than 10, inserted; ovary inferior. Fruit a drupe to 5 mm, oval, purple when mature.

Genus & Specific Name Derivation: Derivation unknown / horn-shaped

Notes: Flowers fragrant.

√ *Physocarpus capitatus* (Pursh) Kuntze

E

PACIFIC NINEBARK   Native

Flowering Time: April–July

Habitat: moist woods, riparian woodland

Description: Deciduous shrub to 2.5 m; with shredding bark. Leaves simple, alternate to 5 cm, toothed and palmately lobed; petiole to 2 cm. Inflorescence head-like; sepals 5, to 3 mm, fused; petals to 3 mm, rounded, white. Stamens many, exserted; pistils 1–5, ovary superior, style thread-like, stigma head-like. Fruits are inflated follicles.

Genus & Specific Name Derivation: Greek: bladder fruit, for the inflated fruit / growing in a head, referring to the head-like inflorescence

Notes: Common name refers to the several layers of peeling, brownish bark exposed on winter twigs.

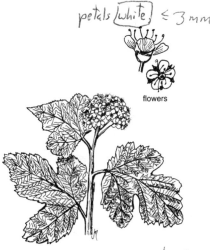

petals white ≤ 3mm

flowers

shrub
Ht. to 2.5m

√ *Potentilla glandulosa* Lindley ssp. *glandulosa*

Sc

STICKY CINQUEFOIL   Native

Flowering Time: March–July

Habitat: woodland

Description: Herbaceous perennial to 30 cm, whole plant glandular-hairy. Leaves basal and stem, compound, 1-pinnate, blade to 30 cm; leaflets to 6 cm, terminal largest; margin lobed and toothed; petiole base sheathing. Inflorescence an open cyme of up to 30 flowers. Sepals triangular, slightly shorter than petals; petals to 10 mm, pale yellow; stamens many; pistils many. Fruit a cluster of achenes to 1 mm, smooth.

Genus & Specific Name Derivation: Latin: diminutive of powerful, for reputed medicinal value / full of glands, referring to the glands on whole plant

Notes: This is one of California's great adapters, ranging from coastal bluffs to alpine slopes.

Photo in K & B plate 49

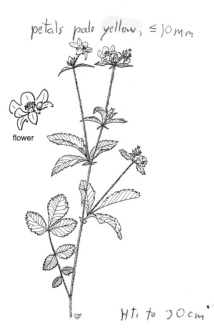

petals pale yellow, ≤ 10mm

flower

Ht. to 30cm

petals [white]

flower
cross-section

fruit
purple-
black

evergreen
large shrub
  or
small tree
Ht. to 15m

√ *Prunus ilicifolia* (Nutt.) Walp. ssp. *ilicifolia*

HOLLY-LEAVED CHERRY   Native

E
SC

Flowering Time: March–June

Habitat: chaparral, open woodland

Description: Evergreen large shrub to small tree to 15 m. Leaves alternate, simple to 5 cm, margin spiny-toothed, wavy, shiny green above, brighter green beneath; petiole to 10 mm. Inflorescence a many flowered raceme. Flowers regular; sepals and petals 5, separate but fused to the top of a hypanthium; petals to 3 mm, white. Stamens more than 15, usually in 2 whorls; ovary superior, style 1, stigma spherical. Fruit a drupe to 3 cm, spherical, red turning purple-black.

Genus & Specific Name Derivation: Latin: name for a plum tree / holly-like, referring to the look of the leaves

Notes: Fresh leaves smell like almonds. Illustration from *Illustrated Flora of the Pacific States.*

Uses Past and Present: Natives pressed the fruit to make a drink; the bark was used to make a tea for treating colds. Some birds eat the fruit; deer eat the twigs and foliage.

leaves slightly fragrant when crushed
Photo in K & B plate 49

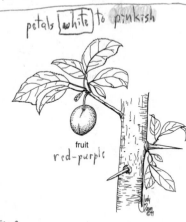

petals [white] to pinkish

fruit
red-purple

Tree

√ *Prunus* sp.

E
SC   ORNAMENTAL PLUM   Nonnative

Flowering Time: February–April

Habitat: disturbed grassland, planted at Day Camp

Description: Deciduous tree, some with spines along the branches. Leaves simple, alternate to clustered. Inflorescence a cluster of 3–5 flowers. Petals white to pinkish; stamens many. Fruit round, green when young, red-purple when mature.

Genus & Specific Name Derivation: Latin: name for a plum tree

Notes: There were several trees near the kiosk on Serpentine Loop, some with green leaves, others purple; these may now have been removed. There are others that were planted in the Day Camp area.

There is one plum along the trail between
Eaton and Big Canyon Parks in San Carlos,
far from any houses in woodland. Not sure
if it is an escaped ornamental or P. subcordata

Prunus subcordata Benth.

PACIFIC PLUM   Native / *SIERRA PLUM*

Flowering Time: March–April

Habitat: woodland

Description: Deciduous large shrub or small tree to 8 m. Leaves alternate, simple to 5 cm, margin finely toothed; petiole to 15 mm. Inflorescence a raceme of 1–7 flowers. Flowers regular; sepals and petals 5, fused to the top of the hypanthium; petals to 10 mm, white; stamens more than 15, exserted; ovary superior. Fruit a pome to 2.5 cm, ovoid, yellow to dark red.

Genus & Specific Name Derivation: Latin: name for a plum tree / nearly heart-shaped, referring to shallowly heart-shaped bases of the leaves

Pyracantha angustifolia (Franchet) C. Schneider

FIRETHORN / PYRACANTHA   Nonnative / China

Flowering Time: March–June

Habitat: disturbed areas in grassland and woodland

Description: Evergreen shrub to 4 m, with spines on the branches. Leaves alternate, simple to 4 cm, often in clusters except at very ends of branches, margin shallowly lobed to toothed. Inflorescence a panicle. Flower regular; sepals 5, fused to the top of the hypanthium, persistent on the fruit; petals 5, separate, white. Stamens more than 10, exserted; ovary partly inferior. Fruit a pome to 8 mm, orange-red when mature.

Genus & Specific Name Derivation: Greek: fire thorn, from color of fruit and irritation caused by thorns / narrow-leaved

Uses Past and Present: Although a nonnative, the fruits are used for jelly. Also, sauces for meats and poultry are made by sweetening the simmered berries.

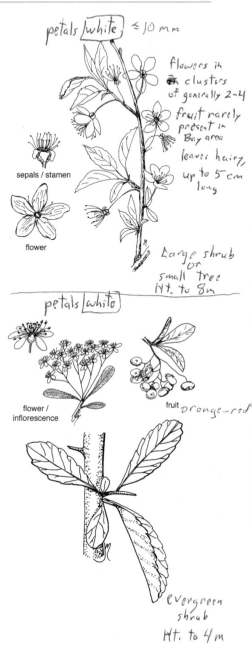

petals white; ≤ 10 mm

flowers in clusters of generally 2–4

fruit rarely present in Bay area

leaves hairy up to 5 cm long

sepals / stamen

flower

Large shrub or small tree Ht. to 8m

petals white

flower / inflorescence

fruit Orange-red

evergreen shrub Ht. to 4 m

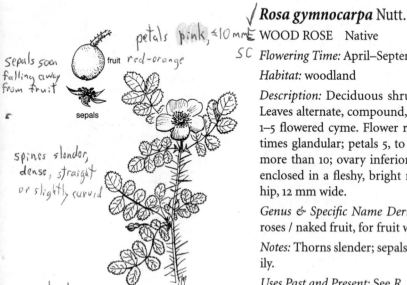

petals pink, ≤20 mm

calyx tube without glandular bristles (generally)

spines stout, few, recurved

sepals persistent on fruit

fruit red-orange

partly evergreen spreading shrub to 2.5 m

Photo in K & B plate 50

√ *Rosa californica* Cham. & Schldl.

CALIFORNIA ROSE   Native

Flowering Time: April–October

Habitat: woodland

Description: Evergreen to deciduous thicket-forming shrub to 2.5 m; with curved thorns on branches. Leaves alternate, compound, sometimes glandular, margin toothed. Inflorescence a 1–10 flowered cyme. Flower regular; sepals 5, separate, sometimes glandular; petals 5, to 2 cm, separate, pink. Stamens more than 10; ovary inferior, pistils many. Fruit are achenes enclosed in a fleshy, bright red-orange hypanthium called a hip, to 2 cm wide.

Genus & Specific Name Derivation: Latin: ancient name for roses / from California

Notes: Thorns stout and generally curved; fruit with evergreen sepals.

Uses Past and Present: Parts used are the dried flower buds, dried leaves, and fruit. Buds used for eyewash. Leaves used as a tea for intestinal inflammation and diarrhea. Fruit used for vitamin C, and to make jam or tea.

petals pink, ≤10 mm

fruit red-orange

sepals soon falling away from fruit

sepals

spines slender, dense, straight or slightly curved

shrub Ht. to 2m

√ *Rosa gymnocarpa* Nutt.

WOOD ROSE   Native

Flowering Time: April–September

Habitat: woodland

Description: Deciduous shrub to 2 m; with slender thorns. Leaves alternate, compound, margin toothed. Inflorescence a 1–5 flowered cyme. Flower regular; sepals 5, separate, sometimes glandular; petals 5, to 10 mm, separate, pink. Stamens more than 10; ovary inferior, pistils many. Fruit are achenes enclosed in a fleshy, bright red-orange hypanthium called a hip, 12 mm wide.

Genus & Specific Name Derivation: Latin: ancient name for roses / naked fruit, for fruit without sepals when ripe

Notes: Thorns slender; sepals deciduous in fruit or fall off easily.

Uses Past and Present: See *R. californica.*

Photo in K & B plate 50

√*Rosa spithamea* S. Watson

E GROUND ROSE   Native

Flowering Time: May–August

Habitat: chaparral, open woodland

Description: Deciduous shrub to 5 dm; with thorns. Leaves alternate, compound, glandular, margin-toothed. Inflorescence a 1–10 flowered cyme. Flower regular; sepals 5, separate, sometimes glandular; petals 5, to 2.5 cm, separate, pink. Stamens more than 10; ovary inferior, pistils many. Fruit are achenes enclosed in a fleshy, bright red-orange hypanthium called a hip, to 10 mm wide.

Genus & Specific Name Derivation: Latin: ancient name for roses / derivation unknown

Notes: Thorns slender, straight; sepals persistent in fruit.

Uses Past and Present: See *R. californica.*

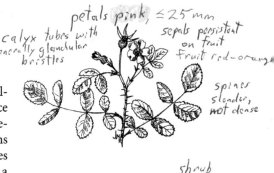

petals pink, ≤25 mm
calyx tubes with generally glandular bristles
sepals persistent on fruit
Fruit red-orange
spines slender, not dense
shrub
Ht. to 0.5 m

√*Rubus discolor* Weihe & Nees

E
SC HIMALAYAN BLACKBERRY   Nonnative / Eurasia

Flowering Time: April–June

Habitat: moist areas, riparian woodland

Description: Arching vine, main stem 5-angled with stout, sharp prickles. Leaves alternate, compound, 1-pinnate, with 3–5 leaflets, green above, whitish beneath, leaflet margin toothed; petiole to cm. Inflorescence a many-flowered panicle. Flowers regular; sepals 5, separate; petals 5, separate, white to pinkish, to 15 mm. Stamens many, exserted; ovary superior, pistils many, styles club-shaped. Fruit an aggregate of tiny separate pistils clumped together, each one called an achene; the whole fruit collectively is called a blackberry.

Genus & Specific Name Derivation: Latin: ancient name for bramble / with different colors referring to the different colors of the upper and lower leaf surfaces

Notes: The 5-angled stem with stout, sharp, widely spaced prickles differentiates it from the native California blackberry.

Uses Past and Present: See *R. ursinus.*

petals white to pinkish, ≤15 mm
flowers
fruit
arching vine

petals white to pale pink, ≤25mm

E SC

vine

Rubus ursinus Cham. & Schldl.

CALIFORNIA BLACKBERRY   Native

Flowering Time: April–June

Habitat: moist areas, riparian woodland

Description: Climbing vine with round stems and slender, weak, straight prickles all along the stem. Leaves alternate, compound, 1-pinnate to 10 cm, with 3 leaflets, margins toothed, green above and below; petiole to 6 cm. Inflorescence a many flowered cyme. Flowers regular; sepals 5, separate, becoming reflexed; petals 5, separate, white to pale pink, to 2.5 cm. Stamens many, exserted; ovary superior, pistils many, styles club-shaped. Fruit an aggregate of tiny separate pistils clumped together, each one called an achene; the whole fruit collectively is called a blackberry.

Genus & Specific Name Derivation: Latin: ancient name for bramble / bear-like

Notes: The round stem and many straight prickles all along the stem differentiate it from Himalayan blackberry. Deer browse on the stems and foliage, and many birds nest in the thickets and eat the fruit.

Uses Past and Present: Natives used the dried berries alone, or mixed them with dried meat to make cakes known as pemmican. Berries used fresh or dried for food. A tea made from the roots was used as a remedy for diarrhea. The leaves can be brewed into a tea. Young shoots can be boiled and eaten. Many animals and birds depend on the fruit as a food source. Many of these same animals use the dense berry thickets for nesting sites and protective cover.

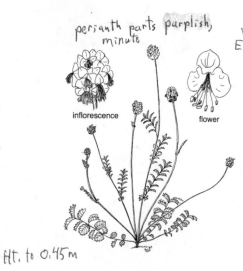

perianth parts purplish, minute

inflorescence   flower

Ht. to 0.45m

Sanguisorba minor Scop. ssp. *muricata* Brig.

E

GARDEN BURNET   Nonnative / Europe

Flowering Time: May–September

Habitat: grassland, woodland

Description: Upright herbaceous perennial to 45 cm. Leaves basal, stem leaves alternate, compound, 1-pinnate, blade to 20 cm; leaflet margin toothed; lower leaves with petioles to 5 cm. Inflorescence a head-like spike of many flowers. Perianth segments minute, purplish; stamens many, filaments thread-like. Fruit a cluster of achenes each to 5 mm, surface bumpy.

Genus & Specific Name Derivation: Latin: blood-absorbing, from styptic properties / small / with rough tubercles, referring to the bumpy tubercles on the fruit

Not in Kozloff and Beidleman. This is the only member of its genus in the S. F. Bay region. distinguished from other herbaceous rosaceae by having no petals, 4 sepals, fruit inside urn-shaped hypanthemum, hardened

Rubiaceae — Madder Family

Annuals or herbaceous perennials, sometimes dioecious. Leaves opposite or appearing whorled, simple. Inflorescence in racemes, panicles, or axillary. Flowers bisexual or unisexual, regular. Sepals 4 or absent; petals 4, fused; stamens 4; pistil 1, ovary inferior, styles 1–2. Fruit a berry, drupe, or capsule. Some are cultivated for important products such as coffee and quinine.

For key to families *see* Group 3. Herbaceous Flowering Plant Families

Key to Herbaceous Plants:

1. Flowers blue-purple .... *Sherardia arvensis* (FIELD MADDER)
1´ Flowers white, yellow to pale green
    2. Fruit sausage-shaped, hairs on outer margin and top ....
    .... *Galium murale* (TINY BEDSTRAW)
    2´ Fruit roundish, 2-lobed, hairy on whole surface or without hairs
        3. Fruit without hairs ....
        .... *Galium porrigens* (CLIMBING BEDSTRAW)
        3´ Fruit with hairs
            4. Leaves mostly in whorls of 4 ....
            .... *Galium californicum* (CALIFORNIA BEDSTRAW)
            4´ Leaves mostly in whorls of 6 or more ....
            .... *Galium aparine* (GOOSE GRASS)

Galium aparine L.

GOOSE GRASS   Native

Flowering Time: March–August

Habitat: woodland

Description: Annual, stem to 9 cm, climbing or low-growing; herbage with small hooked prickles. Leaves opposite appearing whorled with 6–8 leaves, simple to 20 mm. Inflorescence an axillary cluster of several flowers. Sepals 0; petals 4, to 1 mm, whitish; pedicel to 12 mm. Fruit two nutlets, roundish with hooked hairs.

Genus & Specific Name Derivation: Greek: milk, from use of some species in its curdling / clinging

Uses Past and Present: The genus has also been given the common name bedstraw because it was believed that one species, *G. verum*, filled the manger of the infant Jesus.

Photo in K & B plate 5D

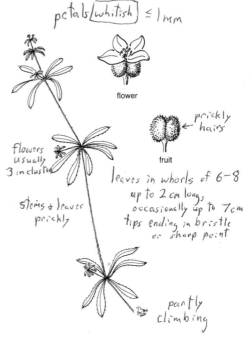

petals (whitish) ≤ 1mm

flower

prickly hairs

fruit

flowers usually 3 in cluster

stems & leaves prickly

leaves in whorls of 6–8 up to 2 cm long, occasionally up to 7 cm tips ending in bristle or sharp point

partly climbing

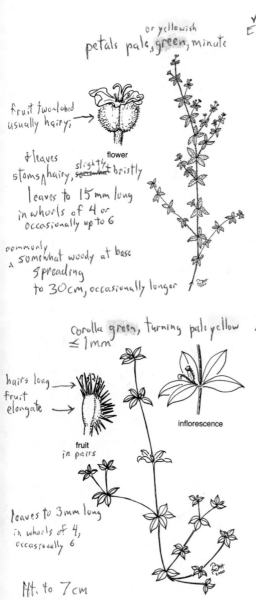

or yellowish

petals pale, green, minute

fruit two-lobed
usually hairy;

flower

+ leaves
stems hairy, slightly, somewhat bristly

leaves to 15 mm long
in whorls of 4 or
occasionally up to 6

commonly
somewhat woody at base
spreading
to 30 cm, occasionally longer

Corolla green, turning pale yellow
≤ 1 mm

hairs long
fruit
elongate

inflorescence

fruit
in pairs

leaves to 3 mm long
in whorls of 4,
occasionally 6

Ht. to 7 cm

√ **Galium californicum** Hook. & Arn.

E ssp. *californicum*

CALIFORNIA BEDSTRAW   Native

Flowering Time: May–July

Habitat: woodland

Description: Spreading herbaceous, dioecious perennial, stems to 30 cm, four-angled; stems and leaf margins bristly-hairy. Leaves opposite appearing whorled with 4 leaves, simple to 15 mm, whole surface and margin hairy, with a point at the tip. Inflorescence axillary, staminate flowers in clusters, several; pistillate flowers usually solitary, petals 4, pale green, minute; ovary 2-lobed. Fruit with or without hairs.

Genus & Specific Name Derivation: Greek: milk, from use of some species in its curdling / from California

Uses Past and Present: See *G. aparine.*

Photo in K&B plate 50

• **Galium murale** (L.) All.

TINY BEDSTRAW   Nonnative / Europe

Flowering Time: March–May

Habitat: woodland

Description: Low-growing annual, stem to 7 cm. Leaves opposite appearing whorled with 4–6 leaves, simple to 3 mm. Inflorescence of 1–2 flowers in axils, sessile. Corolla to 1 mm, green, fading pale yellow. Fruit 2 nutlets, to 1 mm with long white hairs at top and along edges, each nutlet sausage-shaped, 2 nutlets together horseshoe-shaped when mature.

Genus & Specific Name Derivation: Greek: milk, from use of some species in its curdling / walls, growing on walls, referring to the growth habit

Notes: Mature fruit quite different from other *Galiums.*

Uses Past and Present: See *G. aparine.*

2008 Addendum

Galium parisiense WALL BEDSTRAW
Ht. to 25 cm   nonnative

Not in K&B; Key in Jepson Manual:
Annual; corolla lobes 4; nutlets spheric, gen. with
hooked hairs; leaves in whorls of 6, eventually reflexed

√ *Galium porrigens* Dempster var. *porrigens*

E
SC

CLIMBING BEDSTRAW   Native

Flowering Time: March–August

Habitat: woodland

Description: Herbaceous, dioecious, climbing perennial; stems to 15 dm, with clinging tiny prickles. Leaves opposite appearing whorled with 4 leaves, simple to 18 mm. Staminate inflorescence in axillary clusters; pistillate inflorescence generally solitary in leaf axils; corolla yellowish. Fruit without hairs.

Genus & Specific Name Derivation: Greek: milk, from use of some species in its curdling / spreading, referring to the growth habit

Notes: Prickles on stems clasp nearby objects causing plants to climb up them. This species was confused with *G. nuttallii*, but that species only occurs in southern California.

Uses Past and Present: See *G. aparine.*

Photo in K & B plate 50

✗ *Sherardia arvensis* L.

E
SC

FIELD MADDER   Nonnative / Europe

Flowering Time: March–September

Habitat: grassland

Description: Low-growing, matted annual; stem to 10 cm, four-angled. Leaves in whorls of 5–6, simple to 13 mm, tip often pointed. Inflorescence a head-like umbel, axillary in upper leaves. Sepals and petals minute; petals blue-purple, lobe to 1 mm. Fruit 2 nutlets with soft hairs.

Genus & Specific Name Derivation: For Dr. William Sherard (1659–1728) / from the fields

Notes: Often overlooked because of small stature.

Photo in K & B plate 50

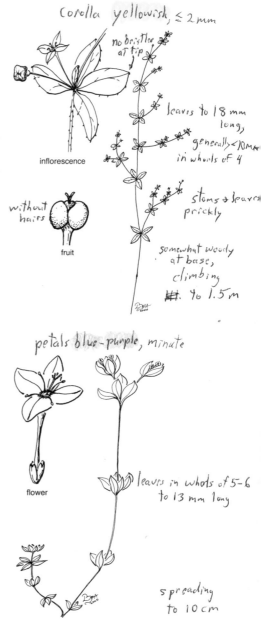

Corolla yellowish, ≤ 2 mm

no bristles at tip

leaves to 18 mm long, generally < 10mm in whorls of 4

inflorescence

without hairs

fruit

stems & leaves prickly

somewhat woody at base, climbing to 1.5 m

petals blue-purple, minute

flower

leaves in whorls of 5-6 to 13 mm long

spreading to 10 cm

Salicaceae — Willow Family

Dioecious large shrubs, small trees, or trees. Leaves alternate, simple, deciduous. Flowers unisexual, regular, in spikes. Perianth absent; staminate flowers with 1–many stamens; pistillate flowers with superior ovary, stigmas 2 or 4. Fruit a capsule; seeds many, minute with silky hairs. Some species are cultivated as ornamentals or used for wood.

For key to woody plants *see* Group 2. Woody Plants

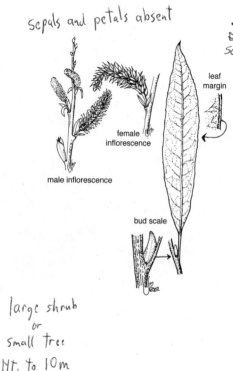

Sepals and petals absent

leaf margin

female inflorescence

male inflorescence

bud scale

large shrub
or
small tree
Ht. to 10 m

√ *Salix lasiolepis* Benth.

ARROYO WILLOW   Native

Flowering Time: February–April

Habitat: riparian woodland

Description: Deciduous large shrub or small tree to 10 m. Leaves alternate, simple to 12 cm, entire to irregularly toothed, slightly rolled under, young leaves hairy, older becoming glabrous, lower surface glaucous, upper surface shiny. Inflorescence a catkin, appearing before the new leaves. Sepals or petals 0; staminate flower with 2 stamens; pistillate flower style minute, ovary glabrous. Staminate and pistillate flowers produced on different trees (dioecious). Fruit a capsule; seeds minute with silky hairs.

Genus & Specific Name Derivation: Latin: ancient name / woolly or shaggy

Notes: The leaves for this species are highly variable. White fluff unfolding from the seed pods can be observed on the mature female catkins and floating in the wind in late spring–summer. Willows are fast-growing plants.

Uses Past and Present: Natives used the pliable new twigs for basket framework and for temporary huts; the bark is one of the original sources of salicylic acid, the active ingredient in aspirin. Ancient Asian records indicate that willow bark has been used to reduce pain for at least 2,400 years. One Spanish place name in the Bay Area from the same root is Sausalito ("sauce" means willow in Spanish).

Saxifragaceae — Saxifrage Family

Herbaceous perennials. Leaves mostly basal, cauline generally alternate. Inflorescence in cymes, racemes or panicles. Flowers bisexual, regular. Hypanthium present; sepals 5; petals 5, separate; stamens 5 or 10; pistils 1 or 2, ovary superior to partly inferior, styles and stigmas generally 2. Fruit a follicle or capsule. Some cultivated ornamentals.

For key to families *see* Group 3. Herbaceous Flowering Plant Families

Key to Herbaceous Plants:

1. Basal leaves simple, not deeply lobed, but may be toothed ....
    .... *Saxifraga californica* (CALIFORNIA SAXIFRAGE)
1′ Basal leaves simple, lobed and toothed
    2. Sepal base rounded to V-shaped , *Petals divided into lobes at the tip* ....
        .... *Lithophragma affine* (WOODLAND STAR)
    2′ Sepal base squared off to blunt , *petals may have some teeth but are not lobed* *at the tip* .... *Lithophragma heterophyllum* (HILL STAR)

✓*Lithophragma affine* A. Gray

E WOODLAND STAR   Native

Flowering Time: February–May

Habitat: woodland

Description: Upright herbaceous perennial to 40 cm, from underground rhizomes; stems short-hairy. Leaves simple to 1.5 cm; basal leaves rounded, margins lobed and toothed; stem leaves alternate 3-parted; petiole to 1.5 cm. Basal leaves often dried up at flowering time. Inflorescence a raceme to 8 cm. Sepals yellow-green, lobes to 4 mm, sepal base rounded to V-shaped, petals separate, 3-lobed and fringed, white, to 1 cm. Stamens inserted, ovary partially inferior. Fruit a capsule.

Genus & Specific Name Derivation: Greek: rock hedge, referring to the habitat / similar to

Notes: The flowers look like stars, and the petals are toothed and fringed like snowflakes.

Uses Past and Present: Roots of some species were used medicinally by natives.

Compare to L. heterophyllum

Photo in K & B plat. 51

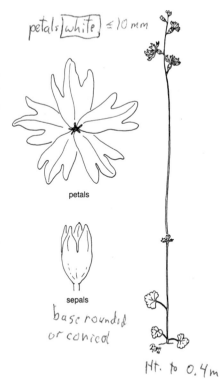

petals $\overline{\text{white}}$ ≤ 10 mm

petals

sepals

base rounded or conical

Ht. to 0.4m

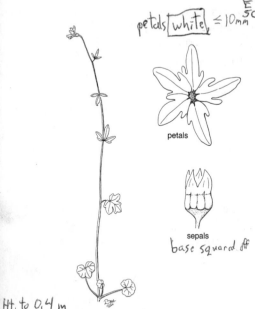

petals white, ≤ 10mm

petals

sepals

base squared off

Ht. to 0.4 m

Lithophragma heterophyllum (Hook. & Arn.) Torrey & A. Gray

HILL STAR   Native

Flowering Time: March–June

Habitat: woodland

Description: Upright herbaceous perennial to 40 cm, from underground rhizomes; stems short-hairy. Leaves simple to 1.5 cm; basal leaves rounded, margins lobed and toothed; stem leaves alternate, 3-parted; petiole to 1.5 cm. Basal leaves often dried up at flowering time. Inflorescence a raceme to 8 cm. Sepals yellow-green, lobes to 4 mm, sepal base squared off, base blunt, petals separate, 3-lobed and fringed, white, to 1 cm. Stamen inserted, ovary partially inferior. Fruit a capsule.

Genus & Specific Name Derivation: Greek: rock hedge, referring to the habitat / diversely-leaved

Uses Past and Present: See *L. affine.*

Compare to L. affine

petals white 2-5 mm

flower

Ht. to ..... cm

Saxifraga californica E. Greene

CALIFORNIA SAXIFRAGE   Native

Flowering Time: February–April

Habitat: woodland

Description: Upright herbaceous perennial from a rhizome. Leaves basal, simple to 10 cm, short-fuzzy-hairy, entire or slightly toothed; petiole to 5 cm. Inflorescence open, stalks red-tinted. Sepals reflexed; petals to 4.5 mm. Stamens 10, anthers orange-red. Fruit 2 small follicles.   petals white

Genus & Specific Name Derivation: Latin: rock-breaking, referring to the habitat / from California

Scrophulariaceae — Figwort Family

Annuals or herbaceous perennials, some root parasites. Leaves alternate or opposite, simple or compound, margin entire, toothed or lobed. Inflorescence in
racemes, spikes, panicles or axillary. Flowers bisexual, irregular or almost regular.
Sepals 4–5, free to fused; petals 4–5, fused; stamens usually 4, often with a 5th sterile stamen (staminode); ovary superior, styles 2, stigma lobes 2. Fruit a capsule;
seeds many. Many used as ornamentals or for medicine, e.g., *Digitalis.*

Family Characteristics

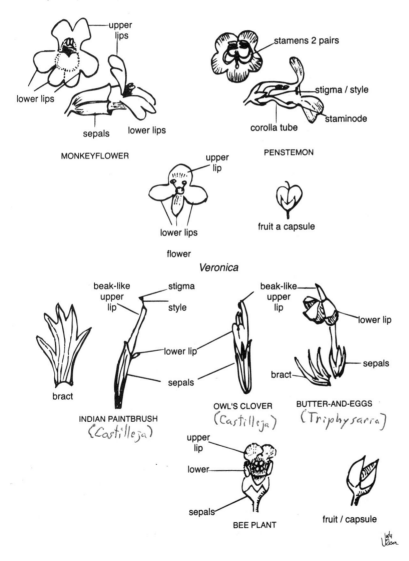

upper
lips

lower lips

sepals   lower lips

MONKEYFLOWER

stamens 2 pairs

stigma / style

staminode

corolla tube

PENSTEMON

upper
lip

lower lips

flower

Veronica

fruit a capsule

beak-like
upper
lip

stigma

style

lower lip

sepals

bract

INDIAN PAINTBRUSH
(Castilleja)

beak-like
upper
lip

lower lip

sepals

bract

OWL'S CLOVER
(Castilleja)

BUTTER-AND-EGGS
(Triphysarra)

upper
lip

lower

sepals

BEE PLANT

fruit / capsule

For key to woody plants *see* Group 2. Woody Plants

For key to families *see* Group 3. Herbaceous Flowering Plant Families

Key to Herbaceous Plants:

1. Upper stem leaves alternate
    2. Upper corolla lip with a beak-like structure
        3. Flowers maroon-red; inflorescence a raceme of many flowers ....
            .... *Pedicularis densiflora* (INDIAN WARRIOR)
        3′ Flowers of other colors
            4. Beak-tip closed, calyx a boat-shaped structure above the corolla
                5. Plant soft-hairy, glandular ....
                    ....*Cordylanthus pilosus* (HAIRY BIRD'S-BEAK)
                5′ Plant bristly-hairy, usually not glandular ....
                    .... *Cordylanthus rigidus* (STIFFLY-BRANCHED BIRD'S-BEAK)
            4′ Beak-tip open, calyx with a definite tube, and gen. with 4 subequal lobes
                6. Plant low-growing, whole plant dark purplish;
                    inflorescence axillary ... *Triphysaria pusilla* (DWARF ORTHOCARPUS)
                6′ Plant upright
                    7. Flowers mostly bright yellow
                        8. Plant usually not branched, corolla yellow ....
                            .... *Castilleja rubicundula* (CREAM SACS)
                        8′ Plant often branched at the base, corolla yellow, beak purple
                            ... *Triphysaria eriantha* (BUTTER-AND-EGGS or JOHNNY-TUCK)
                    7′ Flowers whitish, pale yellow, pink, purple, orange to red
                        9. Flowers whitish to pale yellow ....
                            .... *Castilleja attenuata* (VALLEY TASSELS)
                        9′ Flowers pink, purple, or orange to red
                            10. Flowers pink to purple
                                11. Plant gray-white-hairy ....
                                    .... *Castilleja exserta* (PURPLE OWL'S-CLOVER)
                                11′ Plant slightly hairy ....
                                    .... *Castilleja densiflora* (OWL'S-CLOVER)
                            10′ Flowers orange to red
                                12. Plant densely white-woolly-hairy ....
                                    .... *Castilleja foliolosa* (WOOLLY INDIAN PAINT BRUSH)
                                12′ Plant not densely white-woolly-hairy
                                    but may be slightly hairy ....
                                    .... *Castilleja affinis* (INDIAN PAINT BRUSH)
        2′ Upper corolla lip not beak-like
            13. Corolla with a long narrow basal spur ....
                .... *Linaria canadensis* (BLUE TOADFLAX)
            13′ Corolla without a basal spur but may be slightly sac-like ....
                .... *Antirrhinum vexillo-calyculatum* (WIRY SNAPDRAGON)
1′ Leaves in a basal rosette or upper stem leaves opposite

(handwritten annotations):
"beak" upper lip of corolla

14. Leaves mostly in a basal rosette ....
.... *Mimulus douglasii* (PURPLE MOUSE-EARS)
14´ Upper leaves opposite
   15. Corolla slightly irregular
      16. Inflorescence in axillary racemes ....
      .... *Veronica americana* (AMERICAN BROOKLIME)
      16´ Inflorescence solitary in leaf axils ....
      .... *Veronica persica* (PERSIAN SPEEDWELL)
   15´ Corolla obviously irregular, 2-lipped
      17. Calyx swollen and ribbed; flowers yellow ....
      .... *Mimulus guttatus* (LARGE MONKEYFLOWER)
      17´ Calyx not swollen or ribbed; flowers variously colored
         18. Plants > 5 dm; inflorescence an open panicle ....
         .... *Scrophularia californica* (BEE PLANT/CALIFORNIA FIGWORT)
         18´ Plants < 5 dm; inflorescence in various other arrangements
            19. Flowers pink with white .... *Bellardia trixago* (BELLARDIA)
            19´ Flowers lavender to blue with white
            20. Plants in the woodland; trailing; corolla to 18 mm ....
            .... *Collinsia multicolor* (SAN FRANCISCO COLLINSIA)
            20´ Plants in grassy areas; corolla to 10 mm ...8-12 mm..............
            ...... *Collinsia sparsiflora* (SPARSE-FLOWERED CHINESE HOUSES)

corolla lavender, ≤20mm (handwritten)

J

fruit   flower

Ht. to ... (handwritten)

Antirrhinum vexillo-calyculatum Kellogg var. *vexillo-calyculatum*

WIRY SNAPDRAGON   Native

Flowering Time: April–October

Habitat: woodland

Description: Erect to trailing annual, hairy below inflorescence. Leaves opposite below, alternate above. Inflorescence raceme-like, branched. Calyx lobes unequal; corolla to 2 cm, lavender, throat narrowed; upper lip folded backward, lower lip thrust forward. Fruit a capsule.

Genus & Specific Name Derivation: Greek: nose-like, referring to the corolla, which seems to have a snout / a sail-like petal resembling a small calyx

Notes: This plant climbs by tail-like extensions of the flowering stalk that clasp onto nearby vegetation. Illustration from *Illustrated Flora of the Pacific States.*

Photo in K & B plate 52 (handwritten)

✓ *Bellardia trixago* (L.) All.

BELLARDIA / MEDITERRANEAN LINSEED

Nonnative / Mediterranean

E SC (handwritten)

Flowering Time: April–May

Habitat: grassland, disturbed areas

Description: Upright annual to 15 cm with soft and glandular hairs. Leaves opposite, simple to 3 cm, margin toothed, light green tinged with red; sessile. Inflorescence whorled, each whorl with 3–6 flowers; flowers sessile; bracts leaf-like to 6 mm, light green; sepals 5, to 6 mm, lobed, light green, glandular-hairy; corolla to 2 cm, fused, upper lip pink, lower lip white; stamens and pistil included. Fruit a many-seeded capsule.

Genus & Specific Name Derivation: Bellardi (1740–1826), Italian botany professor / triple

Notes: Roots weakly parasitic mostly with grass roots to obtain minerals. This plant is rapidly reproducing and taking over native grasslands in our area. The first specimens were collected in the Santa Cruz Mountains by Wiggins in 1945.

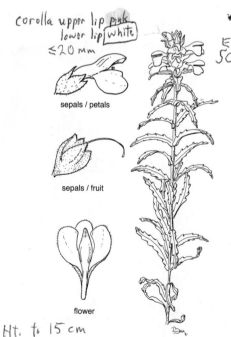

corolla upper lip pink
lower lip white
≤20 mm (handwritten)

sepals / petals

sepals / fruit

flower

Ht. to 15 cm (handwritten)

Photo in K & B plate 52 (handwritten)

✓ *Castilleja affinis* Hook. & Arn. ssp. *affinis*

E
SC

INDIAN PAINTBRUSH, Native COMMON

Flowering Time: March–August

Habitat:, woodland

Description: Herbaceous perennial to 6 dm, covered with short, bristly hairs. Leaves alternate to 8 cm, longer than wide, palmately divided into 3–5 lobes. Inflorescence in a terminal spike. Calyx to 3 cm; corolla to 4 cm, orange-red upper lip extending into a long, pointed beak, lower lip with small rounded lobes. Fruit a capsule to 15 mm.

Genus & Specific Name Derivation: For Domingo Castillejo, a Spanish botanist / related to

Notes: Dense flowering spikes look like they have been dipped in a bucket of brightly colored paints. The tips of the bracts and sepals are brightly colored, adding to the overall color of the inflorescence. Plants are partial parasites with suckers on the roots that extract nutrients from the roots of other plants.

Photo in K & B plate 52

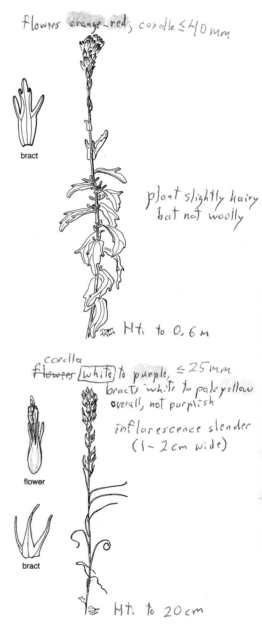

bract

flowers orange-red, corolla ≤ 40 mm

plant slightly hairy but not woolly

Ht. to 0.6 m

✗ *Castilleja attenuata* (A. Gray) Chuang & Heckard

E VALLEY TASSELS   Native

Flowering Time: April–May

Habitat: grassland

Description: Upright annual to 20 cm. Leaves simple, alternate to 2 cm, some 3-lobed. Inflorescence a narrow, terminal spike. Calyx to 20 mm, divided; corolla to 2.5 cm, whitish to purple, linear, beak to 5 mm, lower lip pouches to 4 mm; bracts to 2 cm, lobes 3, tips white or pale yellow. Fruit a capsule to 11 mm.

Genus & Specific Name Derivation: For Domingo Castillejo, a Spanish botanist / tapering

Photo in K & B plate 52

flower

bract

corolla
flowers [white] to purple, ≤ 25 mm
bracts white to pale yellow
overall, not purplish

inflorescence slender
(1 ~ 2 cm wide)

Ht. to 20 cm

flowers *purplish*
corolla lower lip with white pouch,
purple "eye" spots
≤25 mm

flower

stems greenish

plant slightly hairy

Ht. to 0.4 m

✓ *Castilleja densiflora* (Benth.) Chuang & Heckard ssp. *densiflora*

OWL'S-CLOVER, Native   COMMON
E
SC

Flowering Time: March–May

Habitat: grassland

Description: Upright annual to 40 cm, slightly hairy. Leaves alternate, deeply divided into thread-like lobes. Inflorescence in a dense spike at the top of each branch. Calyx to 2 cm, purplish; corolla to 2.5 cm, 3-lipped, upper lip narrow, beak-like, lower lip pouched. Bracts and sepals have purplish tips. Fruit a capsule to 10 mm.   nearly straight

Genus & Specific Name Derivation: For Domingo Castillejo, a Spanish botanist / densely flowered

Notes: Each flower looks like an owl with the rounded flower tube the body, the white pouches the face, with darker purple-pink eye spots. Synonym *Orthocarpus* means "straight fruit." Plants are partial parasites with suckers on the roots that extract nutrients from the roots of other plants.

Compare to C. exserta

flowers purplish

corolla upper "beak" pink
lower lobes pink with
tips yellow-cream, darker "eye" spots   purple

Sepals with pink tips

corolla lobes ≤15 mm

inflorescence purple at tip,
greenish below

stems mainly purplish
or reddish

plant gray-white hairy

Ht. to 0.45 m

✓ *Castilleja exserta* (A. A. Heller) Chuang & Heckard ssp. *exserta*

PURPLE OWL'S-CLOVER   Native
E
SC

Flowering Time: March–May

Habitat: grassland

Description: Densely gray-white-hairy, upright annual to 45 cm, sometimes branched. Leaves alternate, simple, deeply lobed to 3 cm; sessile. Inflorescence a dense spike to 3 cm with many flowers; bracts surrounding each flower green with pink tips. Flowers sessile; calyx to 2 cm base fused, green, tips lobed, pink; petals fused, exserted to 1.5 cm above the sepals, lower petals pink, tips pale yellow-cream with darker spots, upper beak pink-hairy; stigma slightly exserted. Fruit a capsule to 15 mm.   with hooked tip

Genus & Specific Name Derivation: For Domingo Castillejo, a Spanish botanist / protruding

Notes: Each flower looks like an owl with the rounded flower tube the body, the white pouches the face, with darker purple-pink eye spots. Synonym *Orthocarpus* means "straight fruit." Plants are partial parasites with suckers on the roots that extract nutrients from the roots of other plants.

Compare to C. densiflora
Photo in K&B plate 52

Castilleja foliolosa Hook. & Arn.

WOOLLY INDIAN PAINT BRUSH   Native

Flowering Time: March–August

Habitat: serpentine chaparral

Description: Upright, woolly-white-hairy, herbaceous perennial to 45 cm, branched at the base. Leaves alternate, simple to 4 cm, upper 2–3-lobed, white-woolly hairy; sessile. Inflorescence a terminal spike to 20 cm. Flowers sessile, irregular; calyx pale yellow-green, woolly, tips orange-coral; corolla to 1 cm, yellow-green, stigma exserted; stamens included. Bracts 3-lobed, darker at base, tips coral-orange. Fruit a capsule to 15 mm.

Genus & Specific Name Derivation: For Domingo Castillejo, a Spanish botanist / leafy

Notes: Plants are partial parasites with suckers on the roots that extract nutrients from the roots of chamise.

Photo in K & B plate 52

√*Castilleja rubicundula* (Jepson) Chuang & Heckard ssp. *lithospermoides* (Benth.) Chuang & Heckard

CREAM SACS   Native

Flowering Time: April–June

Habitat: grassland

Description: Upright, hairy, glandular annual to 3 dm. Leaves alternate, simple to 3 cm, margin lobed. Inflorescence a dense spike; bracts to 3 cm, green; calyx to 1 cm, divided; corolla to 2.5 cm, yellow; beak to 7 mm, straight, lower lip to 6 mm, with wide pouches. Fruit a capsule to 10 mm.

Genus & Specific Name Derivation: For Domingo Castillejo, a Spanish botanist / reddened / stone-seed-like

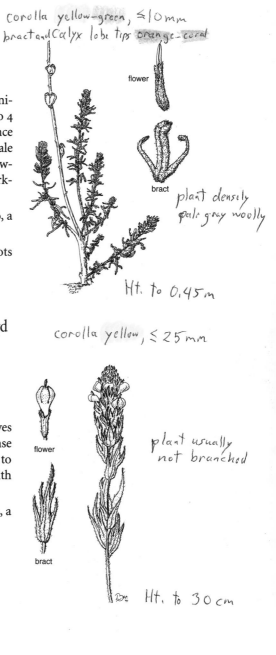

corolla yellow-green, ≤ 10 mm
bract and Calyx lobe tips orange-coral

flower

bract

plant densely pale gray woolly

Ht. to 0.45 m

corolla yellow, ≤ 25 mm

flower

bract

plant usually not branched

Ht. to 30 cm

corolla upper lip whitish with spots
lower lip lavender to blue-purple

on upper stem
flowers, mostly
in whorls of 3 or
more (K & B), at
least near top
of plant

corolla ≤ 20mm

fruit

upper leaves opposite,
≤ 3cm long

Ht. to 0.4m

Collinsia multicolor Lindley & Paxton

SC SAN FRANCISCO COLLINSIA   Native
E

Flowering Time: March–May

Habitat: woodland

Description: Loosely branched annual to 40 cm. Leaves opposite, simple to 3 cm, sessile to clasping. Inflorescence with 1–2
flowers in the leaf axils. Calyx to 6 mm, fused, and lobed;
corolla to 2 cm, 2-lipped with a pouch on lower floral tube,
upper lip whitish, erect, sometimes dotted or lined, lower lip
lavender to bluish purple. Fruit a capsule.

Genus & Specific Name Derivation: For Zaccheus Collins (1764–
1831), a Philadelphia botanist / many-colored

Notes: Listed in *CNPS Inventory of Rare and Endangered Plants
of California* on "List 1B, Plants Rare, Threatened, or Endangered in California and Elsewhere."

corolla lavender to purple
lower lip with purple dots at base
≤ 10mm
(8-12mm)

flowers mostly
in pairs in leaf axils
(K & B, but their
photo shows
solitary)

flower

corolla ≤ 10mm
upper leaves opposite,
≤ 10mm long

Ht. to 15 cm

Collinsia sparsiflora Fischer & C. Meyer var. *collina* (Jepson) V. Newsom

FEW-FLOWERED BLUE-EYED MARY   Native

Flowering Time: March–May

Habitat: serpentine grassland

Description: Low-growing annual to 15 cm. Leaves opposite,
simple to 10 mm, clasping to sessile. Inflorescence open, with
1–3 flowers in the leaf axils. Calyx to 8 mm, fused, remaining
on fruit; corolla to 10 mm, 2-lipped, lavender to purple, lower
lip with purple dots at base. Fruit a spheric capsule.

Genus & Specific Name Derivation: For Zaccheus Collins (1764–
1831), a Philadelphia botanist / sparsely flowered

Notes: So small often overlooked.

This variety of C. sparsiflora not listed in K & B

photo of C. s. var sparsiflora in K & B plate 53

genus Cordylanthus: Next to Castilleja and Triphysaria in keys; upper lip of corolla ("beak") closed; calyx a boat-shaped structure above the corolla

SCROPHULARIACEAE 269

Cordylanthus pilosus A. Gray ssp. *pilosus*

HAIRY BIRD'S-BEAK   Native

Flowering Time: July–October

Habitat: chaparral, grassland

Description: Plant gray-green, tinged with purple, densely soft-hairy, glandular, annual to 60 cm. Leaves alternate, simple to 4 cm, sessile, linear. Inflorescence axillary, sometimes clustered. Calyx to 2 cm; corolla to 2 cm, club-shaped, whitish, yellow-to green-tipped, pouch lightly marked maroon. Outer bracts 1–4, to 2 cm, linear, entire or 3-lobed; inner bract to 2.2 cm, tip pointed to notched. Fruit a capsule.

Genus & Specific Name Derivation: Greek: club-shaped flower / with soft hairs

Notes: Root-parasites on various host plants. The common name refers to the appearance of the corolla tip looking like a bird's beak.

Uses Past and Present: The natives are said to have used the plant medicinally as an emetic (to cause vomiting).

corolla [whitish] yellow or green at tips, pouch with light maroon marks ≤20mm

flower

bracts / flower

inflorescence with ≤4 flowers

plant soft-hairy, glandular

Ht. to 0.6m

Cordylanthus rigidus (Benth.) Jepson ssp. *rigidus*

STIFFLY-BRANCHED BIRD'S-BEAK   Native

Flowering Time: August–October

Habitat: chaparral, grassland

Description: Plant an annual to 60 cm, yellow-green, tinged with purple-red, bristly-hairy, not glandular. Leaves alternate, simple to 2 cm, linear, often in-rolled. Inflorescence axillary sometimes clustered. Calyx to 2 cm; corolla to 2 cm, club-shaped, yellowish, lower side marked maroon, pouch white. Outer bract to 2 cm, usually 3-lobed; inner bract to 2 cm, bristly. Fruit a capsule.

Genus & Specific Name Derivation: Greek: club-shaped flower / rigid, referring to rigid hairs

Notes: See. C. pilosus.

Uses Past and Present: See. C. pilosus.

corolla yellowish, ≤20mm lower side maroon-marked pouch white

flower

bract

inflorescence with generally 5–15 flowers

plant bristly-hairy, not glandular

Ht. to 0.6m

2008 Addendums

Kickxia elatine

Kickxia spuria

Genus Kickxia: leaves gen. alternate; corolla tube base with spur; leaf veins pinnate, margins entire; stems decumbent; plant hairy

SHARP-LEAVED FLUELIN nonnative
leaves ovate to hastate below, hastate to sagittate upward

ROUND-LEAVED FLUELIN nonnative
leaves narrowly to widely ovate or subcordate

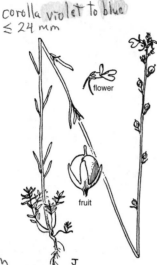

corolla violet to blue
≤ 24 mm

flower

fruit

Ht. to 0.5 m

J

Linaria canadensis (L.) Dum.-Cours.

BLUE TOADFLAX   Native

Flowering Time: February–May

Habitat: woodland

Description: Annual to biennial, stem to 50 cm, slender, with lower nonflowering shoots. Leaves simple to 2.5 cm, linear, lower opposite, upper alternate. Inflorescence in a raceme. Calyx to 3 mm; corolla to 2.4 cm, violet to blue, lips spreading, lower lip longer than upper. Fruit a spheric capsule to 3 mm.

Genus & Specific Name Derivation: Latin: flax, from flax-like leaves / from Canada

Notes: Illustration from *Illustrated Flora of the Pacific States.*

corolla orange to yellow-orange
≤ 40 mm

flower

evergreen shrub
Ht. to 1 m

Mimulus aurantiacus Curtis

STICKY MONKEYFLOWER   Native / *BUSH MONKEYFLOWER*

SC

Flowering Time: March–July

Habitat: chaparral, woodland

Description: Evergreen shrub to 1 m. Leaves opposite, simple to 6 cm, sticky, dark green, often in clusters on the lower stem, margin sometimes rolled under. Inflorescence with 1–3 flowers in the leaf axils. Flowers irregular; sepals 5, fused; petals 5, to 4 cm, fused, bright orange to yellow-orange. Stamens 4 in 2 pairs; ovary superior, stigma 2-lobed. Fruit a capsule.

Genus & Specific Name Derivation: Latin: little mime or comic actor, from face-like corolla / orange, referring to the flower color

Notes: When mature stigma is teased lightly with the fingertip, you can see it close. This occurs naturally when an insect brushes against it. Illustration from *Illustrated Flora of the Pacific States.*

Photo in K & B plate 53

Mimulus douglasii (Benth.) A. Gray

PURPLE MOUSE-EARS   Native

Flowering Time: February–April

Habitat: chaparral, serpentine grassland

Description: Small, upright annual to 4 cm. Leaves basal, simple to 1 cm, sessile. Inflorescence with 1–5 flowers at the leaf base. Calyx to 1.5 cm, hairy; corolla to 4 cm, including the floral tube, lower lips with a pouch below, with yellow stripes going down throat. Fruit a capsule to 7 mm.

Genus & Specific Name Derivation: Latin: little mime or comic actor, from face-like corolla / for David Douglas (1798–1834), collector in American northwest for the Royal Horticultural Society

Notes: So small often overlooked; the flowers bloom one at a time and each flower lasts for only 1–2 days. In times of stress due to unfavorable weather, this flower will close up and self-pollinate.

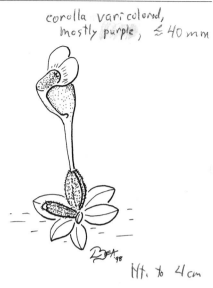

corolla varicolored, mostly purple, ≤ 40 mm

Ht. to 4 cm

Mimulus guttatus DC.

LARGE MONKEYFLOWER   Native/COMMON MONKEYFLOWER

Flowering Time: January–October

Habitat: seeps, swales

Description: Annual or herbaceous perennial, branches to 5 dm. Leaves opposite, simple to 10 cm, margin toothed; petiole to 5 cm. Inflorescence a raceme. Calyx to 3 cm, swollen and ridged; corolla to 4 cm, yellow with orange-red spots; pedicel to 2 cm. Bracts, opposite, fused at the base. Fruit an oval capsule to 12 mm.

Genus & Specific Name Derivation: Latin: little mime or comic actor, from face-like corolla / spotted

Photo in K & B plate 53

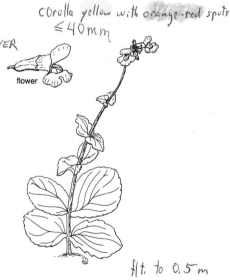

corolla yellow with orange-red spots ≤ 40 mm

flower

Ht. to 0.5 m

corolla deep maroon-red
≤ 35 mm

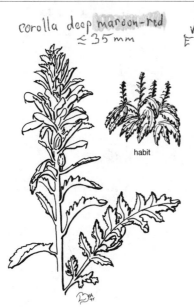

habit

Ht. to 0.5 m

√ *Pedicularis densiflora* Hook.

INDIAN WARRIOR   Native

Flowering Time: January–July

Habitat: woodland

Description: Upright herbaceous perennial with underground rhizomes, stems to 5 dm. Lower leaves alternate, compound to 20 cm, margins lobed and toothed, fern-like; upper leaves smaller, simple, lobed and toothed, often reddish-tinged; petiole to 2 cm. Inflorescence a raceme with many flowers. Calyx to 1.5 cm, hairy, lobes equal; corolla to 3.5 cm, club-like, deep maroon-red, upper lip hood like, lower lip lobed. Bracts purple-red adding to the overall color of the inflorescence. Fruit a capsule to 13 mm.

Genus & Specific Name Derivation: Latin: lice, from belief that ingestion by stock promoted lice infestation / densely flowered

Notes: Root-parasites on various host plants, often oaks in our area.

Photo in K & B plat. 54

corolla redish-brown to maroon
≤ 12 mm

Ht. to 1.5 m

√ *Scrophularia californica* Cham. & Schldl.
ssp. *californica*

BEE PLANT / CALIFORNIA FIGWORT   Native

Flowering Time: February–July

Habitat: chaparral, woodland

Description: Upright branched herbaceous perennial to 12 dm, stems 4-angled, often purple-tinged. Leaves opposite, simple to 20 cm, blade triangular, margin toothed; petiole to 7 cm. Inflorescence an open panicle. Calyx to 4 mm; corolla to 12 mm, reddish-brown to maroon, upper lip hooded, lower lobes smaller. Fruit an ovoid capsule to 8 mm.

Genus & Specific Name Derivation: Latin: scrofula, a disease supposedly cured by some species / from California

Notes: The flowers are a favorite nectar source for bees.

Uses Past and Present: Scrofula is a tuberculosis of the lymph nodes; some species of this genus have rhizome knobs that were supposed to be used to heal this disease.

Photo in K & B photo 54

Triphysaria eriantha (Benth.) Chuang & Heckard ssp. *eriantha*

BUTTER-AND-EGGS / JOHNNY-TUCK   Native

Flowering Time: March–April

Habitat: grassland

Description: Annual to 20 cm, purplish, hairy and glandular. Leaves alternate, simple to 2 cm, 3–7-lobed. Inflorescence a dense raceme; bracts to 1.8 cm, 3–5-lobed. Calyx to 1.3 cm; corolla to 2.5 cm, bright yellow to lighter yellow, beak dark purple, pouches enlarged. Fruit a capsule to 8 mm.

Genus & Specific Name Derivation: Greek: 3 bladders, from lower lip pouches / early flower

photo in K &B plate 54

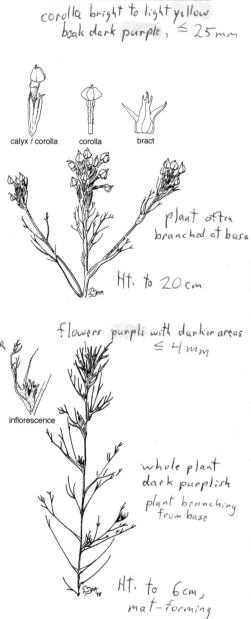

corolla bright to light yellow beak dark purple, ≤ 25mm

calyx / corolla   corolla   bract

plant often branched at base

Ht. to 20 cm

√ *Triphysaria pusilla* (Benth.) Chuang & Heckard

E

DWARF ORTHOCARPUS   Native / DWARF OWL'S-CLOVER

Flowering Time: March–May

Habitat: grassland

Description: Small, slender annual to 6 cm, whole plant purplish in color. Leaves reddish, alternate, simple to 1.5 cm, lower leaves unlobed, upper deeply lobed to compound. Inflorescence sessile in leaf axils. Flowers minute to 4 mm, purple with darker areas. Bracts to 2 cm, leaf-like. Fruits to 6 mm, roundish.

Genus & Specific Name Derivation: Greek: 3 bladders, from lower lip pouches / minute or small, referring to the small flowers or the small stature of the whole plant

Notes: This plant is most obvious when you see a low-growing purplish patch along the trail or in open areas.

flowers purple with darker areas ≤ 4mm

inflorescence

whole plant dark purplish

plant branching from base

Ht. to 6cm, mat-forming

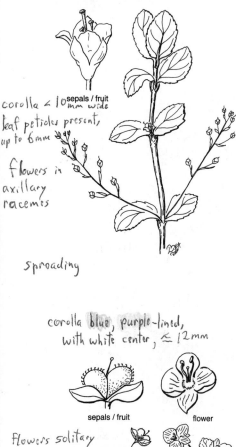

corolla bluish purple with darker veins

corolla < 10 mm wide sepals / fruit

leaf petioles present, up to 6mm

flowers in axillary racemes

spreading

corolla blue, purple-lined, with white center, ≤ 12mm

sepals / fruit   flower

Flowers solitary in leaf axils

spreading to 0.4m

Veronica americana (Raf.) Benth.

AMERICAN BROOKLIME   Native

Flowering Time: May–October

Habitat: riparian woodland, seeps

Description: Spreading herbaceous perennial from a rhizome, stems reddish. Leaves opposite, simple to 3 cm, lower longer, reddish on margins and undersurface, margins toothed; petiole to 6 mm. Inflorescence an axillary raceme; flowers irregular almost appearing regular, bluish-purple with darker veins; calyx to 3 mm, deeply lobed; corolla to 5 mm wide. Fruit a 2-parted capsule to 4 mm.

Genus & Specific Name Derivation: Possibly named for Saint Veronica; the markings on some species resemble the markings on her sacred handkerchief / from America

Notes: The darker lines on the petals are nectar guides. Correct authority from *The Jepson Manual Corrections* — Installment No. 5.

Veronica persica Poiret

PERSIAN SPEEDWELL   Nonnative / Asia Minor

Flowering Time: March–September

Habitat: grassland, woodland

Description: Low-growing annual to 40 cm, stems simple or branched. Leaves opposite, simple to 2.5 cm, margin toothed; petiole short. Inflorescence axillary; pedicel to 3 cm. Calyx to 7 mm; corolla to 12 mm, blue, purple-lined, center white. Fruit a two-parted, heart-shaped capsule.

Genus & Specific Name Derivation: Possibly named for Saint Veronica; the markings on some species resemble the markings on her sacred handkerchief / from Persia

Notes: The darker lines on the petals are nectar guides.

Note: Kozloff and Beidleman give differing descriptions:
V. persica: flowers in racemes X
*   leaf blades longer than wide X*
*   However, they agree with Corelli in that*
*   corolla 7-11 mm wide ✓*
*   leaf blades not heart-shaped ✓, >1cm long ✓*
V. filiformis: flowers solitary in leaf axils ✓
*   corolla up to 8 mm wide X*
*   leaf blades generally <1cm long X*
*   " " about as long as wide ✓*
*   " " somewhat heart-shaped X*

Solanaceae — Nightshade Family

Annuals, herbaceous perennials, or shrubs. Leaves alternate, simple. Inflorescence solitary, in umbel-like clusters, racemes, or panicles. Flowers bisexual, regular. Sepals 5, fused; petals 5, fused; stamens 5; pistil 1, ovary superior, style 1, stigma usually head-like. Fruit a berry or capsule. Some species are widely cultivated for food including tomatoes, peppers, eggplant, potatoes, and as ornamentals, e.g., petunias. Some are toxic, including tobacco and the deadly nightshades.

For key to woody plants *see* Group 2. Woody Plants

√ *Solanum umbelliferum* Eschsch.

E
SC BLUE WITCH   Native

Flowering Time: January–September

Habitat: chaparral, woodland

Description: Evergreen to deciduous shrub to 1 m; stem green, hairy. Leaves alternate, simple to 4 cm, margin entire, upper and lower surface soft-hairy; petiole to 3 mm. Inflorescence umbel-like. Flower regular; sepals 5, to 4 mm, fused; corolla to 2.5 cm wide, fused, blue-purple with green nectar glands at base. Fruit a berry to 14 mm wide, green looking like unripe tomatoes, turning dark purple when mature.

Genus & Specific Name Derivation: Latin: quieting, from narcotic properties / branches of inflorescence all rising from the same point, referring to the umbel-like inflorescence

Notes: Plant is poisonous throughout. Illustration from *Illustrated Flora of the Pacific States.*

Uses Past and Present: Birds feed on the fruit, but this genus is known to have poisonous alkaloids throughout the whole plant.

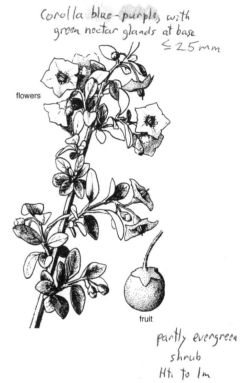

Corolla blue-purple, with green nectar glands at base
≤ 25 mm

flowers

fruit

partly evergreen shrub
Ht. to 1m

Photo in K & B plate 54

Thymelaeaceae — Mezereum Family

Shrubs or trees. Leaves simple, alternate or opposite. Inflorescence in clusters, racemes, umbels, or solitary. Flowers bisexual, regular. Calyx corolla-like, 4-lobed; corolla 0 or inconspicuous; stamens 4; pistil 1, ovary superior. Fruit a drupe or nut. Some cultivated, e.g., *Daphne*.

For key to woody plants *see* Group 2. Woody Plants

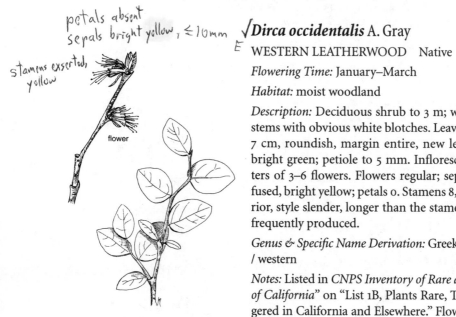

petals absent
sepals bright yellow, ≤ 10mm

stamens exserted, yellow

flower

shrub
Ht. to 3 m

√ *Dirca occidentalis* A. Gray

WESTERN LEATHERWOOD   Native

Flowering Time: January–March

Habitat: moist woodland

Description: Deciduous shrub to 3 m; with flexible branches, stems with obvious white blotches. Leaves alternate, simple to 7 cm, roundish, margin entire, new leaves often clustered, bright green; petiole to 5 mm. Inflorescence axillary in clusters of 3–6 flowers. Flowers regular; sepals to 1 cm, 4-lobed, fused, bright yellow; petals 0. Stamens 8, exserted; ovary superior, style slender, longer than the stamens. Fruit a drupe, infrequently produced.

Genus & Specific Name Derivation: Greek: a fountain in Thebes / western

Notes: Listed in *CNPS Inventory of Rare and Endangered Plants of California"* on "List 1B, Plants Rare, Threatened, or Endangered in California and Elsewhere." Flowers before new leaves fully develop. This is our only native member of this family in California.

Photo in K + B plat. 55

Urticaceae — Nettle Family

Annuals or herbaceous perennials, monoecious or dioecious; stems and leaves sometimes with stinging hairs. Leaves alternate or opposite, simple, entire to toothed. Flowers bisexual or unisexual, regular, in axillary clusters or pendulous racemes or panicles. Sepals 4–5; <u>petals absent</u>; staminate flowers with 4–5 stamens; pistillate flowers with ovary superior, stigma 1. Fruit an achene.

For key to families *see* Group 3. Herbaceous Flowering Plant Families

Key to Herbaceous Plants:

1. Leaves alternate, without stinging hairs, margins entire ....
    .... *Parietaria judaica* (PELLITORY)
1´ Leaves opposite, with stinging hairs, margins toothed ....
    .... *Urtica dioica* (AMERICAN STINGING NETTLE)

√*Parietaria judaica* L.

ℰ PELLITORY   Nonnative / Eurasia and North Africa

Flowering Time: May–October

Habitat: grassland, seeps

Description: Spreading to upright, dioecious, herbaceous perennial to 8 dm, whole plant hairy. Leaves alternate, simple to 9 cm; petiole to 10 cm. Inflorescence a head-like spike in the axils of upper leaf-like bracts. Perianth parts minute, pinkish. Fruit hidden in calyx lobes.

Genus & Specific Name Derivation: Latin: wall dweller, from the habit of some / unknown derivation

Notes: This plant occurs in the area along the underpass just before entering the park.

petals absent
perianth parts minute, pinkish

Ht. to 0.8 m

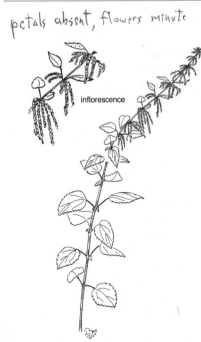

petals absent, flowers minute

inflorescence

Ht. to 3m

Urtica dioica L. ssp. *gracilis* (Aiton) Selander

AMERICAN STINGING NETTLE   Native

Flowering Time: April–September

Habitat: woodland , moist or riparian

Description: Upright herbaceous perennial from a rhizome, stem to 30 dm. Stems densely white hairy, **with stinging hairs.** Leaves opposite, simple, blade to 4 cm, shorter upward, somewhat triangular, margin toothed. Inflorescence a loose, pendent spike-like raceme to 7 cm, in the axils of leaf-like bracts. Individual flowers minute with 4 sepals, petals absent; staminate and pistillate flowers on separate plants. Fruit an achene.

Genus & Specific Name Derivation: Latin: to burn, from stinging hairs / two houses, having separate male and female plants (dioecious) / slender, graceful

Notes: Plant dioecious (male and female flowers on different plants). A rash follows after touching the stinging hairs. The sting contains formic acid and is similar to being stung by certain ants. Plants have a high nitrogen content and are often used as a catalyst to ferment compost heaps by manufacturers that sell purely organic fertilizer. Correct authority from *The Jepson Manual Corrections* — Installment No. 5.

Uses Past and Present: Leaves were used by natives as a raw vegetable or boiled as greens. Stem fibers were used to make bowstrings and in basket making. Nettle leaves were applied to various aching areas, such as rheumatic legs and arms. The boiled roots were used to obtain a yellow dye. Nettles have significant amounts of vitamins A and C, and protein. Plants are reported to be used as a food source for the brown towhee.

Valerianaceae — Valerian Family

Annuals or herbaceous perennials. Leaves in basal rosettes or opposite, simple to compound. Inflorescence in terminal or axillary panicles or clusters. Flowers bisexual or unisexual, radial to bilateral. Calyx absent or 5 or more lobed, fused; petals 5, fused, often spurred at base; stamens 1–3; ovary inferior, style 1, stigma head-like or 3-lobed. Fruit an achene.

For key to families *see* Group 3. Herbaceous Flowering Plant Families

Key to Herbaceous Plants:

1. Lower lip of corolla with red spots .... *Plectritis ciliosa* (PINK PLECTRITIS)   corolla ~~slightly~~ decidedly 2-lipped
1′ Lower lip of corolla without red spots .. *Plectritis macrocera* (WHITE PLECTRITIS)   corolla ~~decidedly~~ slightly 2-lipped

Plectritis ciliosa (E. Greene) Jepson var. *insignis* (Suksd.) D. Morey

PINK PLECTRITIS   Native / LONGSPUR PLECTRITIS

Flowering Time: April–May

Habitat: grassland

Description: Annual to 20 cm. Leaves simple, opposite to 2 cm, green with paler veins; margin entire. Inflorescence a terminal head-like cluster. Sepals 0; corolla to 4 mm, spur slender, pointed; petals 2-lipped, pink, lower lip with 2 red spots. Ovary inferior. Fruit an achene to 3 mm, with wings, hairs on whole surface of wings.

Genus & Specific Name Derivation: Greek: spur / fringed with hairs, referring to the hairs on the wings of the fruit

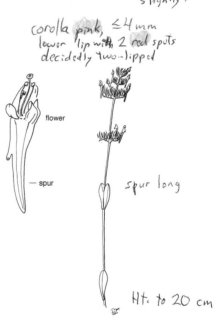

corolla pink, ≤4 mm
lower lip with 2 red spots
decidedly two-lipped

flower

— spur

spur long

Ht. to 20 cm

corolla uniformly [white] to pink,
regular or slightly two-lipped
≤ 3,5 mm

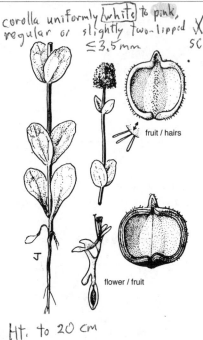

fruit / hairs

flower / fruit

J

Ht. to 20 cm

X ***Plectritis macrocera*** Torrey & A. Gray

SC WHITE PLECTRITIS   Native / LONGHORN PLECTRITIS

Flowering Time: March–April

Habitat: grassland

Description: Upright annual to 20 cm. Leaves simple, opposite to 2 cm, sessile, bright green. Inflorescence a head-like cluster. Flowers sessile; bracts linear, green with pink tips. Sepals 0; petals to 3.5 mm, uniformly pink to white, spur thick, blunt. Fruit an achene 1–2 mm, hairy on margins of wings.

Genus & Specific Name Derivation: Greek: spur / large horn

Notes: Illustration from *Illustrated Flora of the Pacific States.*

Photo in K + B plate 55

Verbenaceae — Vervain Family

Annual, or herbaceous perennials. Leaves opposite, simple, margin usually toothed or lobed. Inflorescence in racemes or spikes. Flowers bisexual, regular; each flower usually subtended by 1 bract. Sepals 5, fused; petals 4–5, fused; stamens usually 4; ovary superior, style 1, stigma lobes 2. Fruit a capsule, or 2 or 4 nutlets. Some species are cultivated as ornamentals e.g. *Lantana*; others cultivated for wood e.g. *Tectona*, teak.

For key to families *see* Group 3. Herbaceous Flowering Plant Families

Verbena lasiostachys Link var. *scabrida* Mold.

VERVAIN Native/*ROBUST VERBENA*

Flowering Time: July–September

Habitat: chaparral, grassland, seeps

Description: Upright perennial to 5 dm, whole plant rough-glandular-hairy. Leaves opposite, simple to 10 cm, margin lobed and toothed, both surfaces rough-hairy. Inflorescence a narrow spike to 10 cm in fruit. Flowers pink-purple, calyx 2 mm, glandular-hairy; corolla 2 mm wide, slightly irregular; bracts narrow. Fruit 4 nutlets to 1.5 mm.

Genus & Specific Name Derivation: Latin: ancient name / shaggy spike / rough, referring to the hairs

Notes: Although *Verbena* is an ancient Latin name, botanist J. Pitton de Tournefort (1656–1708), believed the name was a corruption of *Herbena*, "the good plant," because it was "used among the heathens in their religion and worship."

Uses Past and Present: Leafy twigs used in wreaths for rituals and medicine.

Photo in K & B plate 55

corolla pink-purple, ≤ 2 mm

flower

stem hairs

Ht. to 0.5 m

Viscaceae — Mistletoe Family

Shrubs, generally green, parasitic on above-ground parts of woody plants, dioecious or monoecious. Leaves simple, entire, opposite. Inflorescence in spikes or cymes. Flowers unisexual, regular. Staminate flowers with perianth parts 3–7; anthers sessile; pistillate flowers with perianth parts 2–4; ovary inferior, style unbranched, stigma obscure. Fruit a berry.

For key to woody plants *see* Group 2. Woody Plants

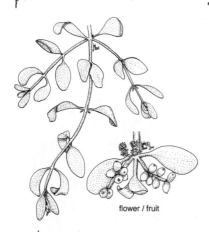

petals absent, sepals greenish

flower / fruit

woody on oak branches

. *Phoradendron villosum* (Nutt.) Nutt.

OAK MISTLETOE   Native

Flowering Time: July–September

Habitat: woodland, oak savanna

Description: Shrub, parasitic on aboveground parts of oaks in our area. Leaves opposite, simple, thick leathery, to 4 cm, densely short-hairy; petiole short. Inflorescence a spike. Flowers unisexual, sepals 2–5-lobed, greenish; petals 0. Staminate spike with 20–30 flowers, pistillate spike with 10–15 flowers. Male and female flowers on different plants (dioecious). Fruit is a berry to 4 mm, pinkish-white, maturing in 2 seasons. The seeds are covered with a sticky substance that permits them to stick to the branches of the host trees.

Genus & Specific Name Derivation: Greek: tree thief, referring to the plant being parasitic / with soft hairs

Notes: The seeds are dispersed by birds. The plant absorbs food from the sap of the host through specialized roots.

Uses Past and Present: This species is collected and sold at Christmas, but the eastern species is the one more commonly used.

Monocotyledons

Arecaceae — Palm Family

Shrubs, trees; evergreen; monoecious or dioecious or flowers bisexual. Leaves palmate, or pinnately compound, alternate, large; base sheathing; petiole long. Inflorescence an axillary panicle; bracts sheathing. Flowers small, sepals and petals 3, fused at the base or free. Stamens 6; pistils 1 or 3, ovary superior, 3 chambers, styles free or fused. Fruit a drupe.

For key to woody plants *see* Group 2. Woody Plants

√ *Washingtonia* sp.

FAN PALM   Planted

Flowering Time: N/A

Habitat: disturbed area in open woodland

Description: Tree to 20 m; with a narrow trunk and an open rounded top. Leaves to 2 m, palmately divided with thread-like fibers, segments folded, fan shaped; petiole margins generally spiny. Flowers regular; sepals and petals white, 3 lobed, located high within the leaves. Fruit black when mature.

Genus & Specific Name Derivation: George Washington / derivation unknown

Notes: Only one tree noted at Edgewood. It is not known if this was planted or seeded by birds or other animals.

Tree

2008 addendums:
Traphycarpus fortunei
WINDMILL PALM   Nonnative

Araceae   Arum family
Arum italicum
ITALIAN LORDS AND LADIES   Nonnative
Zantedeschia aethiopica   CALLA LILY   Nonnative

Cyperaceae — Sedge Family

Annuals or herbaceous perennials; stems terete to triangular, solid. Leaves usually in 3 ranks, alternate, usually sheathing the stem; blades linear, flat to terete, sometimes reduced or absent. Inflorescence in an umbel or open to dense panicle. Flowers bisexual or unisexual, regular, 1–many; each flower subtended by 1 bract. Perianth absent or of scales or bristles; stamens 1–3; ovary superior, seeds 1, styles 1–3, or 2–3 branched. Fruit an achene.

For key to families *see* Group 3. Herbaceous Flowering Plant Families

1.   Flower and fruit enclosed in a closed bract (perigynium) .... *Carex* (SEDGE)
1′   Flower and fruit not enclosed in a closed bract
    2.   Fruit with horizontal crossribs ..... *Eleocharis acicularis* (NEEDLE SPIKERUSH)
    2′   Fruit without horizontal crossribs .... *Eleocharis montevidensis* (SPIKERUSH)

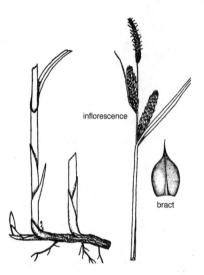

inflorescence

bract

Carex sp.

SEDGE

Flowering Time: N/A

Habitat: moist areas

Description: Herbaceous perennial from rhizomes; stem usually 3-angled, solid. Inflorescence of spikelets in a raceme, panicle or head-like cluster, usually subtended by a spikelet bract. Flowers unisexual; staminate flowers with 3 stamens; pistillate flowers enclosed in a sac-like bract (perigynium); style 1 with 2–4 exserted stigmas. Fruit 2–4 sided.

Genus & Specific Name Derivation: Latin: cutter, from sharp leaf and stem edges / derivation unknown

Notes: Various species have not been identified at Edgewood yet. Remember: "sedges have edges and rushes are round" referring to the shape of the stem. This is mostly true. Illustration from *A California Flora and Supplement.*

Uses Past and Present: Used locally in basketry, matting and for hats and chair seats. The pith has been used for candlewicks.

2008 Addendums (all native)

Carex densa   DENSE SEDGE
Carex praegracilis CLUSTERED FIELD SEDGE
Carex subbracteata SMALL-BRACTED SEDGE
Carex serratodens   BIFID SEDGE
Cyperus eragrostis   TALL CYPERUS

Eleocharis acicularis (L.) Roemer & Schultes var. *acicularis*

NEEDLE SPIKERUSH   Native

Flowering Time: N/A

Habitat: moist areas

Description: Perennial to 15 cm. Leaves to 15 cm, needle-like, sheathing at the base. Inflorescence a terminal, solitary spikelet; flower bracts spiraled, straw-colored with reddish-brown stripes. Stamens 1–3; style 3-branched, base bulb-like. Fruit 3-sided, with ridges and crossbars.

Genus & Specific Name Derivation: Greek: marsh grace / needle shaped, referring to the leaves

Notes: See *Carex.* Illustration from *Illustrated Flora of the Pacific States.*

Uses Past and Present: See *Carex.*

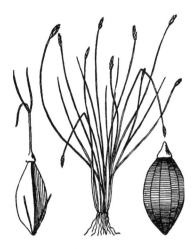

Eleocharis montevidensis Kunth

SPIKERUSH   Native

Flowering Time: N/A

Habitat: moist areas

Description: Herbaceous perennial to 5 dm. Leaves to 15 dm, purplish brown, becoming straw-colored at tip. Inflorescence a spikelet to 8 mm, 10 to many-flowered. Flower bract brownish to yellow, margin translucent. Flower bisexual, style branches 3. Fruit to 1 mm, 3-sided, yellowish brown, shiny.

Genus & Specific Name Derivation: Greek: marsh grace / from Montevideo, Uruguay

Notes: See *Carex.* Illustration from *Illustrated Flora of the Pacific States.*

Uses Past and Present: See *Carex.*

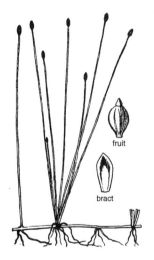

fruit

bract

Iridaceae — Iris Family

Herbaceous perennials from a bulb, corm, or rhizome. Leaves basal and cauline, alternate, simple, linear, sheathing the stem; main veins parallel. Inflorescence solitary or in racemes or panicles. Flowers bisexual, regular. Perianth parts in 2 whorls of 3, petaloid, fused into a tube; stamens 3; <u>ovary inferior</u>, style or style branches 3. Fruit a capsule, 3-parted. Many cultivated, e.g., iris, gladiolus, crocus, freesia. Iris means rainbow, referring to the beautiful colors of the flowers.

Family Characteristics

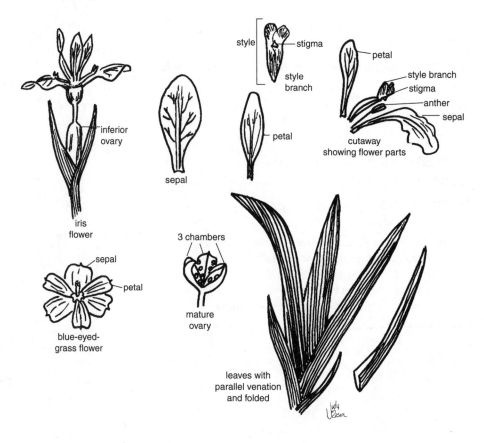

For key to families *see* Group 3. Herbaceous Flowering Plant Families.

Key to Herbaceous Plants:

1. Perianth parts similar .... *Sisyrinchium bellum* (BLUE-EYED-GRASS)
1′ Perianth parts not alike .... *Iris douglasiana* (DOUGLAS' IRIS)

√ CROCOSMIA sp. (probably C₁ X Crocosmiiflora)
F   CROCOSMIA / MONTBRETIA
9c

✓ *Iris douglasiana* Herbert

E

DOUGLAS IRIS   Native

Flowering Time: February–June

Habitat: woodland

Description: Spreading perennial from a tuber-like rhizome. Leaves basal, linear, sharply folded, overlapping. Inflorescence of 2–3 flowers; perianth parts in 2 series of 3, colorful from cream to light or dark lavender with darker veins; sepals narrower than petals, upright; style branches petal-like, arching over stamens; bracts leaf-like, overlapping. Fruit a many-seeded 3-chambered capsule.

Genus & Specific Name Derivation: Greek: rainbow, referring to the flower colors / David Douglas (1798–1834), collector in American northwest for the Royal Horticultural Society

Notes: Leaves poisonous.

Photo in K & B plate 57

perianth parts light to dark lavender with creamy bases and darker veins

Ht. to 0...m

✓ *Sisyrinchium bellum* S. Watson

E
SC

BLUE-EYED-GRASS   Native

Flowering Time: March–May

Habitat: grassland

Description: Upright herbaceous perennial to 35 cm, somewhat spreading. Leaves basal and alternate to 12 cm, folded, flat, linear. Inflorescence 3–5 flowers coming out of a linear bract folded around the pedicel; flowers to 2 cm wide, regular; sepals and petals similar in shape and color, light to dark purple, with a yellow center; stamens somewhat exserted, style and stigma come through the center of the stamens. Fruit to 8 mm, roundish, appearing bumpy.

Genus & Specific Name Derivation: Name used by Theophrastus for Iris-like plant / beautiful

Notes: Blue-eyed-grass actually has blue-purple flowers with a yellow center or eye and it is not a grass; it could more appropriately be called yellow-eyed purple iris.

Uses Past and Present: Spanish Californians made a tea from the roots for fevers.

Photo in K & B plate 57

perianth parts light to dark blue-purple with yellow center

flowers ≤ 20 mm wide

Ht. to 35 cm

2008 Addendums

Chasmanthe floribunda   AFRICAN CORNFLAG Nonnative

Iris spp.   GARDEN IRISES Nonnative

I. foetidissima   BROWN STINKING IRIS Nonnative

I. germanica   BEARDED IRIS Nonnative

Juncaceae — Rush Family

Annuals or herbaceous perennials; stems compressed to cylindrical, hollow or solid. Leaves basal, some stem leaves, alternate; blades linear, flat to terete; petiole sheathing stem. Flowers bisexual, regular, 1–many, in small, axillary clusters. Inflorescence axillary, or in terminal panicles; each flower subtended by 1–3 minute bracts. Perianth parts in 2 whorls of 3, greenish to dark brown; stamens 3 or 6; ovary superior, style usually 3-parted. Fruit a capsule; seeds many.

For key to families *see* Group 3. Herbaceous Flowering Plant Families

Key to Herbaceous Plants:

1. Sheath margins free, overlapping, glabrous; leaf blade margins glabrous; ovary with many seeds
   2. Stem flat .... *Juncus xiphioides* (IRIS-LEAVED RUSH)
   2´ Stem cylindric
      3. Flowers usually solitary .... *Juncus bufonius* (TOAD RUSH)
      3´ Flowers many in a cluster
         4. Stamens 6; fruit with a soft beak ....
            .... *Juncus patens* (SPREADING RUSH)
         4´ Stamens 3; fruit without a soft beak ....
            .... *Juncus effusus* (PACIFIC BOG RUSH)
1´ Sheath margins fused except near tip, hairy;
   leaf blade margins hairy, especially near base; ovary with 3 seeds ....
   .... *Luzula comosa* (COMMON WOOD RUSH)

Juncus bufonius L.

TOAD RUSH   Native

Flowering Time: N/A

Habitat: moist areas

Description: Annual branched from the base to 30 cm. Leaves 1–3 per stem to 1.5 mm wide. Inflorescence in small clusters throughout the plant; lowest bracts leaf-like; bractlets to 2.5 mm. Perianth segments to 7 mm, sepals longer than the petals; stamens 6, stigmas generally 3. Fruit a capsule, seeds minute, many.

Genus & Specific Name Derivation: Latin: to join or bind, from use of stems / of the toad or living in damp places

Notes: Remember: "sedges have edges and rushes are round" referring to the shape of the stem. This is mostly true. Illustration from *Illustrated Flora of the Pacific States.*

Uses Past and Present: Rushes were used locally in basketry and matting.

fruit

perianth parts and fruit   perianth parts

Juncus effusus L. var. *pacificus* Fern. & Wieg.

PACIFIC BOG RUSH   Native

Flowering Time: N/A

Habitat: moist areas

Description: Herbaceous perennial, stems to 13 dm, leafless. Leaves all basal, reduced to brown sheaths. Inflorescence lateral, many-flowered, compact to open; lowermost bract to 25 cm, appearing as a continuation of the stem; perianth parts green-brown to 3.5 mm, stamens mostly 3. Fruit a capsule, shorter or about as long as the perianth scales.

Genus & Specific Name Derivation: Latin: to join or bind, from use of stems / spread-out, loose-spreading, referring to the inflorescence / from the Pacific region

Notes: See *J. bufonius.* Illustration from *Illustrated Flora of the Pacific States.*

Uses Past and Present: Rushes were used locally in basketry and matting.

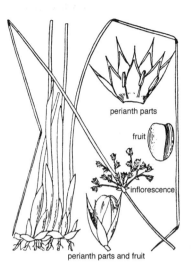

perianth parts

fruit

inflorescence

perianth parts and fruit

Juncus patens E. Meyer

SPREADING RUSH   Native

Flowering Time: N/A

Habitat: moist areas

Description: Herbaceous perennial to 9 dm. Leaves basal, blades 0 or short, sheaths dark brown. Inflorescence lateral, open to compact, lower bract > inflorescence, flowers many. Perianth segments to 3 mm, narrow, spreading in fruit; stamens 6. Fruit shorter to equal to perianth.

Genus & Specific Name Derivation: Latin: to join or bind, from use of stems / spreading out from the stem, referring to the inflorescence

Notes: See *J. bufonius.* Illustration from *Illustrated Flora of the Pacific States.*

Uses Past and Present: Rushes were used locally in basketry and matting.

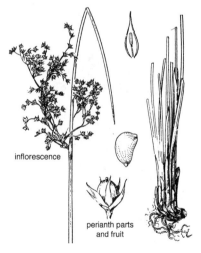

inflorescence

perianth parts
and fruit

2008 Addendum
  Juncus occidentalis   WESTERN RUSH native

Juncus xiphioides E. Meyer

IRIS-LEAVED RUSH   Native

Flowering Time: N/A

Habitat: moist areas

Description: Herbaceous perennial to 8 dm. Leaf blade to 5 dm, 12 mm wide, flat, with crosswalls that can be felt by rubbing your finger along the blade. Inflorescence in clusters with 3–10 flowers; lowest bract < 1 / 2 length of inflorescence. Perianth segments to 3.5 mm, very narrow, green to brown; stamens 6. Fruit equal to greater than the perianth segments.

Genus & Specific Name Derivation: Latin: to join or bind, from use of stems / sword-like, referring to the flattened leaf blades

Notes: See *J. bufonius.* Illustration from *Illustrated Flora of the Pacific States.*

Uses Past and Present: Rushes were used locally in basketry and matting.

fruit

perianth segments
and fruit

X *Luzula comosa* E. Meyer

E
SC
COMMON WOOD RUSH   Native

Flowering Time: N/A

Habitat: moist areas

Description: Herbaceous perennial to 4 dm. Leaf sheath margin with long, soft hairs; blade to 15 cm, to 7 mm wide. Inflorescence umbel-like; flower clusters 1–6, spike-like to 15 mm, 7 mm in diameter; bractlets clear, margins hairy. Perianth segments to 5 mm, dark brown to pale, margins translucent. Fruit equal to or shorter than perianth, green to dark brown.

Genus & Specific Name Derivation: Latin: light; Italian: glow-worm / shaggy-tufted, referring to the hairy bractlets

Notes: See *J. bufonius.* Illustration from *Illustrated Flora of the Pacific States.*

Uses Past and Present: Rushes were used locally in basketry and matting.

Photo in K & B plate 57

Liliaceae — Lily Family

Herbaceous perennials from bulbs, corms, or rhizomes. Leaves basal or cauline, alternate, opposite, or whorled, often sheathing at base. Inflorescence in umbels, spikes, racemes, and some head-like. Flowers bisexual, regular. Perianth in 2 whorls of 3; calyx sometimes petaloid; stamens 3 or 6, sometimes staminodes present, filaments with appendages; style 1, stigma 3-lobed. Fruit a capsule, 3-lobed. Many species cultivated as ornamentals and food; some toxic. Amaryllidaceae and other families included.

Family Characteristics

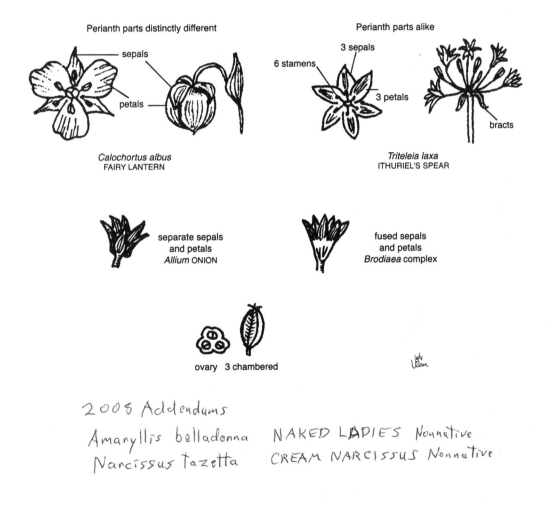

Perianth parts distinctly different

sepals

petals

Calochortus albus
FAIRY LANTERN

Perianth parts alike

3 sepals

6 stamens

3 petals

bracts

Triteleia laxa
ITHURIEL'S SPEAR

separate sepals
and petals
Allium ONION

fused sepals
and petals
Brodiaea complex

ovary   3 chambered

2008 Addendums
Amaryllis belladonna   NAKED LADIES Nonnative
Narcissus Tazetta   CREAM NARCISSUS Nonnative

For key to families *see* Group 3. Herbaceous Flowering Plant Families

Key to Herbaceous Plants:

1. Some stem leaves whorled
    2. Perianth segments strongly recurved ....
    .... *Lilium pardalinum* (LEOPARD LILY/TIGER LILY)
    2´ Perianth segments not recurved
        3. Perianth parts purple to pink, evenly colored ....
        .... *Trillium chloropetalum* (GIANT TRILLIUM)
        3´ Perianth parts brown, purple, mottled yellow ....
        .... *Fritillaria affinis* (MISSION BELLS/CHECKER LILY)
1´ Leaves basal, alternate, or opposite
    4. Perianth parts similar in size and shape *(but not necessarily identical)*
        5. Perianth parts separate (free)
            6. Inflorescence an umbel
                7. Flowers cream-white; leaves narrow, cylindric;
                   plants without an onion odor ....
                   .... *Muilla maritima* (COMMON MUILLA)
                7´ Flowers, white, pink or purple; plants with an obvious onion odor
                    8. Stem and leaves channeled and angled;
                       flowers white with green midveins ....
                       .... *Allium triquetrum* (WILD ONION)
                    8´ Stem cylindric
                        9. Flowers white with darker midveins;
                           found on serpentine ...... *Allium lacunosum* (PITTED ONION)
                        9´ Flowers pink to purple
                            10. Leaves flattened, sickle-shaped ....*Allium falcifolium*
                                (BREWER'S ONION/ SICKLE-LEAVED ONION)
                            10´ Leaves cylindric to channeled
                                11. Inflorescence dense; pedicels to 2 cm ....
                                    .... *Allium dichlamydeum* (COASTAL ONION)
                                11´ Inflorescence open; pedicels to 3 cm ....
                                    .... *Allium peninsulare* (FRANCISCAN ONION)
            6´ Inflorescence in other arrangements
                12. Leaves mostly basal
                    13. Leaf margin wavy; perianth segments white throughout
                        with a darker midvein ....
                        .... *Chlorogalum pomeridianum* (AMOLE/SOAP PLANT)
                    13´ Leaf margin not wavy; perianth segments white to
                        pale yellow with a yellow gland at base
                        14. Mature inflorescence mostly > 25 cm ....
                            .... *Zigadenus fremontii* (FREMONT'S STAR LILY)
                        14´ Mature inflorescence mostly < 25 cm ....
                            .... *Zigadenus venenosus* (DEATH CAMAS)
                12´ Leaves alternate, simple or whorled

    15. Flowers green-yellow with dark brown blotches ....
    .... *Fritillaria affinis* (MISSION BELLS/CHECKER LILY)
    15´ Flowers white to cream
        16. Leaves somewhat succulent, linear ....
        .... *Fritillaria liliacea* (FRAGRANT FRITILLARY)
        16´ Leaves not linear
            17. Inflorescence a raceme or panicle; flowers many, obvious
                18. Inflorescence an open panicle ....
                .... *Smilacina racemosa* (FAT SOLOMON'S SEAL)
                18´ Inflorescence a raceme ....
                .... *Smilacina stellata* (SLIM SOLOMON'S SEAL)
            17´ Inflorescence 1–3 flowers, hidden by leaves ....
            .... *Prosartes hookeri* (HOOKER'S FAIRY BELL)
5´ Perianth parts fused at the base
    19. Inflorescence congested (pedicel < 3 mm)
        20. Perianth tube markedly narrowed at top; inflorescence dense,
        raceme-like .... *Dichelostemma congestum* (OOKOW)
        20´ Perianth tube not markedly narrowed at top, inflorescence a
        dense umbel .... *Dichelostemma capitatum* (BLUE DICKS)
    19´ Inflorescence open
        21. Fertile stamens 3; perianth purple to blue
            22. Plants low-growing, less than 8 cm ....
            .... *Brodiaea terrestris* (DWARF BRODIAEA)
            22´ Plants taller than 8 cm
                23. Anther tip notched; staminodia inrolled toward stamens ....
                .... *Brodiaea coronaria* (HARVEST BRODIAEA)
                23´ Anthers rounded; staminodia not inrolled ....
                .... *Brodiaea elegans* (ELEGANT BRODIAEA)
    21´ Fertile stamens 6
        24. Perianth golden yellow .... *Triteleia ixioides* (GOLDEN BRODIAEA)
        24´ Perianth white, blue or purple
            25. Perianth white to pale blue-purple
                26. Pedicel < 2 cm; perianth tube short ....
                .... *Triteleia hyacinthina* (WHITE BRODIAEA/WILD HYACINTH)
                26´ Pedicel > 2 cm; perianth tube obvious ....
                .... *Triteleia peduncularis* (LONG-RAYED BRODIAEA)
            25´ Perianth blue to purple .... *Triteleia laxa* (ITHURIEL'S SPEAR)
4´ Perianth parts distinctly different
    27. Flowers nodding; perianth closed ....
    .... *Calochortus albus* (WHITE GLOBE LILY/FAIRY LANTERN)
    27´ Flowers erect; perianth open
        28. Petals white to pink .... *Calochortus argillosus* (CLAY MARIPOSA LILY)
        28´ Petals yellow .... *Calochortus luteus* (YELLOW MARIPOSA LILY)

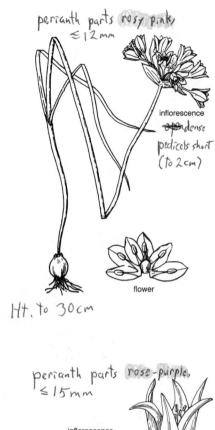

perianth parts rosy pink, ≤ 12mm

inflorescence

~~open dense~~

pedicels short (to 2 cm)

flower

Ht. to 30cm

Allium dichlamydeum E. Greene

COASTAL ONION   Native

Flowering Time: April–June

Habitat: woodland

Description: Herbaceous perennial from a bulb, whole plant to 30 cm. Leaves 3–6, to 30 cm, linear, channeled to cylindric. Inflorescence an open umbel of 5–30 flowers; peduncle to 20 cm; pedicels to 2 cm; perianth segments alike, to 12 mm, rosy-pink; bracts to 2 cm, split in half, pale pink to white; ovary crests 3, minute, 2-lobed. Fruit a capsule, seeds small, black.

Genus & Specific Name Derivation: Latin: garlic / two-cloaked, may refer to the bracts covering the bud

Notes: Leaves have smell of onion. Illustration from *Illustrated Flora of the Pacific States.*

Uses Past and Present: Used as a food and to relieve the pain of insect stings and bites. The juice made into a thick syrup has been used as a treatment for colds and throat irritations.

Allium falcifolium Hook. & Arn.

BREWER'S ONION / SICKLE LEAVED ONION   Native

Flowering Time: April–May

Habitat: serpentine grassland

Description: Herbaceous perennial from a bulb, stems to 20 cm, flattened. Leaves to 30 cm, flattened, sickle-shaped. Inflorescence an umbel of 10–30 flowers; pedicels to 15 cm; perianth segments alike to 15 mm, rose-purple; ovary crests 3, wide. Fruit a capsule, seeds small, black.

Genus & Specific Name Derivation: Latin: garlic / sickle-shaped, referring to leaf shape

Notes: Leaves have smell of onion.

Uses Past and Present: See *A. dichlamydeum.*

Photo in K & B plate 58

perianth parts rose-purple, ≤ 15mm

inflorescence

flower

leaves flattened, sickle-shaped (curved)

stems also flattened

stem cross-section

leaf cross-section

Ht. to 20 cm

Allium lacunosum S. Watson var. *lacunosum*

PITTED ONION   Native

Flowering Time: May–June

Habitat: serpentine chaparral

Description: Herbaceous perennial from a bulb, stem to 35 cm. Leaves to 50 cm, cylindric. Inflorescence an umbel of 5–45 flowers, pedicels to 12 mm; perianth segments alike to 9 mm, white with darker midveins; ovary crests 3, minute, 2-lobed. Fruit a capsule, seeds small, black.

Genus & Specific Name Derivation: Latin: garlic / with pits or deep holes, referring to the fruit

Notes: Leaves have smell of onion.

Uses Past and Present: See *A. dichlamydeum*.

Photo in K & B plate 58

Allium peninsulare Lemmon var. *franciscanum* D. McNeal & F. Ownbey

FRANCISCAN ONION   Native

Flowering Time: April–May

Habitat: woodland

Description: Herbaceous perennial from a bulb, stem to 45 cm. Leaves 2–3, to 60 cm, channeled to cylindric. Inflorescence an umbel of 5–35 flowers; peduncle to 20 cm; pedicels to 3 cm; perianth segments alike to 12 mm, purple, tips recurved; ovary crests 3, minute, 2-lobed. Fruit a capsule, seeds small, black.

Genus & Specific Name Derivation: Latin: garlic / living on a peninsula / from San Francisco

Notes: Listed in *CNPS Inventory of Rare and Endangered Plants of California* on "List 1B, Plants Rare, Threatened, or Endangered in California and Elsewhere." Leaves have smell of onion.

Uses Past and Present: See *A. dichlamydeum*.

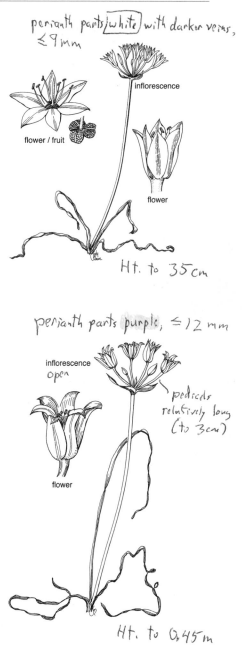

perianth parts (white) with darker veins, ≤9mm

inflorescence

flower / fruit

flower

Ht. to 35cm

perianth parts purple, ≤12 mm

inflorescence open

pedicels relatively long (to 3cm)

flower

Ht. to 0.45m

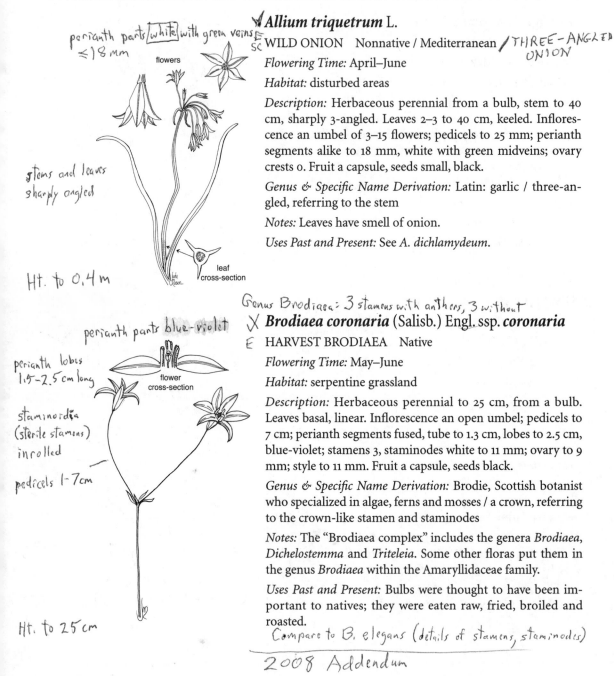

perianth parts white with green veins ≤18 mm

flowers

stems and leaves sharply angled

Ht. to 0.4 m

leaf cross-section

Allium triquetrum L.

WILD ONION   Nonnative / Mediterranean   */THREE-ANGLED ONION*

Flowering Time: April–June

Habitat: disturbed areas

Description: Herbaceous perennial from a bulb, stem to 40 cm, sharply 3-angled. Leaves 2–3 to 40 cm, keeled. Inflorescence an umbel of 3–15 flowers; pedicels to 25 mm; perianth segments alike to 18 mm, white with green midveins; ovary crests 0. Fruit a capsule, seeds small, black.

Genus & Specific Name Derivation: Latin: garlic / three-angled, referring to the stem

Notes: Leaves have smell of onion.

Uses Past and Present: See *A. dichlamydeum.*

Genus Brodiaea: 3 stamens with anthers, 3 without

perianth parts blue-violet

perianth lobes 1.5–2.5 cm long

flower cross-section

staminodia (sterile stamens) inrolled

pedicels 1-7cm

Ht. to 25 cm

Brodiaea coronaria (Salisb.) Engl. ssp. *coronaria*

HARVEST BRODIAEA   Native

Flowering Time: May–June

Habitat: serpentine grassland

Description: Herbaceous perennial to 25 cm, from a bulb. Leaves basal, linear. Inflorescence an open umbel; pedicels to 7 cm; perianth segments fused, tube to 1.3 cm, lobes to 2.5 cm, blue-violet; stamens 3, staminodes white to 11 mm; ovary to 9 mm; style to 11 mm. Fruit a capsule, seeds black.

Genus & Specific Name Derivation: Brodie, Scottish botanist who specialized in algae, ferns and mosses / a crown, referring to the crown-like stamen and staminodes

Notes: The "Brodiaea complex" includes the genera *Brodiaea, Dichelostemma* and *Triteleia.* Some other floras put them in the genus *Brodiaea* within the Amaryllidaceae family.

Uses Past and Present: Bulbs were thought to have been important to natives; they were eaten raw, fried, broiled and roasted.

Compare to B. elegans (details of stamens, staminodes)

2008 Addendum

Amaryllis belladonna   NAKED LADIES   nonnative

✓*Brodiaea elegans* Hoover ssp. *elegans*

E   ELEGANT BRODIAEA   Native

SC *Flowering Time:* May–June

Habitat: grassland

Description: Herbaceous perennial to 50 cm, from a bulb. Leaves basal, linear. Inflorescence an open umbel; pedicels to 10 cm; perianth segments fused, tube to 2 cm, lobes to 3 cm, blue-purple; stamens 3; staminodes white to pale lilac to 9 mm; style to 15 mm. Fruit a capsule, seeds black.

Genus & Specific Name Derivation: Brodie, Scottish botanist who specialized in algae, ferns and mosses / graceful, elegant

Notes: See *B. coronaria.*

Uses Past and Present: See *B. coronaria.*

Compare to B. terrestris (flower + plant size)
Compare to B coronaria (details of stamens, staminodes)
Photo in K & B plate 58

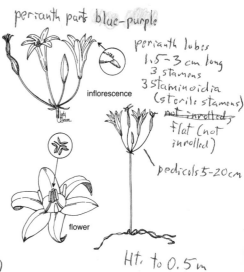

perianth parts blue-purple

perianth lobes
1.5–3 cm long
3 stamens
3 staminoidia
(sterile stamens)
~~not inrolled~~
flat (not inrolled)

inflorescence

flower

pedicels 5–20 cm

Ht. to 0.5 m

✓*Brodiaea terrestris* Kellogg ssp. *terrestris*

E   DWARF BRODIAEA   Native

Flowering Time: March–June

Habitat: grassland

Description: Herbaceous perennial to 7 cm, from a bulb. Leaves basal, linear. Inflorescence an open umbel; pedicels to 2 cm; perianth segments fused, tube to 9 mm, lobes to 16 mm, blue-violet; stamens 3; staminodes white to pale lilac to 5 mm, tip notched; style to 5 mm. Fruit a capsule, seeds black.

Genus & Specific Name Derivation: Brodie, Scottish botanist who specialized in algae, ferns and mosses / growing on the ground, referring to the height of the plant being close to the ground

Notes: See *B. coronaria.*

Uses Past and Present: See *B. coronaria.*

Compare to B. elegans (flower + plant size)
Photo in K & B plate 58

perianth parts blue-violet
perianth lobes ≤ 16 mm long

3 stamens
3 staminoidia

flower

Ht. to 7 cm

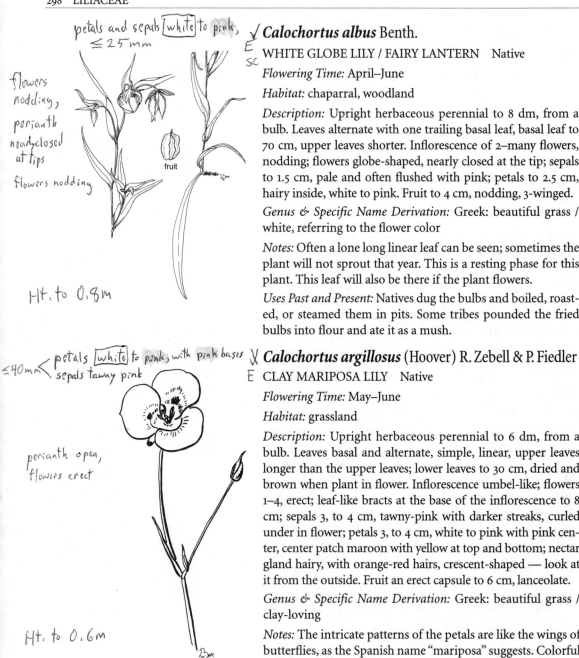

petals and sepals [white] to pink,
≤25mm

flowers
nodding,
perianth
nearly closed
at tips

flowers nodding

fruit

Ht. to 0.8m

petals [white] to pink, with pink bases
sepals tawny pink
≤40mm

perianth open,
flowers erect

Ht. to 0.6m

Calochortus albus Benth.

WHITE GLOBE LILY / FAIRY LANTERN   Native

Flowering Time: April–June

Habitat: chaparral, woodland

Description: Upright herbaceous perennial to 8 dm, from a bulb. Leaves alternate with one trailing basal leaf, basal leaf to 70 cm, upper leaves shorter. Inflorescence of 2–many flowers, nodding; flowers globe-shaped, nearly closed at the tip; sepals to 1.5 cm, pale and often flushed with pink; petals to 2.5 cm, hairy inside, white to pink. Fruit to 4 cm, nodding, 3-winged.

Genus & Specific Name Derivation: Greek: beautiful grass / white, referring to the flower color

Notes: Often a lone long linear leaf can be seen; sometimes the plant will not sprout that year. This is a resting phase for this plant. This leaf will also be there if the plant flowers.

Uses Past and Present: Natives dug the bulbs and boiled, roasted, or steamed them in pits. Some tribes pounded the fried bulbs into flour and ate it as a mush.

Calochortus argillosus (Hoover) R. Zebell & P. Fiedler

CLAY MARIPOSA LILY   Native

Flowering Time: May–June

Habitat: grassland

Description: Upright herbaceous perennial to 6 dm, from a bulb. Leaves basal and alternate, simple, linear, upper leaves longer than the upper leaves; lower leaves to 30 cm, dried and brown when plant in flower. Inflorescence umbel-like; flowers 1–4, erect; leaf-like bracts at the base of the inflorescence to 8 cm; sepals 3, to 4 cm, tawny-pink with darker streaks, curled under in flower; petals 3, to 4 cm, white to pink with pink center, center patch maroon with yellow at top and bottom; nectar gland hairy, with orange-red hairs, crescent-shaped — look at it from the outside. Fruit an erect capsule to 6 cm, lanceolate.

Genus & Specific Name Derivation: Greek: beautiful grass / clay-loving

Notes: The intricate patterns of the petals are like the wings of butterflies, as the Spanish name "mariposa" suggests. Colorful tulip-shaped flowers add color to the grassland in the late spring and early summer when many of the other plants have dried out. At Edgewood we may have this species as well *C. venustus*, white mariposa lily, the final determination was not made as of this printing.

Uses Past and Present: See *C. albus*.

Not in Kozloff and Beidleman

✓ *Calochortus luteus* Lindley

E YELLOW MARIPOSA LILY   Native

Flowering Time: April–June

Habitat: grassland

Description: Upright herbaceous perennial to 5 dm, from a bulb. Leaves basal and alternate, simple to 20 cm, linear, upper leaves longer than the upper leaves; upper leaves dried and brown when plant is in flower. Inflorescence umbel-like; flowers 1–7, erect; leaf-like bracts at the base of the inflorescence to 3 cm; sepals 3, yellow with darker streaks, curled under in flower, to 3 cm; petals 3, yellow with red-brown center, center patch red-brown; nectary gland hairy, with orange-red hairs, crescent-shaped to oblong — look at it from the outside. Fruit an erect capsule to 6 cm.

Genus & Specific Name Derivation: Greek: beautiful grass / yellow

Notes: The intricate patterns of the petals are like the wings of butterflies, as the Spanish name "mariposa" suggests. Colorful tulip-shaped flowers add color to the grassland in the late spring and early summer when many of the other plants have dried out.

Uses Past and Present: See *C. albus.*

Photo in K & B plate 58

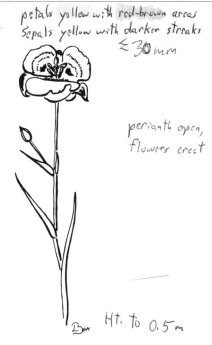

petals yellow with red-brown areas
Sepals yellow with darker streaks
≤ 30 mm

perianth open,
flowers erect

Bar   Ht. to 0.5 m

perianth parts [white] with greenish
≤ 25 mm   or purple veins

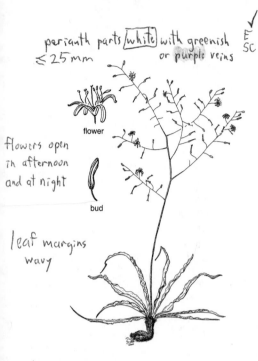

flower

flowers open
in afternoon
and at night

bud

leaf margins
wavy

Ht. to ___ m

√ *Chlorogalum pomeridianum* (DC.) Kunth
E/sc var. *pomeridianum*

AMOLE / SOAP PLANT Native

Flowering Time: May–June

Habitat: all habitats

Description: Upright herbaceous perennial from a bulb. Leaves basal to 70 cm, wavy. Inflorescence a branched panicle; flowers opening in the late afternoon, closing by the next morning; perianth segments to 2.5 cm, similar, spreading, linear, white with green or purple midvein; pedicels to 2.5 cm. Fruit a capsule, spherical to slightly lobed.

Genus & Specific Name Derivation: Greek: green milk or juice / of the afternoon, referring to the flowers opening in the afternoon, past the meridian (12 noon)

Notes: Along the worn trails you can often see the fibrous bulbs sticking out. The Spanish Californians called it "escobeta, little broom." They also called it amole, a name that comes from the Aztecs.

Uses Past and Present: The bulbs were used by natives for soap and the fibers around the bulb were made into brushes. The gummy substance inside the bulb was used as a glue. The whole bulb could be crushed and thrown into a pond or slow stream to stupefy or stun fish, or baked and used as food.

Photo of C. p. var. divaricatum in K & B plate 59

Dichelostemma capitatum (Benth.) A. W. Wood ssp. *capitatum*

BLUE DICKS   Native

Flowering Time: February–May

Habitat: chaparral, grassland, woodland

Description: Herbaceous perennial from a bulb, stem to 50 cm. Leaves to 40 cm, linear, keeled. Inflorescence a head-like umbel; pedicel to 1 mm; perianth segments fused, tube to 12 mm, lobes to 12 mm, blue-purple; stamens 6, 3 smaller and 3 larger with notched appendages. Fruit a capsule, seeds black.

Genus & Specific Name Derivation: Greek: toothed crown, referring to the stamen appendages / head-like, referring to the inflorescence

Notes: The "Brodiaea complex" includes the genera *Brodiaea*, *Dichelostemma* and *Triteleia*. Some other floras put them in the genus *Brodiaea* within the Amaryllidaceae family. Correct authority from *The Jepson Manual Corrections* — Installment No. 5.

Uses Past and Present: Bulbs were thought to have been important to natives; they were eaten raw, fried, broiled, and roasted.

Compare to D. congestum   Photo in K & B plate 60

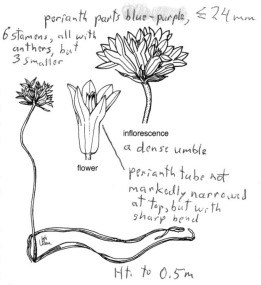

perianth parts blue-purple, ≤ 24 mm

6 stamens, all with anthers, but 3 smaller

inflorescence

a dense umble

flower

perianth tube not markedly narrowed at top, but with sharp bend

Ht. to 0.5 m

Dichelostemma congestum (Sm.) Kunth

OOKOW   Native

Flowering Time: April–May

Habitat: chaparral, grassland, woodland

Description: Herbaceous perennial from a bulb, stem to 50 cm. Leaves to 10 cm, linear, keeled. Inflorescence a dense raceme-like umbel; pedicel to 6 mm; perianth segments fused, tube to 10 mm, narrowed at top, lobes to 10 mm, blue-purple; stamens 3, with notched appendages. Fruit a capsule, seeds black.

Genus & Specific Name Derivation: Greek: toothed crown, referring to the stamen appendages / arranged close together, referring to the inflorescence

Notes: See: *D. capitatum*.

Uses Past and Present: See: *D. capitatum*.

Compare to D. capitatum

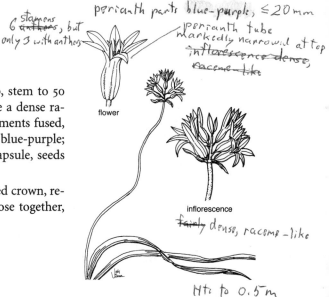

6 stamens, but only 3 with anthers

perianth parts blue-purple, ≤ 20 mm

perianth tube markedly narrowed at top

inflorescence dense, raceme-like

flower

inflorescence

dense, raceme-like

Ht. to 0.5 m

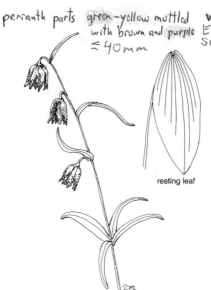

perianth parts green-yellow mottled
with brown and purple
≤ 40 mm

resting leaf

Ht. to 0.45 m

✓*Fritillaria affinis* (Schultes) Sealy var. *affinis*

MISSION BELLS / CHECKER LILY   Native

E
SC

Flowering Time: March–May

Habitat: woodland

Description: Herbaceous perennial to 45 cm, from a bulb. Leaves whorled on the lower part of the stem, alternate above, simple, sessile; whorled leaves to 15 cm, upper leaves to 10 cm. Inflorescence a raceme; flowers hang down; pedicel to 2 cm; perianth segments to 4 cm, green-yellow mottled with brown, green and purple; stamens 6, inserted, style and stigma 3-parted; there is a green-yellow nectar gland at the base of each petal. Fruit a capsule, widely winged.

Genus & Specific Name Derivation: Latin: dicebox, referring to shape of fruit / related to

Notes: In the resting phase a long, ovate leaf will be the only evidence that this plant is here. This leaf is adding nutrients to the bulb; the flowering plant usually does not come up that year. This leaf has been referred to as a nurse leaf.

Photo in K & B plat. 60

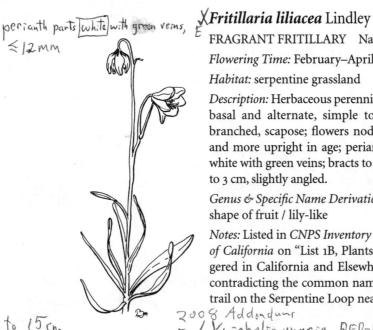

perianth parts white with green veins,
≤ 12 mm

Ht. to 15 cm

✗*Fritillaria liliacea* Lindley

FRAGRANT FRITILLARY   Native

E
E

Flowering Time: February–April

Habitat: serpentine grassland

Description: Herbaceous perennial to 15 cm, from a bulb. Leaves basal and alternate, simple to 7 cm, linear. Inflorescence branched, scapose; flowers nodding downward when young and more upright in age; perianth segments alike, to 1.2 cm, white with green veins; bracts to 3 cm. Fruit an upright capsule to 3 cm, slightly angled.

Genus & Specific Name Derivation: Latin: dicebox, referring to shape of fruit / lily-like

Notes: Listed in *CNPS Inventory of Rare and Endangered Plants of California* on "List 1B, Plants Rare, Threatened, or Endangered in California and Elsewhere." No noticeable fragrance contradicting the common name. Plant can be seen from the trail on the Serpentine Loop near Sunset Entrance.

2008 Addendum
E ✓ Khipholia uvaria RED-HOT POKER Nonnative
E ✓ Leucojum sp. SNOWFLAKE Nonnative

Lilium pardalinum Kellogg ssp. *pardalinum*

LEOPARD LILY / TIGER LILY   Native

Flowering Time: June–July

Habitat: riparian woodland

Description: Upright herbaceous perennial to 10 dm, from a bulb-like rhizome. Leaves mostly whorled but some alternate, simple to 15 cm. Inflorescence 2–4 flowers at the top of the stem; peduncles to 30 cm; perianth parts to 10 cm, orange-red with darker spots toward the base, petals curl backward; stamens, style and stigma exserted, anthers dark orange. Fruit a capsule to 3 cm.

Genus & Specific Name Derivation: Greek: lily / spotted or marked like a leopard

Photo in K & B plat. 60

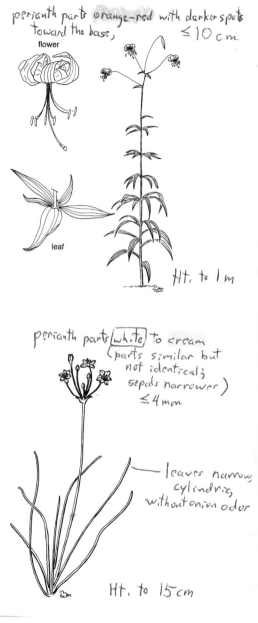

perianth parts orange-red with darker spots toward the base, ≤10 cm

flower

leaf

Ht. to 1 m

Muilla maritima (Torrey) S. Watson

COMMON MUILLA   Native

Flowering Time: March–April

Habitat: grassland

Description: Herbaceous perennial to 15 cm, from a corm. Leaves basal to 8 cm, linear, grass-like; sessile. Inflorescence an umbel on a scapose peduncle; perianth segments to 4 mm, alike, white; pedicel to 2 cm; bracts to 4 mm, whitish. Fruit a spherical capsule to 8 mm.

Genus & Specific Name Derivation: Anagram of *Allium*, from superficial resemblance / growing by the sea

Notes: Very much like the genus *Allium* but no onion odor of the leaves. *Muilla* is *Allium* spelled backwards.

Compare to Allium spp.
Photo in K & B plat. 60

perianth parts white to cream (parts similar but not identical; sepals narrower) ≤4 mm

leaves narrow, cylindric, without onion odor

Ht. to 15 cm

2008 Addendum

Narcissus tazetta   CREAM NARCISSUS nonnative
Narcissus jonquilla   DAFFODIL   nonnative
Narcissus pseudonarcissus DAFFODIL   nonnative

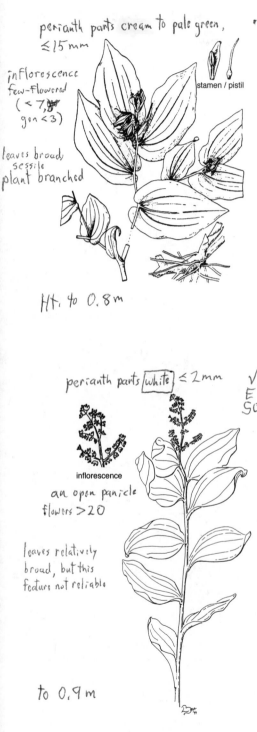

perianth parts cream to pale green, ≤15mm

inflorescence few-flowered (< 7, gen < 3)

stamen / pistil

leaves broad, sessile
plant branched

Ht. to 0.8m

perianth parts white ≤ 2mm

inflorescence

an open panicle
flowers >20

leaves relatively broad, but this feature not reliable

to 0.9m

Prosartes hookeri Torr. /Disporum h.

HOOKER'S FAIRY BELL   Native

Flowering Time: March–May

Habitat: woodland

Description: Upright herbaceous perennial to 80 cm, from a rhizome. Leaves alternate to 15 cm, sessile, strongly veined. Inflorescence umbel-like, terminal; flowers 1-several, drooping, hidden under the leaves; flowers bell-shaped; perianth segments to 15 mm, cream to pale green. Fruit a berry to 9 mm, spherical, red when mature.

Genus & Specific Name Derivation: Derivation unknown / named for either Sir W. J. Hooker or his son Sir J. D. Hooker, both directors of the Royal Botanical Gardens at Kew

Notes: New name accepted by *Jepson Manual* staff, name in *The Jepson Manual* (1993) *Disporum hookeri*. Leaves are very similar to *Smilacina* but the stems of *P. hookeri* branch, and the flowers and fruits are different. Illustration from *Illustrated Flora of the Pacific States.*

Compare to Smilacina spp.

√ **Smilacina racemosa** (L.) Link

E
SC

FAT SOLOMON'S SEAL   Native

Flowering Time: March–May

Habitat: woodlands

Description: Upright to trailing herbaceous perennial to 90 cm, from a creeping rhizome. Leaves alternate, simple to 20 cm, ovate, clasping the stem. Inflorescence an open panicle with more than 20 flowers; perianth segments to 2 mm, alike, white, fragrant. Fruit a berry to 7 mm, spherical, red-speckled when mature.

Genus & Specific Name Derivation: Greek: little smilax, an ancient Greek name / flowers arranged in a raceme, although these are not

Notes: Flowers are arranged in a panicle in this species although the name indicates a raceme. Another common name is false solomon's seal.

Uses Past and Present: The mature berries are eaten by birds. Roots were used to make tea for sore throats and colds and a poultice for swellings, inflammations, and stings, bites, and poison oak rashes.

Compare to S. stellata

Photo in K & B plat. 60

Smilacina stellata (L.) Desf.

SLIM SOLOMON'S SEAL   Native

Flowering Time: February–March

Habitat: woodland

Description: Herbaceous perennial to 70 cm, from a slender rhizome. Leaves alternate, simple to 17 cm, sessile, clasping. Inflorescence a raceme; perianth segments to 6 mm, alike, white. Fruit a roundish berry to 10 mm, reddish-purple when mature.

Genus & Specific Name Derivation: Greek: little smilax, an ancient Greek name / star-shaped referring to the flower

Notes: No discernible fragrance unlike *S. racemosa*. Another common name is slender false Solomon's seal.

Uses Past and Present: See *S. racemosa*.

Compare to S. racemosa

Trillium chloropetalum (Torrey) Howell

GIANT TRILLIUM   Native

Flowering Time: February–April

Habitat: woodland

Description: Herbaceous perennial to 7 dm, from a rhizome. Leaves 3, sessile in a single whorl, each leaf to 15 cm, margin wavy, green with brown mottling. Inflorescence sessile in center of stem leaves; sepals to 7 cm, under-surface green, upper red with green mottling; petals to 11 cm, upright, linear, dark purple, sometimes paler to white; stamens to 2.3 cm, tissue between anther sacs purple; ovary dark purple; styles 3. Fruit a berry-like capsule.

Genus & Specific Name Derivation: Latin: three, referring to the parts of 3's / green petals, referring to occasionally green petals

Notes: Leaf venation netted, unusual since most monocots have parallel leaf veins.

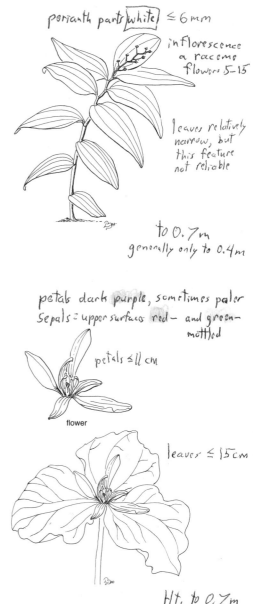

perianth parts white ≤ 6 mm

inflorescence a raceme flowers 5-15

leaves relatively narrow, but this feature not reliable

to 0.7m generally only to 0.4m

petals dark purple, sometimes paler Sepals = upper surface red – and green- mottled

petals ≤ 11 cm

flower

leaves ≤ 15cm

Ht. to 0.7m

Genus *Triteleia* = 6 fertile stamens (with anthers); inflorescence an open umbel

perianth parts **white** with green veins
perianth 1–1,5 cm (?)   lobes ≤ 12mm
tube ≤ 4mm

perianth tube short, hardly noticeable
6 stamens with anthers, attached at one level

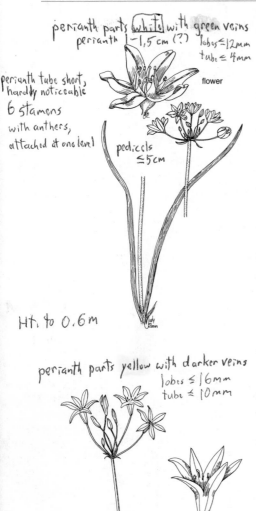

flower

pedicels ≤ 5cm

Ht. to 0.6m

Triteleia hyacinthina (Lindley) E. Greene

WHITE BRODIAEA / WILD HYACINTH   Native

Flowering Time: April–June

Habitat: seeps, swales

Description: Herbaceous perennial from a bulb, stem to 60 cm. Leaves basal to 40 cm. Inflorescence an open umbel; pedicels to 5 cm; perianth segments fused, tube to 4 mm, lobes to 12 mm, white with greenish veins; stamens 6, filament appendages 0. Fruit a capsule, seeds black.

Genus & Specific Name Derivation: Greek: three complete, referring to flower parts in 3's / dark purplish-blue

Notes: The "Brodiaea complex" includes the genera *Brodiaea*, *Dichelostemma* and *Triteleia*. Some other floras put them in the genus *Brodiaea* within the Amaryllidaceae family.

Uses Past and Present: Bulbs were thought to have been important to natives; they were eaten raw, fried, broiled, and roasted.

Compare to *T. peduncularis*

perianth parts yellow with darker veins
lobes ≤ 16mm
tube ≤ 10mm

flower

Ht. to 0.6m

Triteleia ixioides (S. Watson) E. Greene ssp. *ixioides*

GOLDEN BRODIAEA   Native

Flowering Time: April–June

Habitat: woodland

Description: Herbaceous perennial from a bulb, stem to 60 cm. Leaves basal to 40 cm. Inflorescence an open umbel; pedicels to 3 cm; perianth segments fused, golden yellow with darker veins, tube to 1 cm, lobes to 1.6 cm; stamens 6, 3 shorter, filament appendages lobed. Bracts to 7 mm, cream, tinged with red. Fruit a capsule, seeds black.

Genus & Specific Name Derivation: Greek: three complete, referring to flower parts in 3's / iris-like

Notes: See: *T. hyacinthina.*

Uses Past and Present: See: *T. hyacinthina.*

√ *Triteleia laxa* Benth.

ITHURIEL'S SPEAR   Native

Flowering Time: April–June

Habitat: woodland

Description: Herbaceous perennial from a bulb, stem to 70 cm. Leaves basal to 40 cm. Inflorescence an open umbel; pedicels to 9 cm; perianth segments fused, blue-purple, tube to 2.5 cm, lobes to 2 cm; stamens 6, attached at two different levels, filament appendages 0, anthers white to pale purple. Bracts to 1.5 cm, straw-colored when old. Fruit a capsule, seeds black.

Genus & Specific Name Derivation: Greek: three complete, referring to flower parts in 3's / open, not crowded, referring to the flowers in the inflorescence

Notes: See: *T. hyacinthina.*

Uses Past and Present: See: *T. hyacinthina.*

Photo in K & B plate 61

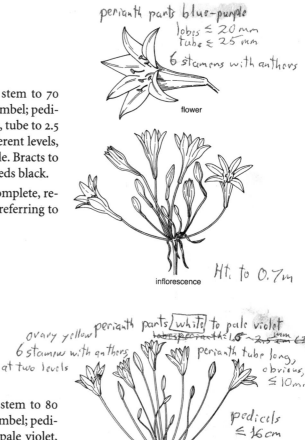

perianth parts blue-purple
lobes ≤ 20 mm
tube ≤ 25 mm
6 stamens with anthers

flower

inflorescence

Ht. to 0.7m

Triteleia peduncularis Lindley

LONG-RAYED BRODIAEA   Native

Flowering Time: April–June

Habitat: grassland

Description: Herbaceous perennial from a bulb, stem to 80 cm. Leaves basal to 40 cm. Inflorescence an open umbel; pedicels to 16 cm; perianth segments fused, white to pale violet, tube to 1 cm, lobe to 1.6 cm; stamens 6 attached at two different levels; ovary bright yellow in flower. Fruit a capsule, seeds black.

Genus & Specific Name Derivation: Greek: three complete referring to flower parts in 3's / with the inflorescence on a definite stalk

Notes: See: *T. hyacinthina.*

Uses Past and Present: See: *T. hyacinthina.*

Compare to T. hyacinthia

ovary yellow
6 stamens with anthers at two levels

perianth parts white to pale violet
lobes perianth 1.6 – 2.5 mm (?)
perianth tube long, obvious, ≤ 10mm

pedicels ≤ 16 cm

inflorescence

Ht. to 0.8 m

Genus Zigadenus: Leaves mostly basal, some along stem, these smaller

Perianth segments more or less free, not forming a tube, whitish
Stems (peduncles) unbranched except for pedicels

perianth parts cream to greenish yellow
≤ 15 mm

mature inflorescence generally >25 cm long

stamens shorter than perianth segments

leaves >10 mm wide

flower

Ht. to 0.9 m

Zigadenus fremontii (Torrey) S. Watson

E
SC

FREMONT'S STAR LILY   Native / *COMMON STAR LILY*

Flowering Time: February–September

Habitat: all habitats

Description: Upright herbaceous perennial from a bulb, stem to 90 cm. Leaves simple, to 50 cm, linear, often folded, basal and alternate along the stem, longer at base, shorter upward. Inflorescence a panicle-like raceme to 40 cm; perianth segments to 15 mm, similar, with greenish-yellow glands. Fruit a cylindric capsule to 35 mm.

Genus & Specific Name Derivation: Greek: yoke-gland, referring to the shape of the gland on perianth parts / Lt. Colonel John Charles Fremont (1813–1890), an army officer and presidential candidate who played a prominent part in the early history of California. The plants he collected were sent to John Torrey, a New York botanist.

Notes: Toxic to humans and livestock, from alkaloids; caused serious illness to some members of Lewis & Clark expedition. Notice how the leaves, which somewhat resemble soap plant, are not eaten by herbivores whereas the soap plant leaves are browsed on. Another common name is death camas.

Uses Past and Present: The poisonous bulbs may have been eaten by mistake.

Compare to Z. venosus
Photo in K & B plate 61

perianth parts [white] ≤ 6 mm
to pale yellow

mature inflorescence generally < 25 cm long

stamens longer than perianth segments

leaves 4-10 mm wide

flower

Ht. to 0.7m

Zigadenus venenosus S. Watson var. venenosus

DEATH CAMAS   Native

Flowering Time: April

Habitat: wet swales

Description: Upright herbaceous perennial from a bulb, stem to 70 cm. Leaves simple, to 40 cm, linear, often folded, basal and alternate along the stem. Inflorescence raceme-like, to 25 cm; perianth segments to 6 mm, glands yellowish green. Fruit a cylindric capsule to 14 mm.

Genus & Specific Name Derivation: Greek: yoke-gland, referring to the shape of the gland on perianth parts / very poisonous

Notes: Illustration from *Illustrated Flora of the Pacific States.* See *Z. fremontii.*

Uses Past and Present: See *Z. fremontii.*

Compare to Z. fremontii
Photo in K & B plate 61

Orchidaceae — Orchid Family

Herbaceous perennials, from rhizomes or corms, some parasitic. Leaves usually alternate, sheathing at the base. Inflorescence solitary or in raceme, spike, or panicle. Flowers bisexual, irregular. Sepals 3, usually similar in shape and color; petals 3, one may have a spur, lower petal different from the other 2 in shape; stamens 1-2, fused to the style and stigma; ovary inferior, style and stigma fused into a column. Fruit a capsule. Many cultivated as ornamentals, some used as food flavoring, e.g., vanilla.

For key to families *see* Group 3. Herbaceous Flowering Plant Families

Key to Herbaceous Plants:

1. Plant nongreen; leaves scale-or bract-like
    2. Perianth with reddish to purplish stripes ....
        .... *Corallorhiza striata* (STRIPED CORALROOT)
    2′ Perianth with reddish to purplish spots ....
        .... *Corallorhiza maculata* (SPOTTED CORALROOT)
1′ Plant green
    3. Leaves mostly basal
        4. Sepals white with green midvein, petals white to pale green
            5. Spur oriented horizontally along the stem ....
                ....*Piperia transversa* (TRANSVERSE-SPURRED PIPERIA)
            5′ Spur curved along stem but not horizontal ....
                .... *Piperia elegans* (ELEGANT PIPERIA/ELEGANT REIN ORCHID)
        4′ Sepals and petals unmarked, green or yellow-green ....
            ....*Piperia elongata* (LONG-SPURRED PIPERIA)
    3′ Leaves along stem, alternate; perianth purple-tinged to pink ....
        .... *Epipactis helleborine* (HELLEBORINE)

perianth parts cream-pink with
≤10mm   darker spots
          (maroon on
          lower flowers)
                    flower

fruit

Ht. to 35 cm

perianth parts cream-pink with darker
≤10mm   stripes
              (maroon on
              lower flowers)
                        flower

fruit

Ht. to 35 cm

Corallorhiza maculata Raf.

SPOTTED CORALROOT   Native

Flowering Time: April–July

Habitat: woodland

Description: Pale cream-pink, herbaceous perennial to 35 cm, from a rhizome. No true leaves but pale pink-brown sheathing bracts along the stem. Inflorescence a raceme to 18 cm with many flowers; flowers irregular; perianth parts to 1 cm, cream-pink with darker spots, lower with darker maroon spots. Ovary inferior, twisting at base, ascending in full fruit. Fruit a capsule to 2 cm.

Genus & Specific Name Derivation: Greek: coral root / bearing spots, referring to the spots on perianth parts

Notes: Rhizome looks coral-like. Whole plant nongreen, saprophytic (dependent on leaf litter for all nutrients).

Photo in K & B plate 62

Corallorhiza striata Lindley

E

STRIPED CORALROOT   Native

Flowering Time: April–June

Habitat: woodland

Description: Pale cream-pink, herbaceous perennial to 35 cm. No true leaves but pale pink-brown sheathing bracts along the stem. Inflorescence a raceme to 18 cm with many flowers; flowers irregular; perianth to 1 cm, cream-pink with darker stripes, lower with darker maroon striping. Ovary inferior, twisting at base, ascending in full fruit. Fruit a capsule to 2 cm.

Genus & Specific Name Derivation: Greek: coral root / striped, referring to the stripes on the perianth segments

Notes: Rhizome looks coral-like. Whole plant nongreen, saprophytic (dependent on leaf litter for all nutrients).

Photo in K & B plate 62

Epipactis helleborine (L.) Crantz

HELLEBORINE   Nonnative / Europe

Flowering Time: May–August

Habitat: woodland

Description: Upright herbaceous perennial to 5 dm. Leaves alternate, simple to 10 cm, sessile. Inflorescence a raceme-like spike; sepals to 1.3 cm, green, purple-tinged; lateral petals to 1.1 cm; lip to 1.2 cm, lower half pouch-like, white to pink. Fruit a pendent capsule to 1.5 cm.

Genus & Specific Name Derivation: Greek: ancient name epipegnus, which was the name for *Helleborus* (a Christmas rose) / named for *Helleborus*

Photo in K & B plate 62

Piperia elegans (Lindley) Rydb.

ELEGANT PIPERIA / ELEGANT REIN ORCHID   Native

Flowering Time: June–August

Habitat: woodland

Description: Herbaceous perennial to 5 dm from a bulb-like tuber. Leaves basal, simple to 15 cm, brown and dried up when plant is in flower. Inflorescence a spike-like raceme to 30 cm; flowers sessile; bracts to 5 mm, green; sepals white, midvein dark green; lateral petals spreading to erect, white to pale green; lip to 7 mm, curved downward, white to pale green; spur to 14 mm, pointed down. Fruit a capsule with many seeds with many seeds.

Genus & Specific Name Derivation: Named for Charles V. Piper (1867–1926), American botanist / elegant

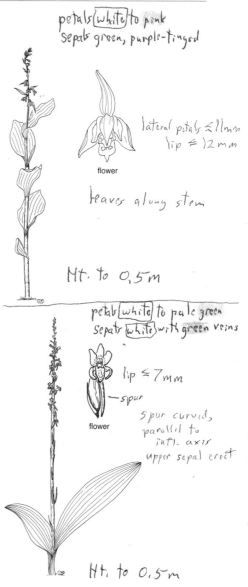

petals white to pink
sepals green, purple-tinged

lateral petals ≤ 11 mm
lip ≤ 12 mm

flower

leaves along stem

Ht. to 0.5 m

petals white to pale green
sepals white with green veins

lip ≤ 7 mm

—spur

spur curved, parallel to infl. axis
upper sepal erect

flower

Ht. to 0.5 m

These two species not in Kozloff and Beidleman

perianth green, unmarked by vein lines

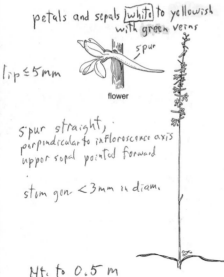

lip ≤ 6mm

spur curved, parallel to infl. axis

upper sepal erect

flower

spur

Ht. to 1 m

Piperia elongata

LONG-SPURRED PIPERIA Native

Flowering Time: June–August

Habitat: woodland

Description: Herbaceous perennial to 10 dm from a bulb-like tuber. Leaves basal, simple to 20 cm. Inflorescence a spike-like raceme to 30 cm, open to dense; flowers sessile; perianth green; upper sepal erect, lower sepals reflexed; lateral petals sickle-shaped, erect; lip to 6 mm, triangular, reflexed; spur to 15 mm, slender, generally pointed down. Fruit a capsule with many seeds.

Genus & Specific Name Derivation: Named for Charles V. Piper (1867–1926), American botanist / elongate referring to the spur

Notes: Illustration from *Illustrated Flora of the Pacific States.*

petals and sepals [white] to yellowish with green veins

lip ≤ 5mm

spur

flower

spur straight, perpendicular to inflorescence axis

upper sepal pointed forward

stem gen. <3mm in diam.

Ht. to 0.5 m

Piperia transversa

TRANSVERSE-SPURRED PIPERIA Native

Flowering Time: June–August

Habitat: woodland

Description: Herbaceous perennial to 5 dm from a bulb-like tuber. Leaves basal, simple to 20 cm. Inflorescence a spike-like raceme to 20 cm, open to dense; flowers sessile; sepals and lateral petals white to yellowish with green midvein; upper sepal pointed forward; lateral petals spreading and curved back; lip to 5 mm, white; spur to 10 mm pointed horizontal to the stem. Fruit a capsule with many seeds.

Genus & Specific Name Derivation: Named for Charles V. Piper (1867–1926), American botanist / transverse referring to the spur direction

Poaceae — Grass Family

Annuals or herbaceous perennials; stems hollow. Leaves basal and/or stem, usually in 2 ranks, alternate, sheathing the stem; sheath margin free or overlapping, usually with a small appendage called a ligule; leaf blades linear, flat or rounded. Spikelets bisexual or unisexual, 1–many. At the base of each spikelet are 1 or 2 bracts called glumes; inside there is an outer lemma and an inner palea; the lemma, and palea, stamens and pistil make-up a floret; there may be 1 or more florets on a spikelet. Some structures have definite awns, attached to the glumes, lemma or both, and looking different from them. Some glumes and lemmas have a sharply pointed elongated tip that is not an awn but may be awn-like. Stamens 1–3; ovary superior, style branches 2. Fruit called a caryopsis. Some species are sources of food, including rice, wheat, and corn. Fruit of many were eaten by natives.

Family Characteristics

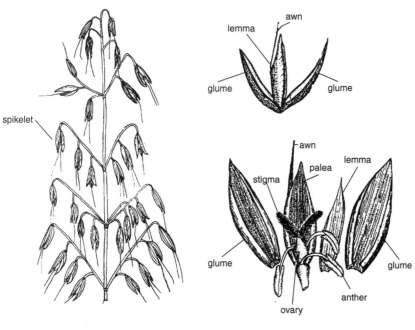

Panicle Inflorescence   Floret

2008 Addendums listed alphabetically

1. Inflorescence open, panicle-like
    2. Spikelets with awns (these are definite structures attached to the glume or lemma)
        3. Glumes and lemmas awned
            4. Both glumes awned
                5. Lemma awn < 5 cm .... *Nassella lepida* (FOOTHILL NEEDLEGRASS)
                5′ Lemma awn > 5 cm .... *Nassella pulchra* (PURPLE NEEDLEGRASS)
            4′ One glume awned .... *Holcus lanatus* (COMMON VELVET GRASS)
        3′ Lemmas with awns, glumes not awned
            6. Awns < 1.5 cm
                7. Awns < 1 cm
                    8. Annual
                        9. Lemma < 2 mm ....
                            .... *Aira caryophyllea* (SILVER EUROPEAN HAIRGRASS)
                        9′ Lemma > 2 mm
                            10. Spikelet < 3 mm wide ....
                                 .... *Deschampsia danthonioides* (ANNUAL HAIRGRASS)
                            10′ Spikelet > 3 mm wide .. *Bromus hordeaceus* (SOFT CHESS)
                    8′ Perennial
                        11. Lemma awned at or below middle
                            12. Spikelets on short pedicels ....
                                 .... *Deschampsia elongata* (SLENDER HAIRGRASS)
                            12′ Lower spikelets on long pedicels ....
                                 .... *Trisetum cernuum* (NODDING TRISETUM)
                        11′ Lemma awned from or near tip
                            13. Lemma tip 2-lobed
                                14. Awn curved ....
                                     .... *Danthonia californica* (CALIFORNIA WILD OATGRASS)
                                14′ Awn straight
                                    15. Lemmas soft-hairy ....
                                         .... *Bromus laevipes* (WOODLAND BROME)
                                    15′ Lemmas scabrous *Festuca elmeri* (ELMER'S FESCUE)
                            13′ Lemma tip entire *Festuca californica* (CALIFORNIA FESCUE)
                7′ Awns > 1 cm
                    16. Spikelet on a long pedicel ....
                         .... *Bromus carinatus* (CALIFORNIA BROME)
                    16′ Spikelet sessile or on a short pedicel ....
                         .... *Vulpia microstachys* var. *pauciflora* (PACIFIC FESCUE)
            6′ Awns > 1.5 cm
                17. Awns < 2.5 cm
                    18. Inflorescence a dense panicle
                        19. Stem generally glabrous .. *Bromus madritensis* (RED BROME)
                        19′ Stem generally puberulent ....
                             .... *Bromus madritensis* ssp. *rubens* (SPANISH BROME)
                    18′ Inflorescence open .... *Bromus sterilis* (POVERTY BROME)

17´ Awns > 2.5 cm
  20. Glumes longer than lemma
    21. Lemma hairy to tip, awn bent
      22. Lemma fork to 1 mm .... *Avena fatua* (WILD OAT)
      22´ Lemma fork > 1 mm *Avena barbata* (SLENDER WILD OAT)
    21´ Lemma sometimes hairy at base, awn straight ....
      .... *Avena sativa* (CULTIVATED OAT)
  20´ Glumes shorter than lemma . *Bromus diandrus* (RIPGUT GRASS)
2´ Spikelets without awns
  23. Annual
    24. Glumes and lemmas papery, lemma wider than long
      25. Spikelets < 5 mm .... *Briza minor* (LITTLE QUAKING GRASS)
      25´ Spikelets > 5 mm .... *Briza maxima* (BIG QUAKING GRASS)
    24´ Glumes and lemmas membranous, lemma longer than wide ....
      .... *Poa annua* (ANNUAL BLUEGRASS)
  23´ Perennial
    26. Lower glume with 1 vein .... *Agrostis hallii* (HALL'S BENT GRASS)
    26´ Lower glume with more than 1 vein
      27. Spikelet > 5 mm
        28. Glume tips and margins often tinged purple ....
        .... *Poa secunda* (ONE-SIDED BLUEGRASS)
        28´ Glume back often tinged with purple ....
        .... *Melica californica* (CALIFORNIA MELIC)
      27´ Spikelet < 5 mm
        29. Lemma back and margin hairy ....
        .... *Melica torreyana* (TORREY'S MELIC)
        29´ Lemma glabrous or minutely scabrous ....
        .... *Melica imperfecta* (SMALL-FLOWERED MELIC)
1´ Inflorescence spike-like, branches not easily seen
  30. Flowers with awns
    31. Both glumes and lemmas awned
      32. Annual
        33. Glumes awn-like
          34. Awns < 5 cm
            35. Glumes hairy, some awns > 2 cm ....
            .... *Hordeum murinum* var. *leporinum* (FARMER'S FOXTAIL)
            35´ Glumes not hairy, lemma awns < 2 cm ....
            .... *Hordeum marinum* ssp. *gussoneanum*
                                (MEDITERRANEAN BARLEY)
          34´ Some awns > than 5 cm ....
          .... *Taeniatherum caput-medusae* (MEDUSA HEAD)
        33´ Glumes not awn-like
          36. Inflorescence more or less 1-sided ....
          .... *Cynosurus echinatus* (HEDGEHOG DOGTAIL)
          36´ Inflorescence not 1-sided ....
          .... *Polypogon monspeliensis* (ANNUAL BEARD GRASS)

32′ Perennial
    37. Glumes awn-like
        38. Lemma awn < 3 cm
            .... *Hordeum brachyantherum* (MEADOW BARLEY)
        38′ Lemma awn > 3 cm .... *Elymus multisetus* (BIG SQUIRRELTAIL)
    37′ Glumes not awn-like .... *Elymus glaucus* (BLUE WILDRYE)
31′ Either the glumes or lemmas awned
    39. Glumes awned, margin with long hairs ....
        .... *Phleum pratense* (CULTIVATED TIMOTHY)
    39′ Lemmas awned, glumes not awned
        40. Annual
            41. Awns < 1 cm
                42. Glume usually 1, spikelets 2-ranked ....
                    ....*Lolium multiflorum* (ITALIAN RYEGRASS)
                42′ Glumes 2
                    43. Glumes much longer than lemma, lemma hidden
                        within glumes, inflorescence rounded ....
                        .... *Gastridium ventricosum* (NIT GRASS)
                    43′ Glumes and lemma about equal in length, spikelets
                        appressed to the stem, inflorescence very narrow ....
                        .... *Scribneria bolanderi* (SCRIBNER'S GRASS)
            41′ Awns > 1 cm
                44. Lemma margin with stiff bristles ....
                    .... *Brachypodium distachyon* (PURPLE FALSEBROME)
                44′ Lemma margin with soft hairs, glabrous or minutely scabrous
                    45. Lower glume < 1/2 upper glume length
                      46. Lemma margin with long hairs near tip ....
                        .... *Vulpia myuros* var. *hirsuta* (FOXTAIL)
                      46′ Lemma margin glabrous to minutely scabrous ....
                        .... *Vulpia myuros* (RATTAIL FESCUE)
                45′ Lower glume > 1/2 upper glume length ....
                  .... *Vulpia bromoides* (SIX-WEEKS FESCUE)
        40′ Perennial
            47. Spikelets, including awns > 1 cm ....
            .... *Leymus triticoides* (ALKALI RYEGRASS)
            47′ Spikelets < 1 cm
                48. Spikelets on short pedicels ....
                .... *Deschampsia elongata* (SLENDER HAIRGRASS)
                48′ Lower spikelets on long pedicels ....
                .... *Trisetum cernuum* (NODDING TRISETUM)
30′ Flowers without awns
    49. Plant > 10 dm
        50. Annual .... *Phalaris minor* (MEDITERRANEAN CANARY GRASS)
        50′ Perennial
            51. Inflorescence > 5 cm ....*Phalaris aquatica* (HARDING GRASS)

51′ Inflorescence < 5 cm
    52. Lower florets wide .... *Phalaris canariensis* (CANARY GRASS)
    52′ Lower florets awl-like ... *Phalaris californica* (CALIFORNIA CANARY GRASS)
49′ Plant < 10 dm
    53. Glume generally 1, inflorescence 2-ranked...
    .... *Lolium perenne* (PERENNIAL RYEGRASS)
    53′ Glumes more than 1 .... *Koeleria macrantha* (JUNEGRASS)

Agrostis hallii Vasey

HALL'S BENT GRASS   Native

Flowering Time: May–July

Habitat: woodland

Description: Perennial to 10 dm. Inflorescence to 15 cm, panicle-like; spikelet with 1 floret. Glumes and lemmas without awns; lemma with a tuft of hairs at base. The fruit is called a caryopsis, also a grain.

Genus & Specific Name Derivation: Greek: pasture / for H. M. Hall (1874–1932), botanist and authority of the Asteraceae of Southern California. He was also in charge of the University of California Herbarium at Berkeley in 1902 and was an honorary curator until 1932

Notes: Illustration from *Illustrated Flora of the Pacific States.*

Uses Past and Present: Native grasses were used for lining steam-cooking pits, stringing food for drying, spreading on floors, and as bedding.

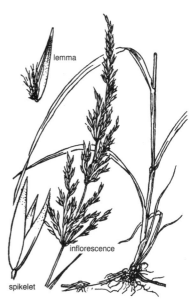

Aira caryophyllea L.

SILVER EUROPEAN HAIRGRASS   Nonnative / Europe

Flowering Time: March–June

Habitat: grassland

Description: Annual to 5 dm. Inflorescence panicle-like; spikelet with 2 or more florets. Glumes without awns; lemma awns to 3 mm. The fruit is called a caryopsis, also a grain.

Genus & Specific Name Derivation: Greek: a grass / nut-leaf

Notes: Illustration from *Illustrated Flora of the Pacific States.*

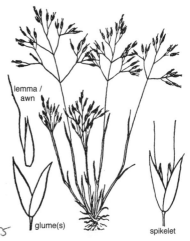

2008 Addendum
Agrostis exarata   WESTERN BENT GRASS
                          Native

Avena barbata Link

SLENDER WILD OAT   Nonnative / Europe

Flowering Time: February–June

Habitat: grassland, disturbed areas

Description: Annual to 6 dm. Inflorescence panicle-like; spikelet with 2 or more florets. Glumes without awns; lemma with stiff red hairs, awn to 4 cm, bent. The fruit is called a caryopsis, also a grain.

Genus & Specific Name Derivation: Latin: oats / with tufts of hairs, bearded, referring to the hairs on the lemma

Notes: Illustration from *Illustrated Flora of the Pacific States.*

Uses Past and Present: Cultivated for grain, hay.

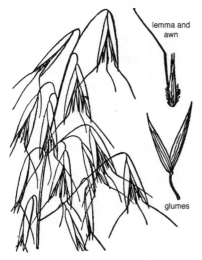

Avena fatua L.

WILD OAT   Nonnative / Europe

Flowering Time: February–July

Habitat: grassland, disturbed areas

Description: Annual to 12 dm. Inflorescence panicle-like; spikelet with 2 or more florets. Glumes without awns; lemma with stiff brown or whitish hairs, awn to 4 cm, bent. The fruit is called a caryopsis, also a grain.

Genus & Specific Name Derivation: Latin: oats / simple

Notes: Illustration from *Illustrated Flora of the Pacific States.*

Uses Past and Present: Cultivated for grain, hay.

Avena sativa L.

CULTIVATED OAT   Nonnative / Europe

Flowering Time: April–June

Habitat: disturbed areas

Description: Annual to 9 dm. Inflorescence panicle-like; spike-let with 2 or more florets. Glume without awns; lemma without hairs or sometimes hairy at base, awn to 15 mm, straight. The fruit is called a caryopsis, also a grain.

Genus & Specific Name Derivation: Latin: oats / planted, cultivated

Notes: Illustration from *Illustrated Flora of the Pacific States.*

Uses Past and Present: Cultivated for grain, hay.

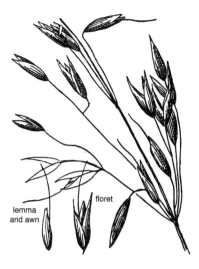

floret

lemma and awn

Brachypodium distachyon (L.) Beauv.

PURPLE FALSEBROME   Nonnative / Europe

Flowering Time: April–May

Habitat: disturbed areas

Description: Annual to 4 dm. Inflorescence to 8 cm, spike-like; spikelet with 2 or more florets. Glumes without awns; lemma awn to 11 mm. The fruit is called a caryopsis, also a grain.

Genus & Specific Name Derivation: Greek: short foot, from short, thick spikelet in some species / two-branched, two-spiked

Notes: Illustration from *Manual of the Grasses of the United States.*

lemma and awn

glumes

spikelets
>5 mm

Briza maxima L.

BIG QUAKING GRASS   Nonnative / Europe

Flowering Time: April–August

Habitat: disturbed areas along trails

Description: Annual to 6 dm. Inflorescence to 10 cm, panicle-like; spikelet with 2 or more florets. Glumes and lemmas not awned. The fruit is called a caryopsis, also a grain.

Genus & Specific Name Derivation: Greek: a kind of grain / large

Notes: Illustration from *Illustrated Flora of the Pacific States.*

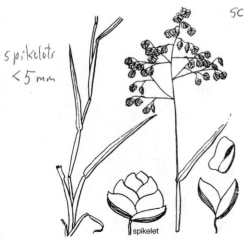

spikelets
<5 mm

spikelet

Briza minor L.

SC LITTLE QUAKING GRASS   Nonnative / Europe

Flowering Time: January–June

Habitat: grasslands and disturbed areas

Description: Annual to 5 dm. Inflorescence to 20 cm, panicle-like; spikelet with 2 or more florets. Glumes and lemmas not awned. The fruit is called a caryopsis, also a grain.

Genus & Specific Name Derivation: Greek: a kind of grain / small

Notes: Illustration from *Illustrated Flora of the Pacific States.*

✓ *Bromus carinatus* Hook. & Arn. var. *carinatus*

CALIFORNIA BROME   Native

Flowering Time: May–October

Habitat: grassland

Description: Perennial to 15 dm. Inflorescence to 20 cm, panicle-like; spikelet with 2 or more florets. Glumes without awns, pointed; lemma awn to 15 mm. The fruit is called a caryopsis, also a grain.

Genus & Specific Name Derivation: Greek: ancient name / keeled

Notes: Illustration from *Illustrated Flora of the Pacific States.*

Uses Past and Present: Native grasses were used for lining steam-cooking pits, stringing food for drying, spreading on floors, and as bedding.

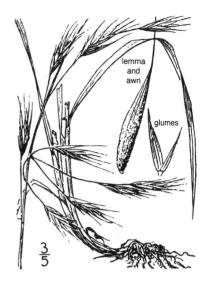

✓ *Bromus diandrus* Roth

RIPGUT GRASS   Nonnative / Europe

Flowering Time: April–July

Habitat: chaparral, grassland

Description: Annual to 8 cm. Inflorescence to 25 cm, panicle-like; spikelet with 2 or more florets. Glumes without awns; lemma awn to 5 cm. The fruit is called a caryopsis, also a grain.

Genus & Specific Name Derivation: Greek: ancient name / two-stamen

Notes: Illustration from *Illustrated Flora of the Pacific States.*

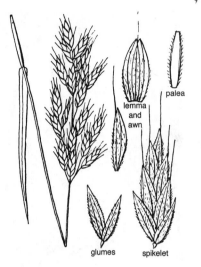

Bromus hordeaceus L.

SOFT CHESS   Nonnative / Eurasia

Flowering Time: March–July

Habitat: grassland, chaparral, woodland

Description: Annual to 7 dm. Inflorescence to 13 cm, panicle-like; spikelet with 2 or more florets. Glumes without awns; lemma awn to 10 mm. The fruit is called a caryopsis, also a grain.

Genus & Specific Name Derivation: Greek: ancient name / Hordeum-like

Notes: Illustration from *Illustrated Flora of the Pacific States.*

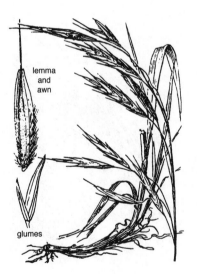

Bromus laevipes Shear

WOODLAND BROME   Native

Flowering Time: May–August

Habitat: woodland

Description: Perennial to 14 dm. Inflorescence to 27 cm, panicle-like; spikelet with 2 or more florets. Glumes without awns; lemma awn to 7 mm. The fruit is called a caryopsis, also a grain.

Genus & Specific Name Derivation: Greek: ancient name / polished

Notes: Illustration from *Illustrated Flora of the Pacific States.*

Uses Past and Present: Native grasses were used for lining steam-cooking pits, stringing food for drying, spreading on floors, and as bedding.

Bromus madritensis L. ssp. *madritensis*

SPANISH BROME   Nonnative / Europe

Flowering Time: April–June

Habitat: grassland, disturbed areas

Description: Annual to 5 dm. Inflorescence to 11 cm, panicle-like; spikelet with 2 or more florets. Glumes without awns; lemma awn to 2.5 cm. The fruit is called a caryopsis, also a grain.

Genus & Specific Name Derivation: Greek: ancient name / from Madrid

Notes: Illustration from *Illustrated Flora of the Pacific States.*

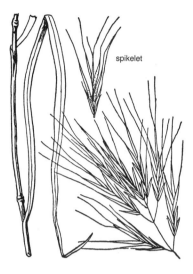

spikelet

Bromus madritensis L. ssp. *rubens* (L.) Husnot

RED BROME   Nonnative / Europe

Flowering Time: March–June

Habitat: grassland, disturbed areas

Description: Annual to 5 dm. Inflorescence to 8 cm, panicle-like; spikelet with 2 or more florets. Glumes without awns; lemma awn to 2.5 cm. The fruit is called a caryopsis, also a grain.

Genus & Specific Name Derivation: Greek: ancient name / from Madrid / blushed with red

Notes: Illustration from *Illustrated Flora of the Pacific States.*

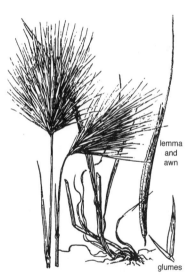

lemma and awn

glumes

Bromus sterilis L.

POVERTY BROME   Nonnative / Eurasia

Flowering Time: April–June

Habitat: disturbed areas

Description: Annual to 8 dm. Inflorescence to 25 cm, panicle-like; spikelet with 2 or more florets. Glumes without awns; lemma awn to 3 cm. The fruit is called a caryopsis, also a grain.

Genus & Specific Name Derivation: Greek: ancient name / infertile

Notes: Illustration from *Illustrated Flora of the Pacific States.*

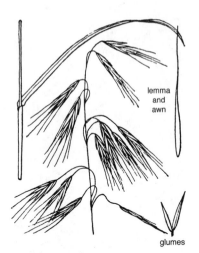

lemma
and
awn

glumes

√ *Cynosurus echinatus* L.

HEDGEHOG DOGTAIL   Nonnative / Europe

Flowering Time: May–August

Habitat: disturbed areas along trails

Description: Annual to 5 dm. Inflorescence to 4 cm, panicle-like, dense; spikelets compressed, with 2 or more florets per spikelet. Glumes with short awns; lemma awn to 10 mm. The fruit is called a caryopsis, also a grain.

Genus & Specific Name Derivation: Greek: dog tail, from shape of inflorescence / hedgehog-like prickles

Notes: Illustration from *Manual of the Grasses of the United States.*

lemma
and
awn

Photo in K + B plate 63

2008 Addendum
Dactylis glomerata   ORCHARD GRASS Nonnative

✗ *Danthonia californica* Bolander var. *californica*

CALIFORNIA WILD OATGRASS   Native

Flowering Time: May–July

Habitat: grassland

Description: Perennial to 10 dm. Inflorescence to 6 cm, panicle-like; spikelet with 2 or more florets. Glumes without awns; lemma awn to 12 mm. The fruit is called a caryopsis, also a grain.

Genus & Specific Name Derivation: For E. Danthoine of France, early 19th century / from California

Notes: Illustration from *Illustrated Flora of the Pacific States.* Correct name derivation from *The Jepson Manual Corrections* — Installment No. 7.

Uses Past and Present: Native grasses were used for lining steam-cooking pits, stringing food for drying, spreading on floors, and as bedding.

floret

Deschampsia danthonioides (Trin.) Munro

ANNUAL HAIRGRASS   Native

Flowering Time: April–August

Habitat: moist areas, meadows

Description: Annual to 6 dm. Inflorescence panicle-like; spikelet with 2 or more florets. Glumes without awns, pointed; lemma awn to 9 mm. The fruit is called a caryopsis, also a grain.

Genus & Specific Name Derivation: From J. L-Deslongchamps, of France, born 1774 / Danthonia-like

Notes: Illustration from *Illustrated Flora of the Pacific States.* Correct authority from *The Jepson Manual Corrections* — Installment No. 7.

Uses Past and Present: Native grasses were used for lining steam-cooking pits, stringing food for drying, spreading on floors, and as bedding.

spikelet

spikelet

Deschampsia elongata (Hook.) Munro

SLENDER HAIRGRASS   Native

Flowering Time: May–August

Habitat: woodland, chaparral

Description: Perennial to 7 dm. Inflorescence panicle-like; spikelet with 2 or more florets. Glumes without awns; lemma awn to 5 mm. The fruit is called a caryopsis, also a grain.

Genus & Specific Name Derivation: From J. L-Deslongchamps, of France, born 1774 / long

Notes: Illustration from *Illustrated Flora of the Pacific States.* Correct authority from *The Jepson Manual Corrections* — Installment No. 7.

Uses Past and Present: Native grasses were used for lining steam-cooking pits, stringing food for drying, spreading on floors, and as bedding.

• *Elymus glaucus* Buckley ssp. *glaucus*

BLUE WILDRYE   Native

Flowering Time: April–June

Habitat: grassland, woodland, chaparral

Description: Plant a tough, woody perennial; to 14 dm. Inflorescence to 16 cm, spike-like, open to dense; spikelet with 2 or more florets. Glumes short-awned; lemma awn to 3 cm. The fruit is called a caryopsis, also a grain.

Genus & Specific Name Derivation: Greek: ancient name for millet / with a whitish coating

Notes: Illustration from *Illustrated Flora of the Pacific States.*

Uses Past and Present: Native grasses were used for lining steam-cooking pits, stringing food for drying, spreading on floors, and as bedding.

glumes   spikelet

Elymus glaucus x *E. multisetus*

SQUIRRELTAIL HYBRID   Native

Flowering Time: May–August

Habitat: grassland

Description: Plant a tough and woody perennial to 10 dm. Inflorescence to 20 cm, branched, branches not easily seen; spikelet with 2 or more florets. Glumes awned; lemma awn to 4 cm. The fruit is called a caryopsis, also a grain.

Genus & Specific Name Derivation: Greek: ancient name for millet / covered with a white or waxy film / multi-bristled

Notes: Illustration from *Illustrated Flora of the Pacific States.* Hybrid between *Elymus glaucus* and *Elymus multisetus*. Synonym *Sitanion hansenii*.

Uses Past and Present: Native grasses were used for lining steam-cooking pits, stringing food for drying, spreading on floors, and as bedding.

inflorescence

Elymus multisetus (J. G. Smith) Burtt Davy

BIG SQUIRRELTAIL   Native

Flowering Time: April–August

Habitat: serpentine grassland

Description: Plant a tough and woody perennial to 6 dm. Inflorescence to 17 cm, excluding awns, branched, branches not easily seen; spikelet with 2 or more florets. Glumes awn-like; lemma awn to 10 cm. The fruit is called a caryopsis, also a grain.

Genus & Specific Name Derivation: Greek: ancient name for millet / multi-bristled, referring to the awn-like glumes

Notes: Illustration from *Illustrated Flora of the Pacific States.*

Uses Past and Present: Native grasses were used for lining steam-cooking pits, stringing food for drying, spreading on floors, and as bedding.

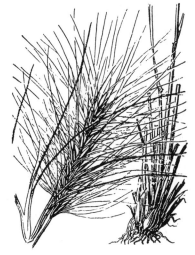

Photo in K & B plate 64

spikelet

Festuca californica Vasey

CALIFORNIA FESCUE   Native

Flowering Time: March–July

Habitat: chaparral, woodland

Description: Perennial to 12 dm. Inflorescence to 27 cm, open, panicle-like; spikelet with 2 or more florets. Glume not awned; lemma awn to 2.5 mm. The fruit is called a caryopsis, also a grain.

Genus & Specific Name Derivation: Latin: ancient name / from California

Notes: Illustration from *Illustrated Flora of the Pacific States.*

Uses Past and Present: Native grasses were used for lining steam-cooking pits, stringing food for drying, spreading on floors, and as bedding.

inflorescence

Festuca elmeri Scribner & Merr.

ELMER'S FESCUE   Native

Flowering Time: May–June

Habitat: woodland

Description: Perennial to 10 dm. Inflorescence to 20 cm, open, panicle-like; spikelet with 2 or more florets. Glume not awned; lemma awn to 5 mm The fruit is called a caryopsis, also a grain.

Genus & Specific Name Derivation: Latin: ancient name / for A. D. E. Elmer (1870–1942), collector in California, Washington and the Philippine Islands

Notes: Illustration from *Illustrated Flora of the Pacific States.*

Uses Past and Present: Native grasses were used for lining steam-cooking pits, stringing food for drying, spreading on floors, and as bedding.

2008 Addendum
Festuca arundinacea TALL FESCUE
Nonnative

Gastridium ventricosum (Gouan) Schinz & Thell.

NIT GRASS   Nonnative / Europe

Flowering Time: May–August

Habitat: grassland, disturbed areas

Description: Annual to 4 dm. Inflorescence to 9 cm, panicle-like, narrow; spikelets 1-flowered. Glumes not awned; lemma awn to 5 mm. The fruit is called a caryopsis, also a grain.

Genus & Specific Name Derivation: Greek: small pouch, from swollen spikelet base / expanded below

Notes: Illustration from *Illustrated Flora of the Pacific States.*

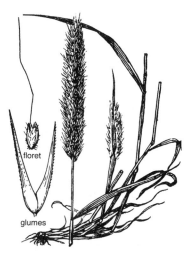

Holcus lanatus L.

COMMON VELVET GRASS   Nonnative / Europe

Flowering Time: May–August

Habitat: moist areas in grassland, chaparral

Description: Perennial to 20 dm. Inflorescence to 15 cm, panicle-like; spikelet with 2 or more florets. Glumes not awned; lemma awn to 1 mm. The fruit is called a caryopsis, also a grain.

Genus & Specific Name Derivation: Latin: a grass / woolly, referring to the hairiness of the whole plant

Notes: Illustration from *Illustrated Flora of the Pacific States.*

Uses Past and Present: Cultivated for forage, hay.

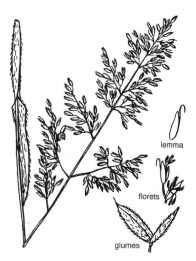

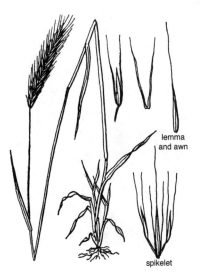

lemma
and awn

spikelet

Hordeum brachyantherum Nevski

MEADOW BARLEY Native

Flowering Time: April–June

Habitat: grassland, woodland

Description: Perennial to 9 dm. Inflorescence to 10 cm, spike-like, dense, purplish; spikelet with 2 or more florets. Glumes awn-like; lemma awn to 2 cm. The fruit is called a caryopsis, also a grain.

Genus & Specific Name Derivation: Latin: ancient name for barley / short anthers

Notes: Illustration from *Illustrated Flora of the Pacific States.*

Uses Past and Present: Native grasses were used for lining steam-cooking pits, stringing food for drying, spreading on floors, and as bedding.

spikelet

Hordeum marinum Hudson ssp. *gussoneanum* (Parl.) Thell.

MEDITERRANEAN BARLEY Nonnative / Europe

Flowering Time: May–June

Habitat: grassland, disturbed areas

Description: Annual to 5 dm. Inflorescence to 7 cm, spike-like, dense; spikelet with 2 or more florets. Glumes awn-like; lemma awn to 8 mm. The fruit is called a caryopsis, also a grain.

Genus & Specific Name Derivation: Latin: ancient name for barley / for the Sierra Morena / for G. Gussone (1787–1866), professor of botany, Naples; worked on the flora of southern Italy and Sicily

Notes: Illustration from *Illustrated Flora of the Pacific States.*

Hordeum murinum L.
var. *leporinum* (Link) Arcang.

FARMER'S FOXTAIL   Nonnative / Europe

Flowering Time: February–July

Habitat: grassland

Description: Annual to 11 dm. Inflorescence to 8 cm, spike-like, dense; spikelet central and lateral. Glume awn-like; lemma awn to 5 cm. The fruit is called a caryopsis, also a grain.

Genus & Specific Name Derivation: Latin: ancient name for barley / mouse-gray / hair-like, referring to the awn-like glumes

Notes: Illustration from *Illustrated Flora of the Pacific States.*

Photo in K & B plate 84

spikelet

Koeleria macrantha (Ledeb.) J. A. Schultes

JUNEGRASS   Native

Flowering Time: April–July

Habitat: grassland, chaparral

Description: Perennial to 7 dm. Inflorescence to 15 cm, panicle-like, compact; spikelet with 2 or more florets. Glumes and lemmas not awned but with small-pointed tips. The fruit is called a caryopsis, also a grain.

Genus & Specific Name Derivation: For G. L. Koeler, of Germany, born 1765 / large anther

Notes: Illustration from *Illustrated Flora of the Pacific States.* Correct authority from *The Jepson Manual Corrections* — Installment No. 7.

Uses Past and Present: Native grasses were used for lining steam-cooking pits, stringing food for drying, spreading on floors, and as bedding.

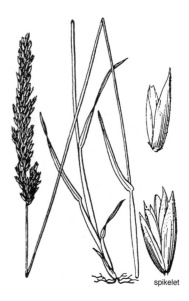

spikelet

2008 Addendum

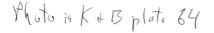

Lamarckia aurea   GOLDENTOP GRASS nonnative

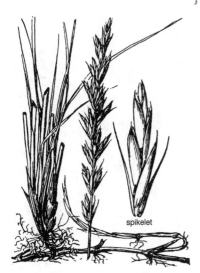

spikelet

, *Leymus triticoides* (Buckley) Pilger

ALKALI RYEGRASS   Native

Flowering Time: May–July

Habitat: woodland, chaparral

Description: Plant a tough and woody perennial to 13 dm. Inflorescence to 20 cm, spike-like, narrow; spikelet with 2 or more florets. Glumes awl-like; lemma awn to 3 mm. The fruit is called a caryopsis, also a grain.

Genus & Specific Name Derivation: Anagram of *Elymus* / unknown derivation

Notes: Illustration from *Illustrated Flora of the Pacific States.*

Uses Past and Present: Native grasses were used for lining steam-cooking pits, stringing food for drying, spreading on floors, and as bedding.

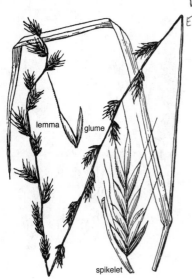

lemma   glume

spikelet

√ *Lolium multiflorum* Lam.

E ITALIAN RYEGRASS   Nonnative / Europe

Flowering Time: April–October

Habitat: grassland, disturbed areas

Description: Annual, biennial, or short-lived perennial to 8 dm. Inflorescence to 30 cm, spike-like; spikelet with 2 or more florets. Glume 1, not awned; lemma awn to 8 mm. The fruit is called a caryopsis, also a grain.

Genus & Specific Name Derivation: Latin: ancient common name for ryegrass / multi-flowered, referring to the spikelets

Notes: Illustration from *Illustrated Flora of the Pacific States.*

Photo in K & B plate 641

Lolium perenne L.

PERENNIAL RYEGRASS   Nonnative / Europe

Flowering Time: April–September

Habitat: grassland, disturbed areas

Description: Perennial to 8 dm. Inflorescence to 8 dm, spike-like; spikelet with 2 or more florets. Glume 1, glume and lemmas not awned. The fruit is called a caryopsis, also a grain.

Genus & Specific Name Derivation: Latin: ancient common name for ryegrass / perennial

Notes: Illustration from *Illustrated Flora of the Pacific States.*

spikelet

Melica californica Scribner

CALIFORNIA MELIC   Native

Flowering Time: March–June

Habitat: grassland, woodland

Description: Perennial to 13 dm. Inflorescence to 30 cm, panicle-like; spikelet with 2 or more florets. Glumes and lemmas not awned. The fruit is called a caryopsis, also a grain.

Genus & Specific Name Derivation: Latin: honey, or old Italian name for a plant with sweet sap / from California

Notes: Illustration from *Illustrated Flora of the Pacific States.*

Uses Past and Present: Native grasses were used for lining steam-cooking pits, stringing food for drying, spreading on floors, and as bedding.

spikelet

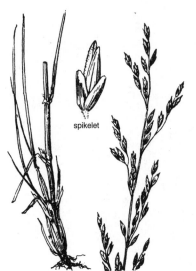

spikelet

Melica imperfecta Trin.

SMALL-FLOWERED MELIC   Native

Flowering Time: March–June

Habitat: chaparral, woodland

Description: Perennial to 11 dm. Inflorescence to 36 cm, panicle-like; spikelet with 2 or more florets. Glumes and lemmas not awned. The fruit is called a caryopsis, also a grain.

Genus & Specific Name Derivation: Latin: honey, or old Italian name for a plant with sweet sap / not perfect

Notes: Illustration from *Illustrated Flora of the Pacific States.*

Uses Past and Present: Native grasses were used for lining steam-cooking pits, stringing food for drying, spreading on floors, and as bedding.

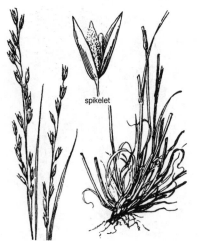

spikelet

Melica torreyana Scribner

TORREY'S MELIC   Native

Flowering Time: March–June

Habitat: grassland, chaparral, woodland

Description: Perennial to 10 dm. Inflorescence to 25 cm, panicle-like; spikelet with 2 or more florets. Glumes and lemmas not awned. The fruit is called a caryopsis, also a grain.

Genus & Specific Name Derivation: Latin: honey, or old Italian name for a plant with sweet sap / for John Torrey (1796–1873), American botanist

Notes: Illustration from *Illustrated Flora of the Pacific States.*

Uses Past and Present: Native grasses were used for lining steam-cooking pits, stringing food for drying, spreading on floors, and as bedding.

Nassella lepida (A. Hitchc.) Barkworth

FOOTHILL NEEDLEGRASS   Native

Flowering Time: April–June

Habitat: grassland, chaparral

Description: Perennial to 10 dm. Inflorescence to 55 cm, panicle-like; spikelets 1-flowered. Glumes short-awned; lemma awn to 5 cm. The fruit is called a caryopsis, also a grain.

Genus & Specific Name Derivation: Latin: nassa, a basket with a narrow neck / elegant, graceful

Notes: Illustration from *Illustrated Flora of the Pacific States.*

Uses Past and Present: Native grasses were used for lining steam-cooking pits, stringing food for drying, spreading on floors, and as bedding.

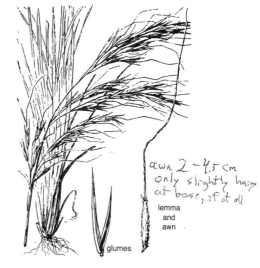

awn 2 – 4.5 cm only slightly hairy at base, if at all

lemma and awn

glumes

Nassella pulchra (A. Hitchc.) Barkworth

PURPLE NEEDLEGRASS   Native

Flowering Time: March–June

Habitat: grassland

Description: Perennial to 10 dm. Inflorescence to 60 cm, panicle-like; spikelets 1-flowered. Glumes short-awned; lemma awn to 10 cm. The fruit is called a caryopsis, also a grain.

> 5 cm

Genus & Specific Name Derivation: Latin: nassa, a basket with a narrow neck / beautiful, handsome

Notes: Illustration from *Illustrated Flora of the Pacific States.*

Uses Past and Present: Native grasses were used for lining steam-cooking pits, stringing food for drying, spreading on floors, and as bedding.

awn 4–10cm hairy at base

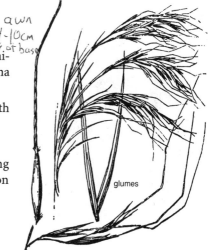

glumes

sterile
lemma

glumes and fertile lemma

Phalaris aquatica L.

HARDING GRASS   Nonnative / Mediterranean

Flowering Time: June–September

Habitat: disturbed areas

Description: Perennial to 15 dm. Inflorescence to 11 cm, panicle-like, cylindric, dense; spikelet compressed. Glumes and lemmas not awned. Fertile lemma to 4 mm, sterile lemma much shorter. The fruit is called a caryopsis, also a grain.

Genus & Specific Name Derivation: Greek: ancient name for grass with shiny spikelets / water, growing in moist areas

Notes: Illustration from *Manual of the Grasses of the United States.*

floret

glumes

Phalaris californica Hook. & Arn.

CALIFORNIA CANARY GRASS   Native

Flowering Time: May–November

Habitat: moist areas

Description: Perennial to 15 dm. Inflorescence to 5 cm, panicle-like, cylindric, dense; spikelet compressed. Glumes and lemmas not awned. Lemmas mostly equal in length. The fruit is called a caryopsis, also a grain.

Genus & Specific Name Derivation: Greek: ancient name for grass with shiny spikelets / from California

Notes: Illustration from *Illustrated Flora of the Pacific States.*

Uses Past and Present: Native grasses were used for lining steam-cooking pits, stringing food for drying, spreading on floors, and as bedding.

Phalaris canariensis L.

CANARY GRASS   Nonnative / Mediterranean

Flowering Time: April–July

Habitat: disturbed areas

Description: Annual to 10 dm. Inflorescence to 4 cm, panicle-like, cylindric, dense; spikelet compressed. Glumes and lemmas not awned. The fruit is called a caryopsis, also a grain.

Genus & Specific Name Derivation: Greek: ancient name for grass with shiny spikelets / from the Canary Islands or bird food for canaries

Notes: Illustration from *Illustrated Flora of the Pacific States.*

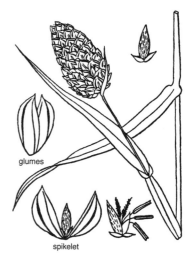

glumes

spikelet

Phalaris minor Retz.

MEDITERRANEAN CANARY GRASS

Nonnative / Mediterranean

Flowering Time: April–July

Habitat: disturbed areas

Description: Annual to 10 dm. Inflorescence to 6 cm, panicle-like, cylindric, dense; spikelet compressed. Glumes and lemmas not awned. The fruit is called a caryopsis, also a grain.

Genus & Specific Name Derivation: Greek: ancient name for grass with shiny spikelets / small

Notes: Illustration from *Illustrated Flora of the Pacific States.*

floret

glumes

2008 Addendum
Phalaris paradoxa   PARADOX CANARY GRASS nonnative

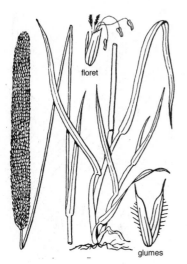

Phleum pratense L.

CULTIVATED TIMOTHY   Nonnative / Eurasia

Flowering Time: May–July

Habitat: disturbed areas

Description: Perennial to 10 dm. Inflorescence to 18 cm, panicle-like, cylindric, dense; spikelet sessile, compressed. Glumes awned; lemma not awned. The fruit is called a caryopsis, also a grain.

Genus & Specific Name Derivation: Greek: a marsh reed / from meadows

Notes: Illustration from *Illustrated Flora of the Pacific States.* Common name Timothy is from Timothy Hanson, 19th century U.S. agrologist who brought the grass from New York to use in domestic pastures.

Poa annua L.

ANNUAL BLUEGRASS   Nonnative / Europe

Flowering Time: February–September

Habitat: grassland, disturbed areas

Description: Annual to biennial to 2 dm. Inflorescence to 10 cm, panicle-like; spikelet with 2 or more florets. Glumes and lemmas not awned. The fruit is called a caryopsis, also a grain.

Genus & Specific Name Derivation: Greek: ancient name / annual

Notes: Illustration from *Illustrated Flora of the Pacific States.*

2008 Addendum

Poa pratensis ssp. pratensis
KENTUCKY BLUEGRASS native (?)

Poa secunda J. S. Presl ssp. *secunda*

ONE-SIDED BLUEGRASS   Native

Flowering Time: February–May

Habitat: grassland

Description: Perennial to 10 dm. Inflorescence to 15 cm, panicle-like; spikelet with 2 or more florets. Glumes and lemmas not awned. The fruit is called a caryopsis, also a grain.

Genus & Specific Name Derivation: Greek: ancient name / turned to one side

Notes: Illustration from *Illustrated Flora of the Pacific States.*

Uses Past and Present: Native grasses were used for lining steam-cooking pits, stringing food for drying, spreading on floors, and as bedding.

spikelet

inflorescence

Polypogon monspeliensis (L.) Desf.

ANNUAL BEARD GRASS   Nonnative / Europe

Flowering Time: April–October

Habitat: moist areas, drainages, seeps

Description: Annual to 10 dm. Inflorescence to 17 cm, plume-like, densely flowered, panicle-like, compact, dense; spikelet 1-flowered. Glumes and lemma awned. The fruit is called a caryopsis, also a grain.

Genus & Specific Name Derivation: Greek: much bearded / from Montpellier, south France

Notes: Illustration from *Illustrated Flora of the Pacific States.*

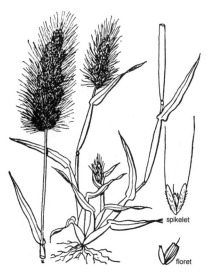

spikelet

floret

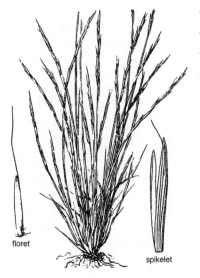

floret

spikelet

Scribneria bolanderi (Thurber) Hackel

SCRIBNER'S GRASS   Native

Flowering Time: March–June

Habitat: disturbed areas

Description: Annual to 3 dm. Inflorescence to 11 cm, spike-like; spikelets 1-flowered. Glumes without awns; lemma awn to 4 mm. The fruit is called a caryopsis, also a grain.

Genus & Specific Name Derivation: For Frank L. Scribner (1851–1938), an American agrostologist / for H. N. Bolander (1831–1897), of Geneva, plant collector in California and Oregon

Notes: Illustration from *Illustrated Flora of the Pacific States.*

Uses Past and Present: Native grasses were used for lining steam-cooking pits, stringing food for drying, spreading on floors, and as bedding.

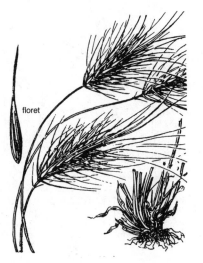

floret

Taeniatherum caput-medusae (L.) Nevski

MEDUSA HEAD   Nonnative / Eurasia

Flowering Time: June–July

Habitat: disturbed areas

Description: Annual to 6 dm. Inflorescence to 5 cm, excluding awns; spikelet with 2 or more florets. Glumes awn-like; lemma awn to 7 cm. The fruit is called a caryopsis, also a grain.

Genus & Specific Name Derivation: Greek: ribbon-awned / Medusa's head

Notes: Illustration from *Illustrated Flora of the Pacific States.*

Uses Past and Present: Synonym *Elymus caput-medusae.*

2008 Addendum
Trisetum canescens TALL TRISETUM
native

Trisetum cernuum Trin.

NODDING TRISETUM   Native

Flowering Time: April–August

Habitat: woodland

Description: Perennial to 8 dm. Inflorescence to 30 cm, panicle-like; spikelet with 2 or more florets. Glumes without awns; lemma awn to 12 mm. The fruit is called a caryopsis, also a grain.

Genus & Specific Name Derivation: Latin: three bristle / drooping

Notes: Illustration from *Illustrated Flora of the Pacific States.*

Uses Past and Present: Native grasses were used for lining steam-cooking pits, stringing food for drying, spreading on floors, and as bedding.

spikelet

Vulpia bromoides (L.) S.F. Gray

SIX-WEEKS FESCUE   Nonnative / Europe

Flowering Time: March–May

Habitat: grassland, chaparral

Description: Annual to 5 dm. Inflorescence to 15 cm, panicle-like, narrow, dense; spikelet with 2 or more florets. Glumes without awns; lemma awn to 12 mm. The fruit is called a caryopsis, also a grain.

Genus & Specific Name Derivation: For J. S. Vulpius, pharmacist-botanist from Baden, Germany / brome-like

Notes: Illustration from *Illustrated Flora of the Pacific States.*

spikelet

2008 Addendum
Triticum aestivum   COMMON WHEAT nonnative

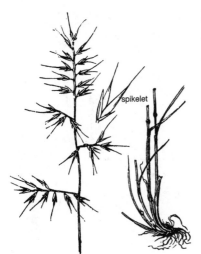

spikelet

Vulpia microstachys (Nutt.) Munro var. *pauciflora* (Beal) Lonard & Gould

PACIFIC FESCUE   Native

Flowering Time: April–May

Habitat: grassland

Description: Annual to 8 dm. Inflorescence to 24 cm, panicle-like; spikelet with 2 or more florets. Glumes without awns; lemma awn to 12 mm. The fruit is called a caryopsis, also a grain.

Genus & Specific Name Derivation: For J. S. Vulpius, pharmacist-botanist from Baden, Germany / small spike-like / few-flowered

Notes: Illustration from *Illustrated Flora of the Pacific States.* Correct authority from *The Jepson Manual Corrections* — Installment No. 7.

Uses Past and Present: Native grasses were used for lining steam-cooking pits, stringing food for drying, spreading on floors, and as bedding.

spikelet

Vulpia myuros (L.) C. Gmelin var. *hirsuta* Hack.

FOXTAIL   Nonnative / Europe

Flowering Time: March–May

Habitat: grassland, chaparral

Description: Annual to 8 dm. Inflorescence to 25 cm, panicle-like, narrow, dense; spikelet with 2 or more florets. Glumes without awns; lemma margin hairy, awns to 15 mm. The fruit is called a caryopsis, also a grain.

Genus & Specific Name Derivation: For J. S. Vulpius, pharmacist-botanist from Baden, Germany / mouse-tailed / hairy

Notes: Illustration from *Illustrated Flora of the Pacific States.* Correct authority for var. from *The Jepson Manual Corrections* — Installment No. 7.

Vulpia myuros (L.) C. Gmelin var. *myuros*

RATTAIL FESCUE   Nonnative / Europe

Flowering Time: March–May

Habitat: grassland, chaparral

Description: Annual to 8 dm. Inflorescence to 25 cm, panicle-like, narrow, dense; spikelet with 2 or more florets. Glumes without awns; lemma margin glabrous, awns to 15 mm. The fruit is called a caryopsis, also a grain.

Genus & Specific Name Derivation: For J. S. Vulpius, pharmacist-botanist from Baden, Germany / mouse-tailed

Notes: Illustration from *Illustrated Flora of the Pacific States.*

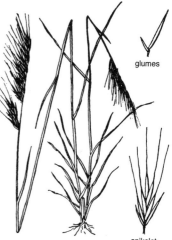

glumes

spikelet

2008 Addendum

Typhaceae — Cattail family

Typha angustifolia   NARROW-LEAVED CATTAIL
native

Glossary

achene. A dry, indehiscent fruit with 1 seed; as in Asteraceae. (See fruit types illustration.)

alternate. Referring to the leaf arrangement in which each node bears 1 leaf along the stem. (See the leaf arrangement illustration.)

anagram. A word formed by rearranging its letters.

annual. Completing a life cycle from germination to reproduction and death in one year or growing season.

anther. Pollen-producing part of the stamen. (See the flower illustration.)

appressed. Pressed against.

awn. A bristle-like appendage as a part of a larger structure, as in the glumes and lemmas of some Poaceae, or as a separate part, as in the pappus of some Asteraceae.

axil. Formed at a node by a flower, leaf or branch (adjective: axillary). (See the inflorescence types illustration.)

beak. With a prolonged or thickened tip.

biennial. Completing a life cycle from germination to reproduction and death in two years or growing seasons.

bisexual. Flower with both fertile stamens and fertile pistils.

bract. A reduced or modified, leaf-like structure at the base of the primary inflorescence. (See the flower illustration.)

bractlet. A reduced or modified, leaf-like structure below the secondary inflorescence.

calyx. Collective term for the sepals, which enclose the flower in bud.

capsule. A dry dehiscent fruit with more than one chamber, and many seeds, this is a common fruit in many families. (See fruit types illustration.)

caryopsis. The fruit of the Poaceae family.

catkin. A spike composed of unisexual flowers with inconspicuous perianth parts, often hanging downward. As in Fagaceae and Salicaceae.

cauline. On the stem of the plant, often referring to leaves.

chaff. Dry bracts; in Asteraceae, a dry, persistent bract on a receptacle.

coma. A tuft of hairs, usually occurring on a seed. As in some Onagraceae.

conic. Shaped like a cone.

corm. A thick underground stem.

corolla. Collective term for the petals.

corymb. A flat-topped or rounded inflorescence in which the pedicels are of varying length (as in yarrow).

cyme. A branched inflorescence in which the terminal flowers open before the lateral ones on any axis. (See the inflorescence types illustration.)

dehiscent. Splitting open at maturity to release contents.

deciduous. Falling at the end of one season of growth or life.

decumbent. Stems whose bases lie or rest on the ground, but the distal portions ascend or curve upward.

dichotomous. Branching repeatedly in pairs or forks.

dioecious. Plants unisexual, the staminate and pistillate flowers on separate plants of the same species. *Both flowers and plants unisexual*

evergreen. Remaining green during the dormant season. Referring to plants that retain their leaves throughout the year.

follicle. A dry, many-seeded fruit opening along one side. (See fruit types illustration.)

flower. Collective term for the sepals, petals, stamens, and pistil. (See the flower illustration).

frond. The stem including the leaf as in the ferns.

gall. Abnormal growth caused by insects, bacteria or fungus.

glabrous. Surfaces without hairs.

glandular. With gland-like hairs or secretions.

glaucous. Covered with a white to gray waxy coating.

head. A compact inflorescence with many flowers clustered together, common in the Asteraceae family.

herbaceous perennial. A plant that lives for more than one year. The above ground parts die back each year, however the underground parts resprout when conditions are favorable (as in bulbs, tubers etc.)

hypanthium. Structure derived from the fusion of the sepals, petals and stamens, often forming a tube as in the Onagraceae family.

indehiscent. A fruit that does not open by means of sutures, lids, pores, or teeth to release contents.

indusium. In ferns, the appendage that covers or encloses the sorus or sori.

inflorescence. The arrangement of flowers on the stem. (See the inflorescence types illustration)

involucre. One or more whorls of bracts, usually below 1 or more flowers, as in the Asteraceae family.

irregular. Referring to the flowers where either the sepals or the petals do not all look alike.

lanceolate. Shaped like a lance; narrow, tapered at the tip, the widest point in the lower half.

leaf arrangement. The way the leaves are arranged on the stem. (See the leaf arrangement illustration.)

legume. A type of fruit in the Fabaceae family. (See fruit types illustration.)

linear. Shape that is long, narrow and with a uniform width.

lobe. A segment or division of a structure as in the sepals, petals, leaf blade, or ovary.

margin. The edge of a leaf blade or perianth part.

membranous. With the consistency of a membrane; usually thin and soft.

monoecious. Plants bisexual, with both kinds of unisexual flowers (staminate and pistillate) produced on the same plant. *Flowers unisexual, plants bisexual*

nectary. Gland-like structure that secretes nectar.

node. The joint of a stem at which leaves are attached and axillary buds are produced.

nutlet. A small, dry, indehiscent fruit with one seed as in the Boraginaceae and Lamiaceae families. (See fruit types illustration.)

oblong. Shape that is longer than broad, but with parallel sides.

opposite. Referring to leaf arrangements in which each node bears two leaves opposite each other. (See the leaf arrangement illustration.)

ovary. The part of the pistil that encloses the ovules and that develops into a fruit after pollination. (See the flower illustration.)

ovate. Outline in the shape of an egg, with the attachment at the widest end.

ovoid. A three dimensional structure with the shape of an egg.

palea. A chaff-like or scale-like bract. In the Poaceae family the upper and smaller of two bracts subtending a flower.

palmate. Radiating from one common point, like the fingers of an open hand; usually used to describe the venation or lobbing of a leaf. (See the leaf types illustration.)

panicle. A compound raceme-like inflorescence. (See the inflorescence types illustration.)

papilionaceous. An irregular corolla in the Fabaceae family composed of a banner, 2 wings and 2 additional petals usually fused into a keel.

pappus. Modified calyx in the Asteraceae family composed of awns, bristles, or scales.

pedicel. The stalk to a single flower. (See the flower illustration.)

peduncle. The stalk to an inflorescence

peltate. A structure that is attached toward the middle, rather than the margin.

pendent. Hanging downward.

perennial. Living for more that two years or growing seasons; flowering and fruiting repeatedly throughout the life of the plant.

perianth. Collective term for the calyx and corolla. (See the flower illustration.)

petal. One segment or lobe of the corolla. (See the flower illustration.)

petiole. A stalk to an individual leaf blade that connects it to the stem. (See the leaf types illustration.)

phyllaries. The individual bracts below the flower head, collective term is involucre. As in the Asteraceae family.

pinnate. Radiating in 2 rows from a linear axis, like the parts of a feather; used to describe the veins or lobes of a leaf and the arrangement of leaflets in a pinnately compound leaf. (See the leaf types illustration.)

pistil. Female reproductive structure of a flower, composed of the ovary, style and stigma. (See the flower illustration.)

pistillate. A unisexual flower with only pistils.

prostrate. Used to describe stems that are laying flat on the ground.

pubescent. Used to describe a surface with short, soft hairs.

raceme. A simple inflorescence composed of a single stem bearing flowers. (See the inflorescence types illustration.)

rachis. The central axis of an inflorescence or a pinnately compound leaf.

recurved. Curved gradually, either downward or backward.

reflexed. Bent downward.

regular. Referring to the sepals and petals where each look alike.

reniform. Kidney-shaped.

revolute. Margins that are rolled toward the lower surface.

rhizome. A horizontal, underground stem with scale-like leaves that produce leafy shoots.

rosette. Leaves that are crowded and arranged at the base of the plant. (See the leaf arrangement illustration.)

samara. An indehiscent fruit with wing-like appendages, as in the Aceraceae family.

scabrous. Surface that feels rough to the touch; covered with short, stiff hairs.

scape. An inflorescence and peduncle usually arising directly from a basal rosette of leaves (adjective: scapose).

scarious. Used to describe leaf or bract margins that are thin, dry, tan to brownish, and often translucent.

schizocarp. A dry indehiscent fruit that separates into two or more segments as in the Apiaceae family. (See fruit types illustration.)

sepal. One segment or lobe of the calyx. (See the flower illustration.)

septum. A dividing wall or membrane, referring to the inner fruit segment in the Brassicaceae family.

serrate. Margins with teeth, often referring to the leaf margins.

sessile. Attached directly by the base, such as leaves without petioles and flowers without pedicels.

silicle. A dry fruit in the Brassicaceae family in which two halves split away from a septum or partition. The fruit is usually as long as it is wide. (See the fruit types illustration.)

silique. A dry fruit in the Brassicaceae family in which two halves split away from a septum or partition. The fruit is usually more than twice as long as wide. (See the fruit types illustration.)

sinus. The indentation or cleft between the lobes or a margin.

sorus. The part of a fern leaf or leaflet that bears sporangia (plural: sori).

spike. A simple inflorescence composed of a single stem bearing sessile flowers. (See the inflorescence types illustration.)

spine. A stiff, sharp-pointed structure.

sporangium. The sac or case-like structure enclosing spores in plants not producing seeds. As in the ferns.

spore. A simple, reproductive, single-celled structure capable of developing into a new individual. As in the ferns.

sporophyll. A leaf that produces sporangia and spores; also the cone-like structures in some fern allies.

spur. A slender, tubular or sac-like projection from either a petal or sepal and usually contains nectar.

stamen. Male reproductive structure of a flower, usually composed of the filament and anther. (See the flower illustration.)

staminate. A unisexual flower with only stamens.

stellate. Star shaped, often referring to hairs.

stipule. An appendage at the base of the petiole, or leaf that is variable in form but is often leaf-like.

subtend. Located below or beneath a structure.

tomentose. Covered with densely interwoven, usually matted hairs.

tubercle. Covered with wart-like or tuber-like projections.

umbel. An inflorescence with pedicels of equal length and arising from a common point (adjective: umbellate). (See the inflorescence types illustration.)

unisexual. Having one sex, referring to the flowers which can be either male or female in some species.

whorl. Referring to a leaf arrangement in which 3 or more leaves or flowers originate from the same point. (See the leaf arrangement illustration.)

Flower

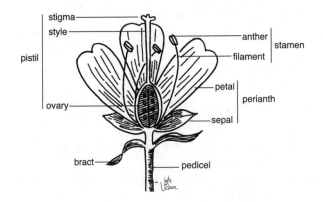

Inflorescence Types

cyme

head

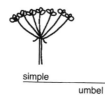

panicle

raceme

spike

axillary

coiled cluster

<u>simple</u>   compound

umbel

Fruit Types

achenes   capsule   follicle   legume or pod   nutlets

schizocarp   silicles   siliques

Leaf Types

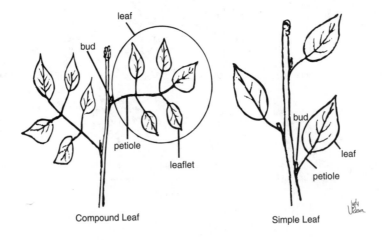

Compound Leaf

Simple Leaf

Compound Leaves

palmate   pinnate   bipinnate   tripinnate

Simple Leaves

simple
margin entire

simple
margin toothed

pinnately lobed

palmately lobed

Leaf Arrangement

alternate

opposite

whorled

basal

Bibliography

Abrams, L. R., Ferris R. S. (1940-1960). *Illustrated Flora of the Pacific States, Washington, Oregon and California.* Four Volumes. Stanford University Press, Stanford, California.

Bossard, C. D., Randall, J. M, M. C. Hoshovsky (2000). *Invasive Plants of California's Wildlands.* University of California Press, Berkeley, California.

Clark, C. B. (1977). *Edible and Useful Plants of California.* University of California Press, Berkeley, California.

Dale, N. (1985). *Flowering Plants The Santa Monica Mountains, Coastal & Chaparral Regions of Southern California.* Capra Press, Santa Barbara, California.

Friends of Edgewood Natural Preserve. *Friends of Edgewood Natural Preserve, Docent Training Manual.* 1999-2000

Gledhill, D. (1996). *The Names of Plants.* Cambridge University Press, New York, New York.

Hickman, J. C. (Editor). (1993). *The Jepson Manual: Higher Plants of California.* University of California Press, Berkeley, California.

Hitchcock, A. S. (1971). *Manual of the Grasses of the United States.* Volume One and Two. Dover Publications, Inc. New York, New York.

Junak, S.; Ayers, T.; Scott, R.; Wilken, D.; Young, D. (1995). *A Flora of Santa Cruz Island.* Santa Barbara Botanic Garden, Santa Barbara, California and in collaboration with The California Native Plant Society, Sacramento California.

Keator, G. (1994). *Plants of the East Bay Parks.* Roberts Rinehart Publishers, Inc., Niowat, Colorado.

Kruckeberg, A. R. (1984). *California Serpentines: Flora, Vegetation, Geology, Soils, and Management Problems.* University of California Press, Berkeley, California.

Moore, M. (1993). *Medicinal Plants of the Pacific West.* Red Crane Books, Santa Fe, New Mexico.

Munz, P. A. and Keck, D. D (1972). *A California Flora with Supplement.* University of California Press, Berkeley, California.

Pojar, J. and MacKinnon, A. (1994). *Plants of Coastal British Columbia.* Lone Pine Publishing, Vancouver, British Columbia, Canada.

Oraduff, (2010), California Plant Life. Univ Calif. Press,

San Mateo County Parks and Recreation Division, Environmental Services Agency (1997). Edgewood Park and Natural Preserve Master Plan. San Mateo County, California.

Sierra, E., Schlegel, F. (1964). Nueva compuesta adventicia para Chile, la Urospermum picroides (L.) Desf. Boletín de la Universidad de Chile 51: 27-28.

Thomas, J. H. (1961). Flora of the Santa Cruz Mountains of California. Stanford University Press, Stanford, California.

Tibor, D. P. and Rare Plant Scientific Advisory Committee, Convening Editor. (2001). Inventory of Rare and Endangered Plants of California (Sixth Edition). California Native Plant Society, Sacramento, California.

Web Pages Used

Jepson Flora Project, Jepson Online Interchange. Editors: B. G. Baldwin, S. Boyde, B. J. Ertter, R. W. Patterson, T. J. Rosatti, and D. H. Wilken (http://ucjeps.berkeley.edu/interchange.html)

California Plant Names, Word Meanings and Name Derivations By Michael Lloyd Charters. (http://www.calflora.net/botanicalnames/index.html)

Friends of Edgewood Natural Preserve (http://www.friendsofedgewood.org/)

Plant Index

About the Author

A California native **Toni Corelli** grew up near Edgewood Natural Preserve and developed her love for nature by exploring the surrounding area. She received her degree in botany from San Jose State University. She is on the board of the Santa Clara Valley Chapter of the California Native Plant Society and The Friends of Edgewood Natural Preserve. She has her own consulting business documenting the natural resources of public open space lands in the Bay Area. She teaches, lectures, and leads walks throughout the Santa Cruz Mountains. She is a docent for Jasper Ridge Biological Preserve, Edgewood Natural Preserve, and Pescadero Marsh. She is the Curator of the Carl W. Sharsmith Herbarium at San Jose State University and Associate Curator of the Teaching Herbarium at Jasper Ridge Biological Preserve. She is the author of *The Rare and Endangered Plants of San Mateo and Santa Clara County,* and coauthor of *The Natural History of the Fitzgerald Marine Preserve.*

About the Illustrators

In the spring of 1997 **Judy Mason** retired from a full-time indoor office career of 34 years. Being retired allows her more time in nature to draw, volunteer, teach, and share her lifetime love of wildflowers. Among the original drawings in this book are some of her drawings illustrated in *The Shrubs of Henry Coe State Park,* originally published in 1988 and *The Trees of Henry Coe State Park,* published in 2004. Judy and Toni developed courses in wildflower families and sunflowers, along with creating the workbooks for the courses, which Judy illustrated. Judy continues to capture wildflowers in watercolor and now with her most recent passion using a digital camera. Judy and her husband Don are docents at Jasper Ridge Biological Preserve at Stanford University.

Linda Bea Miller has been a nature lover and outdoor enthusiast since her youth. Specializing in pen, ink drawings, etching, and watercolor, she has spent the last twenty years drawing flowers and plants. An experienced backpacker, she is also active in outdoor education, particularly for women and children. She is currently on the board of directors of several Bay Area educational organizations specializing in environmental education and teaching women how to be comfortable camping and backpacking in the wilderness.